Sylvester Expansion Theorem

$$F_i = \prod_{\substack{i=1 \\ j \neq i}}^{n} \left(\frac{A - \lambda_j I}{\lambda_i - \lambda_j} \right)$$

LINEAR NETWORKS AND SYSTEMS

McGRAW-HILL ELECTRICAL AND ELECTRONIC ENGINEERING SERIES

Frederick Emmons Terman, Consulting Editor
W. W. Harman and J. G. Truxal,
Associate Consulting Editors

LINEAR
NETWORKS
AND
SYSTEMS

BENJAMIN C. KUO
Professor of Electrical Engineering
University of Illinois

McGRAW-HILL BOOK COMPANY
New York   St. Louis   San Francisco
Toronto   London   Sydney

LINEAR NETWORKS AND SYSTEMS

Library of Congress Catalog Card Number 66-26579

35640

1234567890 MP 7432106987

PREFACE

In recent years, the systems concept has been receiving more and more emphasis in the curriculum of electrical engineering. One of the areas most directly affected, perhaps, is automatic control systems, in which the state-variable method has completely revolutionized design theory. Whereas most of the recently published books on systems theory have been at the graduate level, this book is written with the intention of bringing state and systems concepts to the undergraduate curriculum and to network analysis.

Students majoring in electrical engineering have long been taught how to write loop and node equations, and from all indications this will continue, no matter how the curriculum is changed. Although the loop and node equations derive from Kirchhoff's laws, the practical aspects of the methods were seldom questioned. In the days when computers were not available or in their infancy, when every calculation had to be done by hand, using pencil and paper, it was natural to rely on the loop-and-node-equations methods, which are relatively easy to formulate. With the advent of analog and digital computers, however, the modern approach is to have the engineers formulate the problems and equations, leaving the drudgery of computation to the computer. It is natural to search for still other methods that may be superior to the conventional methods from the viewpoint of computation. Indeed, from the academic standpoint, many educators would agree that in the educational aspects of network analysis, emphasis is usually placed on how network equations are written, and little consideration is given to their solution, once they are written. In a course on network analysis, students are rarely asked to obtain the complete solution of a multiloop network containing resistances, capacitances, and inductances. Most of the academic problems, of course, involve trivial situations, where pencil-and-paper solutions are feasible.

The material covered in this book is intended for use in a course on linear networks and systems analysis at the junior level. It should be preceded by an introductory course in elementary network theory in which basic concepts and theorems of electric networks are introduced. A major portion of the material in this book was successfully class-tested in an intermediate circuit course for honor students in electrical engineering at the University of Illinois.

Chapters 1 and 2 provide some discussion as an introduction to the systems concept and representations of deterministic signals and network elements.   Since matrix symbols are used to some extent in the text, Chapter 3 gives a brief coverage of elementary matrix algebra.   In Chapter 4 the method of network analysis through graph theory is discussed.   Mesh and node equations of electric networks are formulated, using the methods of cut-sets and tie-sets.   This approach is necessary since it paves the way to the general method of writing state equations for electric networks, covered in Chapter 6.   Chapter 5 introduces the state concept and the definitions of state variables, state equations, etc. Continuous-data as well as discrete-data systems are considered.   Various methods of writing state equations for electric networks are discussed in Chapter 6.   These include the inspection method, the equivalent-source method, and the graph-theory method.   Networks with mutual inductances, dependent sources, all-inductance nodes, and all-capacitance loops are considered.

The author firmly believes that signal flow graphs are handy tools for analyzing linear networks and systems.   Chapter 7 introduces both Mason's signal flow graph and Coates' flow graph, and a comparison of the two methods is made.   Chapters 8 and 9 deal with the conventional Fourier and Laplace transforms and the application of Laplace-transform methods to network analysis.   The z transformation, designed to be used for discrete-data systems, is introduced in Chapter 10.   Chapters 11 and 12 treat the topics on transfer functions and the state diagrams, which are the signal flow graphs for state equations.

Homework problems are provided at the end of each chapter, except for Chapter 2.   A solution manual with a detailed solution for each problem in the book, for use by the instructors, is available upon request from the publisher.

The author is grateful to Dr. J. G. Truxal of the Brooklyn Polytechnic Institute and Dr. T. J. Higgins of the University of Wisconsin for their valuable suggestions, particularly in connection with the revisions of the final manuscript.   The encouragement and interest of Dean W. L. Everitt and Dr. E. C. Jordan, Head of the Electrical Engineering Department of the University of Illinois, have been invaluable in the preparation of the manuscript.   Thanks is also due to Mr. C. G. Preston of the University of Illinois, who did the final artwork for the book.

Benjamin C. Kuo

CONTENTS

LINEAR NETWORKS AND SYSTEMS

ONE

SYSTEMS AND SIGNALS

1-1 GENERAL CONCEPTS AND DESCRIPTIONS OF SYSTEMS

Many phenomena and elements in the physical world may be described as systems. A system is not necessarily tangible; whenever there is an interconnection of physical or social events which may lead to actions and reactions of various forms, a system is said to exist. Thus we may envision various types of systems, which may be described as systems of economy, systems in governments, autopilot systems in airplanes and missiles, electric power distribution systems, and many others, indeed too numerous to mention. Above all, human beings are perhaps the most complicated systems in existence.

Usually, a system is activated by some sort of external signals known as *inputs, excitations,* or *commands.*   In response to the input signals, the system will perform certain duties and will fulfill certain objectives in the form of *responses,* or simply *outputs.*   This *input-to-output* link can also

1

be described by a *cause-and-effect* relationship which often plays a vital role in the study of the behavior of physical systems.

A system may have more than one input and one output. In an electronic amplifier, for instance, an input noise component due to the 60-cycle power supply may cause a hum in the audio output. The acts of setting the volume and the tune controls on the amplifier may be regarded as input signals which lead to variations in quality in the volume and tune of the output. An automobile is considered to have several inputs and outputs. The steering and control on the accelerator by the human operator are considered as input excitations to the system, whereas the heading, position and speed, and acceleration of the automobile are the output responses. A human being, of course, has many inputs and many forms of outputs. In addition, a human being is able to make decisions, to think by himself, and make predictions. This is why human beings represent a unique class of intellectual systems which are virtually irreplaceable by man-made machines.

In view of the foregoing discussion, it is customary to depict a system by the block diagram shown in Fig. 1-1. In general, more detailed diagrams of various degrees than that shown in Fig. 1-1 may be drawn for

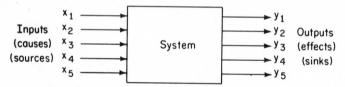

Fig. 1-1   Block diagram of a system.

the system to describe the cause-and-effect relationships between the signals in the system.

Representation of a physical system by a model and mathematical expressions is an important first step in the analysis of the system. This process allows us to use the available mathematical and topological tools, such as differential equations, Laplace and Fourier transformations, block diagrams, and signal flow graphs, to describe the many complex relationships and interactions between the signals and elements in a system.

By far the most powerful and most versatile among the methods of portraying physical systems is the graphical representation. For instance, network or circuit models are often very realistic in the portrayal of actual electric systems or electric circuits, and great success has been achieved by electrical engineers in using them to predict and to correlate with experimental results.   A circuit model allows the engineer to analyze the actual system mathematically with pencil and paper. On the other hand, when direct studies of the actual system with pencil and paper become impractical because of the complex nature of the system, computations may be carried out by an analog model such as an electronic analog computer.   An electronic analog computer consists of sets of electric circuits and elements which may be used to simulate complex physical systems of many varieties.   In this case, a simple set of computing elements may be used to enforce certain basic phenomena and relationships that may exist in a given system.   By connecting these basic computing elements in accordance with the mathematical relations of the physical system, the computer signals are made to follow the behavior of the signals in the actual system.   We have to keep in mind, however, that some of the mathematical models, especially those used in linear analysis, merely represent the physical reality in some idealized form.   These linearized models are used for the sake of simplicity in representation and analysis of a practical system, which otherwise would be too difficult or impossible to analyze.   Strictly speaking, all practical systems are nonlinear to some extent.   The extent of the nonlinear behavior of a system or an element depends on the nature of the signals and excitations, as well as on the environment of operations.   Quite often, an element or a system may be replaced by a linear model if the signals to which it is applied lie within a limited range.

Linearity

Just what is the definition of *linearity* (or nonlinearity)?   Linearity implies that the principle of superposition[1,2]† holds.   In other words, assuming that y_1 is the response of a system to an input x_1, and y_2 is the response to input x_2, if the application of the signal $x_1 + x_2$ results in the response $y_1 + y_2$, we say that the principle of superposition holds, and the system is linear.   The test just described must be satisfied for all possible values of x_1 and x_2.   Any system that does not satisfy the test described above is said to be nonlinear.   For instance, Fig. 1-2 shows the input-output relationship (gain) of an electronic amplifier.   It is apparent that the overall gain characteristic of this amplifier is nonlinear, since the principle of superposition will not be satisfied in this case (especially for large input signals).   However, if we restrict the magnitude of the input signal to be less than 0.5 volt, the amplifier may be considered a linear device, and its gain can then be approximated by a constant K

† Superscripts refer to the numbered bibliography listed at the end of the chapter.

which is equal to the slope of the linear portion of the curve. In view of this simple illustration, we can state that the functional characteristics (such as the gain of the amplifier) of a linear system must be independent of the input signals. Therefore the resistance R of a linear resistor must be independent of the current that flows through it and of the voltage across it. Similar statements can be made for a linear inductor and capacitor.

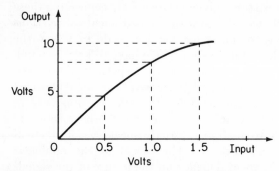

Fig. 1-2 Gain characteristic of an electronic amplifier.

In addition to the linear and nonlinear properties, an element of a system can also be classified as *time-variant* or *time-invariant, passive* or *active, bilateral* or *unilateral,* and in other categories if necessary.

Time variancy

A time-invariant element is one whose value or characteristic does not vary as a function of time. A time-variant element has just the opposite property. One should not confuse the nonlinear property with the time-variant one. An element whose value varies with time is still considered to be linear as long as it is independent of its input signals. However, it is possible for an element to have both nonlinear and time-varying characteristics. For instance, the resistance of a certain resistor may be thought of as depending on the current that flows through it, in addition to being variant with time. The resistance can then be denoted by $R(i,t)$. Of course, any system that contains a resistor or any other element with such characteristics is also said to be nonlinear and time-variant.

Bilateral and unilateral elements

An element (with two terminals) is called a *bilateral element* if signals can be transmitted with identical properties through either end.   Resistors and inductors are common examples of bilateral elements.   Transistors and vacuum tubes are examples of *unilateral elements*, since signals are not transmitted equally in both directions through these devices.

Active and passive elements

Active elements in physical systems are generally considered as energy sources.   Devices such as voltage generators, vacuum tubes, and transistors are common examples of active elements in electric systems.   Any device which exhibits a negative-resistance property, such as a tetrode, is also known as an active element since the negative energy dissipated in a negative resistance is considered to be a positive generated energy.

On the other hand, a passive element may be an energy sink or an energy storage.   For instance, a mechanical spring is a passive element, for it stores potential energy.   An electrical analog of the spring is a capacitor which stores potential energy in electrical form.

In general, when a physical element is supplied by a voltage or current source across its terminals, if the total net energy delivered to the element from $t = 0$ to $t = \infty$ is *positive*, the element is said to be passive; otherwise, it is active.

Dynamic systems[3,4]

The concepts of *dynamic systems* play an important role in the study of physical systems.   An important feature of dynamic systems is that they have memory capabilities.   A network with a capacitor is a typical example of a dynamic system since it is capable of storing potential energy.   On the other hand, an all-resistor network is not a dynamic system since it does not have the ability to retain any information once the input excitations are removed.   The past, present, and future of a dynamic system are fully represented by a set of variables known as the *state variables*.   For instance, the voltage across a capacitor is often designated as a state variable since it completely describes the "state" of the capacitor at any time.   Dynamic systems are usually described by differential equations.   When a system of first-order differential equations is used, the equations are called the *state equations*.

1-2 SIGNALS

Signals and excitations play an important role in the analysis and design of physical systems, since they must act as *causes* to all the *effects* of the system. In general, we may classify all signals in two major categories, *actual signals* and *test signals*, although many other classifications are possible and are often necessary. The first group includes signals that actually exist and are actually being applied to systems under practical conditions. It is not always possible, however, to describe a practical signal by accurate mathematical means. Quite often, the actual input signal of a system is not even known when the system is still on the design board or in the testing stage. For example, in designing a radar tracking system, one does not know ahead of time the paths and the speed of the targets which are to be tracked. Furthermore, these input signals most likely will be different under various circumstances. For these simple reasons, we have often found it necessary to fabricate hypothetical test signals which may be used for the prediction of system responses when the systems are operating under actual conditions. The test signals are not necessarily the true signals to which the systems are actually subjected. They are used simply because they are generally simple to describe mathematically, and they can form and simulate a great variety of actual signals. For instance, we show later that a linear system is completely defined by its response to an impulse-function input. Therefore, although the impulse function does not exist physically in the true sense of its definition, it can be used in numerous ways to aid in the analysis and understanding of linear systems.

In analyzing the performance of an electric filter or circuit, we often use a sinusoidal input signal and vary the frequency of the signal over a wide range. In this way, the responses that correspond to the various sinusoidal inputs may provide a qualitative indication of the properties of the filter circuit when other inputs which are resolvable into sums of sinusoidal components are applied. One of the difficulties encountered in the design of a feedback control system is that the actual input of the system is often unpredictable. However, as a test signal for design purposes, it is customary to use a unit step function, which is defined as having a jump discontinuity from zero to unity at $t = 0$. Therefore many design criteria are specified with respect to this kind of idealized test signal. It is not difficult to see why a step-function input can be an adequate test signal for some systems, since its discontinuous nature is equivalent to the application of numerous sinusoidal signals covering the entire frequency spectrum simultaneously.

Signals are also classified as *deterministic* or *random*. For example, the sinusoid and the unit step function mentioned in the preceding paragraph belong to the class of signals called deterministic signals. These signals have one distinct characteristic in common: their past, present, and future values are completely defined at any instant of time. Other examples of deterministic signals are the ramp function t, parabolic function t^2, exponential function e^{-t}, etc.

Random signals, sometimes also known as stochastic signals, are random functions of time. These signals, unlike the deterministic ones, can be described only by their statistical properties. For a random voltage signal, for instance, one can no longer say specifically that at time equals 1 sec the magnitude of the signal is equal to, say, 2 volts; rather, he should specify what is the *probability* that the voltage will lie between v_1 volts and v_2 volts at a given instant of time. Noise and disturbances in receivers and transmitters of communication systems and radar systems, for example, are random signals. Thermal noise due to randomly excited electrons in a conductor is another example of a random signal. Because all these signals are random in nature and are unpredictable, they must be described by statistical and probabilistic means.

1-3 MATHEMATICAL DESCRIPTIONS OF DETERMINISTIC SIGNALS

In order to carry out a successful mathematical study of the performance of a system, it is necessary, first, to achieve a mathematical description of the system's signals and excitations. After the input signals and the system are defined mathematically, we can proceed to establish definite relationships between them to arrive at the output responses. We consider all deterministic signals as belonging to one of the following two groups: *periodic signals* and *aperiodic signals*.

Periodic signals (sinusoidal functions)

A function $f(t)$ is said to be periodic with a period T if

$$f(t) = f(t \pm nT) \tag{1-1}$$

where n is any positive integer. In other words, a periodic function simply repeats itself after each period T. The sinusoidal signal and the periodic square wave shown in Fig. 1-3 are well-known examples of periodic functions in engineering studies. For the following reasons the

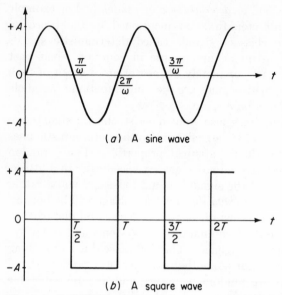

(a) A sine wave

(b) A square wave

Fig. 1-3 *Periodic functions.*

sinusoid is also perhaps the most important periodic signal in the science of electrical engineering:

1 The power generated by most electric generators varies sinusoidally with respect to time. Almost all modern electric power transmission systems have sinusoidally varying voltages and currents.
2 Most nonsinusoidally varying periodic functions can be expanded into Fourier series which consist of sinusoidal harmonic components. Therefore a sinusoid may be regarded as a fundamental entity for periodic functions.
3 Sinusoidal functions are easy to handle mathematically. The derivative and the integral of a sine wave are still sine waves.
4 The output response of a linear system to a sinusoidal input with a given frequency is still a sinusoidal signal with the same frequency. The changes in the amplitude and the phase shift between the input and the output sinusoidal signals indicate the characteristic of the system at that particular frequency. Therefore sinusoidal signals are often used as test signals in linear-system analysis.

A sinusoidal signal may be represented by

$$f(t) = A \sin (\omega t + \phi) \tag{1-2}$$

where A = amplitude

ω = angular frequency, radians/sec

ϕ = phase angle, radians

The period of the sine wave is the time it takes the sine wave to go through one complete cycle, and it is designated by

$$T = \frac{2\pi}{\omega} = \frac{1}{f} \quad \text{sec} \tag{1-3}$$

where f is the frequency in cycles per second.

To compare the phase shifts between different sine waves, it is convenient to represent the sine function by a rotating vector whose length is A. The vector is considered to rotate around its end in the counterclockwise direction at an angular velocity of ω radians/sec. The projection of the vector on the vertical axis at any time gives the magnitude of the sine wave at the corresponding instant. The angle made by the vector with the horizontal axis at the starting position ($t = 0$) gives the phase shift ϕ. Figure 1-4 illustrates three sine-wave signals with different phase-shift conditions. The starting positions of the rotating vectors are also shown in the accompanying figures. We see that the waveform $f_1(t)$ in Fig. 1-4a is "leading" the function $f_2(t)$ in Fig. 1-4b by a phase angle of ϕ_1. Similarly, the sine wave $f_2(t)$ in Fig. 1-4b "leads" $f_3(t)$ in Fig. 1-4c by ϕ_2. We can also say that $f_3(t)$ "lags" $f_2(t)$ by ϕ_2. The lead and lag properties of these sine functions are thus best shown by the relative positions of the rotating vectors. A comparison of the phase-lead or phase-lag properties of sine waves can also be made on the time-axis plots of Fig. 1-4. If we regard the $t = 0$ axis as reference and consider that the three waves are moving toward the left with the same speed, we notice that $f_1(t)$ is clearly ahead of $f_2(t)$ by an angle ϕ_1, and $f_3(t)$ can be regarded as behind $f_2(t)$ by ϕ_2. Of course, it is possible to regard $f_3(t)$ as "leading" $f_2(t)$ by an angle of $2\pi - \phi_2$.

One of the most important applications of the sine wave is that it can be used to represent nonsinusoidal periodic functions. We show later that any periodic signal $f(t)$ that satisfies a certain set of conditions can be expanded in a Fourier series.[5]

$$f(t) = \frac{a_0}{T} + \frac{2}{T} (a_1 \cos \omega t + a_2 \cos 2\omega t + a_3 \cos 3\omega t + \cdots$$
$$+ b_1 \sin \omega t + b_2 \sin 2\omega t + b_3 \sin 3\omega t + \cdots) \tag{1-4}$$

In expression (1-4), ω denotes the frequency, or 2π times the inverse of the period T of the periodic function; the $\cos \omega t$ and $\sin \omega t$ terms are

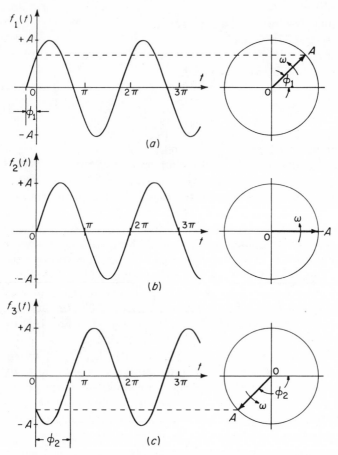

Fig. 1-4   Sine waves with different phase shifts and the corresponding rotating vectors.

called the fundamental components of the series, and the remaining terms are the harmonics. The constants $a_0, a_1, a_2, \ldots, b_1, b_2, \ldots$ are termed the Fourier coefficients and are determined from knowledge of $f(t)$. Thus we see that when a linear system is subjected to a non-sinusoidal periodic signal $f(t)$, its output response can be computed by adding up all the responses due to each sine-wave component of $f(t)$ acting alone.

We can also describe nonsinusoidal periodic signals by graphical addition and subtraction of aperiodic signals. For instance, the periodic square wave shown in Fig. 1-3 can be constructed by a sequence of delayed step functions.   However, we postpone the discussion of this subject until after the aperiodic signals have been discussed.

Aperiodic signals

An aperiodic signal is one that does not repeat itself during any finite time interval; or in simple words, it is not periodic.   Many test signals used in testing and designing systems and networks, such as the step function, ramp function, parabolic function, and impulse function, all fall into this category.   The descriptions and properties of some of the more important nonperiodic signals are given below.

The unit step function

The unit step function $u(t)$ is depicted in Fig. 1-5.   It is defined to have a value of unity for time greater than zero, and zero for time less than

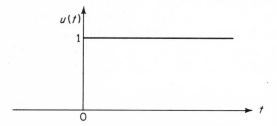

Fig. 1-5   The unit step function.

zero.   The function is not defined at time equals zero.   In other words,

$$u(t) = 1 \qquad t > 0$$
$$u(t) = 0 \qquad t < 0 \qquad\qquad\qquad (1\text{-}5)$$
$$u(t) \text{ is not defined at } t = 0$$

Therefore the following statements can be made:

$$\lim_{t \to 0^+} u(t) = 1 \qquad \lim_{t \to 0^-} u(t) = 0$$

which state that the limit of the function as time approaches zero from the left $(t \to 0^-)$ is zero, whereas the limit as time approaches zero from the right $(t \to 0^+)$ is unity.   Clearly, the unit step function is discontinuous at $t = 0$.   In practice, a step function may be simulated by such actions as the sudden closing of a switch connected to a battery, a sudden twist of a shaft, or a sudden thrust of force.

In defining the unit step function, we have introduced a concept of zero time $(t = 0)$.   Just when is time zero?   In making analytical studies of systems, we often find it necessary to mark a time reference for comparing the excitation with the response.   Zero time is used simply as a convenient time reference, which, indeed, could be at one o'clock, three minutes past two, or any other time of the day.   It simply signifies the "closing of a switch" to start a certain event.   Therefore, with this time reference, the period before $t = 0$ represents "history," $t = 0$ is "present," and any time greater than zero is "future."   In more general terms, we may use $t = t_0$ as a time reference, where t_0 is not necessarily zero.   The choice of this general reference is necessary when we have a chain of events occurring one after another.

In addition to being used as test signals, the unit step function is also often used for the construction of other signals and waveforms. Any time function $f(t)$ which is defined only for time greater than zero is apparently not altered when it is multiplied by the unit step function. Thus the unit step function can be used as a switch to start or end any signal at any time we desire.   For instance, the unit ramp function $u_r(t)$

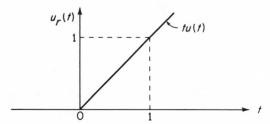

Fig. 1-6   The unit ramp function.

shown in Fig. 1-6 may be regarded as the product of the function t and $u(t)$.   Therefore a ramp function is defined as

$$u_r(t) = t \qquad t > 0 \qquad\qquad (1\text{-}6)$$
$$u_r(t) = 0 \qquad t < 0$$

Since $u(t)$ is zero for all time less than zero, the negative portion of t is eliminated when it is multiplied by $u(t)$.

Any time function $f(t - T)$, which is zero for $t < T$, is unaltered when it is multiplied by a delayed unit step function $u(t - T)$, where the latter is $u(t)$ shifted to the right by T.   However, if $f(t)$ is defined only for $t > 0$ and is multiplied by $u(t - T)$, the product function $f(t)u(t - T)$ will be zero for t less than T since the shifted unit step function *switches on* $f(t)$ only after $t = T$.   Several simple examples illustrating the role of

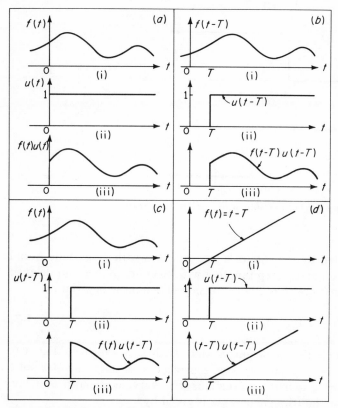

Fig. 1-7 *Waveforms illustrating the applications of the unit step function for the switching on and switching off of a signal.   In all figures, (iii) = (i) × (ii).*

switching played by the unit step function are shown in Fig. 1-7.   We show in the following section that a great variety of signals and waveforms can be formed by using simple signal components and the unit step function as a switching device.

A rectangular pulse of height E and of duration t_1 to t_2 $(t_1 < t_2)$ is shown in Fig. 1-8a.   Figure 1-8b and c shows that this rectangular pulse

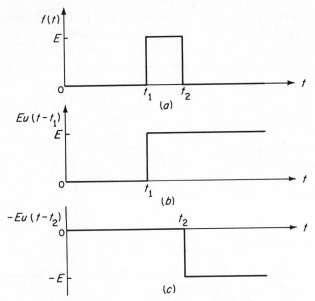

Fig. 1-8   Forming a rectangular pulse with two step functions.

can be represented by the sum of a step function with magnitude E and delayed by time t_1 and a step function with magnitude $-E$ and delayed by time t_2.   Therefore the time expression of the pulse is given by

$$f(t) = E[u(t - t_1) - u(t - t_2)] \tag{1-7}$$

A triangular pulse of height E and width t_2 is shown in Fig. 1-9. The figure also depicts a step-by-step construction of the triangular pulse by means of a set of four ramp functions with varying amounts of delay. The equation for the triangular pulse is given by

$$f(t) = f_1(t) + f_2(t) + f_3(t) + f_4(t)$$

$$= E\left[\frac{t}{t_1} u(t) - \frac{t - t_1}{t_1} u(t - t_1) - \frac{t - t_1}{t_2 - t_1} u(t - t_1) \right.$$

$$\left. + \frac{t - t_2}{t_2 - t_1} u(t - t_2)\right] \quad (1\text{-}8)$$

The composition of signals, of course, is not restricted to signals formed by straight-line segments.   Figure 1-10 shows a signal composed

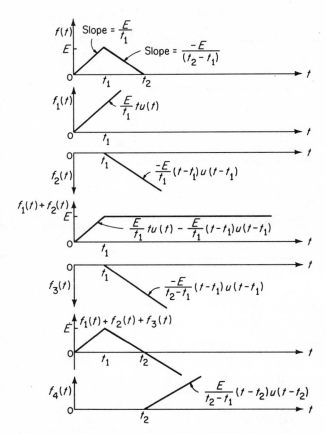

Fig. 1-9 *Waveforms illustrating the construction of a triangular pulse by a set of ramp functions.* $f(t) = f_1(t) + f_2(t) + f_3(t) + f_4(t).$

of sections of t^2 and a unit step function.   The signal is described by

$$f(t) = t^2 u(t) - (t-1)^2 u(t-1) - u(t-3) \qquad (1\text{-}9)$$

The impulse function

The impulse function is a mathematical concept often used to express certain types of discontinuities in physical systems.   Unlike the deterministic signals discussed in the preceding sections, the impulse function cannot be generated physically.

The impulse function can be used to explain the jump discontinuities

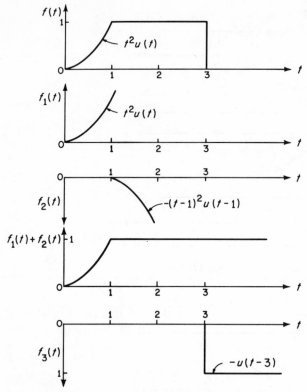

Fig. 1-10 $f(t) = f_1(t) + f_2(t) + f_3(t)$
$$= t^2 u(t) - (t-1)^2 u(t-1) - u(t-3)$$

in currents and voltages in capacitors and inductors.   It is shown in the next chapter that the voltage across a capacitor cannot jump instantaneously unless the current in the capacitor exhibits an impulse function. Similarly, the current in an inductor can be discontinuous only if the voltage across it is an impulse function.   In Chap. 10 it is shown that the impulse function can be used to approximate the outputs of samplers in discrete-data systems.

There are many different definitions of the impulse function, and the subject continues to be controversial among mathematicians and engineers.   From the engineering viewpoint, the impulse function can be defined as a pulse whose amplitude is infinitely large and pulsewidth infinitesimally small and such that the area under the pulse is finite. Actually, the shape of the pulse is immaterial.   For all practical purposes,

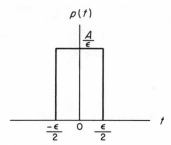

Fig. 1-11   A rectangular pulse.

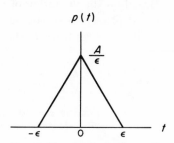

Fig. 1-12   A triangular pulse.

it can be a rectangular pulse as shown in Fig. 1-11 or a triangular pulse as shown in Fig. 1-12. Referring to these two pulse configurations, the *impulse function*, sometimes simply called *impulse*, is defined as

$$\delta(t) = \lim_{\epsilon \to 0} p(t) \tag{1-10}$$

Notice that, in each case, as $\epsilon \to 0$, the areas under the pulses are equal to A. The impulse is thus said to be of *strength A*. When $A = 1$, the impulse is called the *unit impulse*.

The foregoing description of an impulse function is purely for the convenience of engineers, who often have to regard an impulse function as a signal in a physical system.

From a mathematical sense, the impulse function $\delta(t)$ is often treated as a special type of function having certain properties. An ordinary function $f(t)$ usually has a property such that its value at any $t = t_0$ is specified by $f(t_0)$. However, the impulse function belongs to a concept called the *generalized function*,[6] or the *distribution function*. A generalized function differs from an ordinary function in that it is defined by a functional relationship rather than its value at a point. The impulse function is defined as a generalized function possessing the following properties:

$$\delta(t) = 0 \qquad t \neq 0 \tag{1-11}$$

$$\int_{-\infty}^{\infty} \delta(t) \, dt = 1 \tag{1-12}$$

$$\int_{-\infty}^{\infty} \delta(t) f(t) \, dt = f(0) \tag{1-13}$$

for any function $f(t)$ which is continuous at $t = 0$.

Based on the definition of the impulse function given above, several important properties of $\delta(t)$ are derived as follows:

1. If $f(t)$ is continuous at $t = t_0$, then

$$\int_{-\infty}^{\infty} f(t)\delta(t - t_0)\, dt = f(t_0) \tag{1-14}$$

Proof   Letting $\tau = t - t_0$ in (1-14) and from (1-13),

$$\int_{-\infty}^{\infty} f(\tau + t_0)\delta(\tau)\, d\tau = f(t_0) \tag{1-15}$$

2. The derivative of the unit step function is the unit impulse function; i.e.,

$$\frac{du(t)}{dt} = \delta(t) \tag{1-16}$$

Proof   Let us form the integral

$$\int_{-\infty}^{\infty} \frac{du(t)}{dt} f(t)\, dt \tag{1-17}$$

where $f(t)$ is continuous at $t = 0$, and $f(\infty) = 0$. Integrating by parts, (1-17) becomes

$$\int_{-\infty}^{\infty} \frac{du(t)}{dt} f(t)\, dt = \int_{-\infty}^{\infty} f(t)\, du(t)$$

$$= f(t)u(t) \Big|_{-\infty}^{\infty} - \int_{-\infty}^{\infty} u(t) \frac{df(t)}{dt}\, dt \tag{1-18}$$

Since $f(\infty) = 0$, and in view of the property of the unit step function, (1-18) gives

$$\int_{-\infty}^{\infty} \frac{du(t)}{dt} f(t)\, dt = - \int_{0}^{\infty} \frac{df(t)}{dt}\, dt = f(0) - f(\infty) = f(0) \tag{1-19}$$

Now comparing (1-19) with (1-13), we conclude that

$$\frac{du(t)}{dt} = \delta(t) \tag{1-20}$$

PROBLEMS

1-1 Indicate which of the following equations are linear and which are nonlinear:

(a) $\dfrac{d^2y(t)}{dt^2} + 3t\dfrac{dy(t)}{dt} + 2y(t) = 0$

(b) $\dfrac{d^2y(t)}{dt^2} + 3y(t)\dfrac{dy(t)}{dt} + 2y(t) = 5$

(c) $\dfrac{dy(t)}{dt} + t^2 = 1$

(d) $\dfrac{2\,d^2y(t)}{dt^2} + \left[\dfrac{dy(t)}{dt}\right]^2 + y(t) = 0$

1-2 Indicate which of the equations in Prob. 1-1 are time-variant and which are invariant.

1-3 Write the functional relationships for the aperiodic waveforms shown in Fig. P1-1.

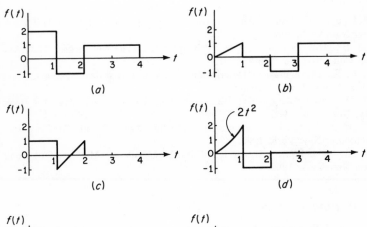

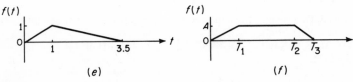

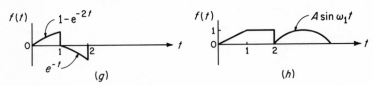

Fig. P1-1

1-4   Write functional expressions for the periodic functions shown in Fig. P1-2.

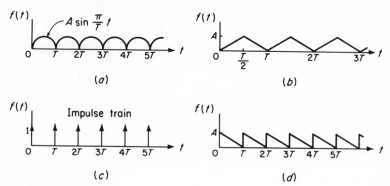

Fig. P1-2

BIBLIOGRAPHY

1   Brenner, E., and M. Javid: "Analysis of Electric Circuits," McGraw-Hill Book Company, New York, 1959.
2   Friedland, B., O. Wing, and R. Ash: "Principles of Linear Networks," McGraw-Hill Book Company, New York, 1961.
3   Kalman, R. E.: Mathematical Description of Linear Dynamical Systems, *J. on Control*, ser. A, vol. 1, no. 2, 1963.
4   Zadeh, L. A., and C. A. Desoer: "Linear System Theory," McGraw-Hill Book Company, New York, 1963.
5   Wylie, C. R. Jr.,: "Advanced Engineering Mathematics," 3d ed., McGraw-Hill Book Company, New York, 1966.
6   Papoulis, A.: "The Fourier Integral and Its Applications," McGraw-Hill Book Company, New York, 1962.

ADDITIONAL REFERENCES

Lynch, W. A., and J. G. Truxal: "Introductory System Analysis," McGraw-Hill Book Company, New York, 1961.
Van Valkenburg, M. E.: "Network Analysis," 2d ed., Prentice-Hall, Inc., Englewood Cliffs, N.J., 1964.

TWO

LINEAR NETWORK ELEMENTS

2-1 INTRODUCTION

The elements found in an electric network may generally be described as *active* or *passive*. Passive elements are usually found in the form of resistors, capacitors, and inductors (including transformers). The symbolic representations of these basic elements are depicted in Fig. 2-1. In this text we consider that these elements are not only passive, but also linear, bilateral, and time-invariant. The active elements found in systems and networks are usually energy sources, or could be considered as such. Devices such as generators, vacuum tubes, transistors, and negative resistors are well-known examples of active electric elements.

An active element may be in whole or in part represented by a current source or a voltage source. Furthermore, these active sources are classified as ideal or nonideal, dependent or independent.

The symbolic representations of nonideal voltage and current sources

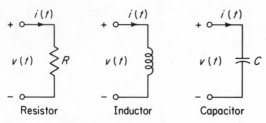

Resistor   Inductor   Capacitor

Fig. 2-1   Symbolic representations of passive elements in electric networks.

are shown in Fig. 2-2.   In these devices, Z_g represents the impedances associated with the sources.   These nonideal sources are characterized by the fact that the terminal voltage $v(t)$ of the voltage source depends on the current that flows through the source, and the current $i(t)$ which flows out of the terminal of the current source also depends upon the terminal voltage.   In Fig. 2-2, if Z_g becomes zero in the voltage source

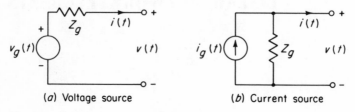

(a) Voltage source   (b) Current source

Fig. 2-2   Symbolic representations of nonideal sources.

and infinite in the current source, the terminal voltage of the voltage source and the current in the current source are no longer functions of the load conditions.   The sources then become *ideal* sources.   The symbolic representations of an ideal voltage source and an ideal current source are shown in Fig. 2-3.

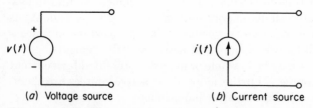

(a) Voltage source   (b) Current source

Fig. 2-3   Symbolic representations of ideal sources.

In the case of dependent sources, the source voltage and the source current depend upon a voltage or a current which appears at another part of the network.   Typical circuit diagrams of dependent voltage and current sources are shown in Fig. 2-4.   In reality, the voltage and current

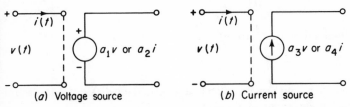

(a) Voltage source   (b) Current source

Fig. 2-4   *Symbolic representations of dependent sources.*

sources shown in Fig. 2-2 are used to represent physical signals and generators, whereas those of Fig. 2-4 are generally used to represent vacuum tubes and transistors.

2-2   MATHEMATICAL DESCRIPTIONS OF PASSIVE ELEMENTS

The mathematical relationships between the currents and the voltages in passive network elements are established by conducting experiments involving these elements.   Based on these experimental results, general conclusions are drawn concerning the mathematical relations between currents and voltages in the elements involved.   In many situations these conclusions are regarded as physical laws.   We here review the voltage-current relationships in R, L, and C elements, using the concept of cause and effect.

Resistance (Ohm's law)

The voltage-current relation in a resistor can be written (see Fig. 2-5)

$$v_R(t) = Ri_R(t) \tag{2-1}$$

or

$$i_R(t) = Gv_R(t) \tag{2-2}$$

where $G = 1/R$ = conductance in mhos.   In (2-1), the current $i_R(t)$ may be regarded as the *excitation*, or *cause*, and $v_R(t)$ is the *effect*.   In (2-2), $v_R(t)$ may be considered as the *cause*, and $i_R(t)$, the *effect*.   Since the resistor considered here is a bilateral element, the vi relation for a resistor

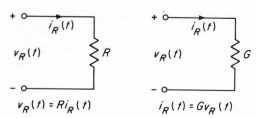

$$v_R(t) = Ri_R(t) \qquad i_R(t) = Gv_R(t)$$

Fig. 2-5 Voltage-current relations in a resistor.

may be expressed by either Eq. (2-1) or (2-2), regardless of the actual cause-and-effect assignment of i and v.

Capacitance (Coulomb's law)[1]

The current-voltage relationship for a capacitor can be expressed as

$$i_c(t) = C\,\frac{dv_c(t)}{dt} \qquad (2\text{-}3)$$

or

$$v_c(t) = \frac{1}{C}\int_{0^-}^{t} i_c(\tau)\,d\tau + v_c(0^-) \qquad (2\text{-}4)$$

where the constant C is the capacitance and is measured in *farads*. In expression (2-3) we may regard $v_c(t)$ as an applied voltage to the capacitor terminals; the resulting current $i_c(t)$ is directly proportional to the time rate of change of this voltage. The interpretation of (2-4) is such that a current $i_c(\tau)$ is sent through the capacitor, and the voltage measured at any time $t > -\infty$ across C is $v_c(t)$. It is shown that $v_c(t)$ is proportional to the integral of $i_c(\tau)$ from 0 to t plus the initial voltage $v_c(0^-)$ across the capacitor. It is often convenient to choose a time reference $t_0 (0 < t_0 < t)$ and assume that the complete past history of the capacitor before $t = t_0$ is contained in the "initial voltage" $v_c(t_0^-)$. In this case, the parallel of (2-4) is

$$v_c(t) = \frac{1}{C}\int_{t_0^-}^{t} i_c(\tau)\,d\tau + v_c(t_0^-) \qquad (2\text{-}5)$$

In expressions (2-4) and (2-5), we have introduced a limiting time concept. The symbol t_0^- means "approaching t_0 from the left." In general, if $v_c(t)$ is discontinuous at $t = t_0$, $v_c(t_0^-)$ will be different from $v_c(t_0^+)$.

As an alternative, we may write

$$v_c(t) = \frac{1}{C} \int_{t_0^+}^{t} i_c(\tau)\, d\tau + v_c(t_0^+) \tag{2-6}$$

The two equations (2-5) and (2-6) imply that the voltage $v_c(t)$ across the capacitor, measured at any time t, is completely defined by the initial capacitor voltage $v_c(t_0)$ and the behavior of i_c between t_0 and t.

Since $v_c(t_0)$ is a voltage, it can be represented by an equivalent source. The voltage-current relationship of (2-5) is demonstrated by an equivalent circuit as shown in Fig. 2-6.

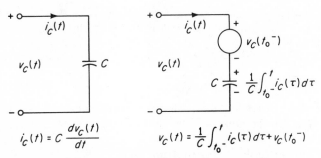

$$i_c(t) = C\,\frac{dv_c(t)}{dt} \qquad\qquad v_c(t) = \frac{1}{C}\int_{t_0^-}^{t} i_c(\tau)\,d\tau + v_c(t_0^-)$$

Fig. 2-6   Voltage-current relations in a capacitor.

It is interesting to take the difference between (2-5) and (2-6). By this process, we get

$$
\begin{aligned}
v_c(t_0^+) - v_c(t_0^-) &= \frac{1}{C}\int_{t_0^-}^{t} i_c(\tau)\, d\tau - \frac{1}{C}\int_{t_0^+}^{t} \ddot{i}_c(\tau)\, d\tau \\
&= \frac{1}{C}\int_{t_0^-}^{t_0^+} i_c(\tau)\, d\tau = \frac{\Delta q(t_0)}{C}
\end{aligned}
\tag{2-7}
$$

where $\Delta q(t_0)$ denotes the instantaneous flow of charge into (or out of) C during the interval of $t_0^+ - t_0^-$.   Of course, $\Delta q(t_0)$ is nonzero only if $v_c(t)$ has a jump discontinuity at t_0.

As a simple illustration of these concepts, consider the network shown in Fig. 2-7.   Assuming that the switch is closed at $t = t_0$, the current in the capacitor for $t \geq t_0$ is given by

$$i_c(t) = C\,\frac{dv_c(t)}{dt} = CV\,\frac{du(t - t_0)}{dt} \tag{2-8}$$

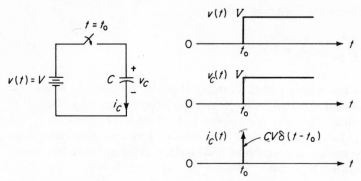

Fig. 2-7   Jump discontinuity in capacitor voltage.

The derivative of a unit step function at $t = t_0$ is a unit impulse function at t_0.   Therefore (2-8) becomes

$$i_c(t) = CV \, \delta(t - t_0) \qquad (2\text{-}9)$$

This result shows that, in order for the capacitor voltage to have a jump discontinuity, the current in the capacitor must have an infinite magnitude, which is physically impossible.

To check the result of (2-9), we write, from (2-7),

$$\Delta q(t_0) = \int_{t_0^-}^{t_0^+} i_c(\tau) \, d\tau = VC \int_{t_0^-}^{t_0^+} \delta(\tau - t_0) \, d\tau = VC$$

Therefore

$$v_c(t_0^+) - v_c(t_0^-) = \frac{\Delta q(t_0)}{C} = V \qquad (2\text{-}10)$$

which is as expected.

Inductance (Faraday's law)

The current-voltage relationships for linear inductors can be written

$$v_L(t) = L \frac{di_L(t)}{dt} \qquad (2\text{-}11)$$

or

$$i_L(t) = \frac{1}{L} \int_{t_0^-}^{t} v_L(\tau) \, d\tau + i_L(t_0^-) \qquad (2\text{-}12)$$

or

$$i_L(t) = \frac{1}{L} \int_{t_0^+}^{t} v_L(\tau) \, d\tau + i_L(t_0^+) \tag{2-13}$$

where $i_L(t_0^-)$ and $i_L(t_0^+)$ are the initial currents in the inductor at $t = t_0^-$ and $t = t_0^+$, respectively.   The constant L is the inductance in *henrys*.

Again, t_0^- refers to measuring toward t_0 from the left, and t_0^+ is approaching from the right.   The two equations (2-12) and (2-13) imply that the current in an inductor L, measured at any time t, is completely defined by the initial inductor current $i_L(t_0)$, measured at an earlier time, and by the behavior of v_L between t_0 and t.

We can also write (2-12) as

$$i_L(t) = \frac{1}{L} \int_{t_0^-}^{t} v_L(\tau) \, d\tau + \frac{\lambda(t_0^-)}{L} \tag{2-14}$$

where $\lambda(t_0^-)$ denotes the flux linkage that links with the inductor just prior to time t_0.   The equivalent circuit for an inductor is shown in Fig. 2-8.

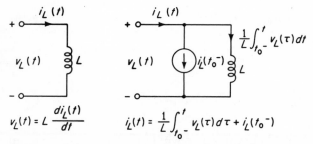

Fig. 2-8   *Voltage-current relations in an inductor.*

Subtracting (2-12) from (2-13) gives

$$i_L(t_0^+) - i_L(t_0^-) = \frac{1}{L} \int_{t_0^-}^{t_0^+} v_L(\tau) \, d\tau = \frac{\Delta\lambda(t_0)}{L} \tag{2-15}$$

where

$$\Delta\lambda(t_0) = \lambda(t_0^-) - \lambda(t_0^+)$$

and is the instantaneous transfer of flux linkage at $t = t_0$.   Clearly, $\Delta\lambda(t_0)$ is nonzero only if $i_L(t)$ has a jump discontinuity at t_0.

As a simple illustrative example of the jump phenomenon in inductor current, consider the circuit shown in Fig. 2-9.   Opening the switch at

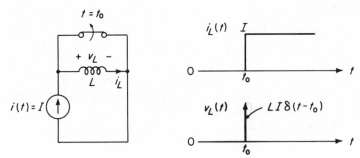

Fig. 2-9   Jump discontinuity in inductor current.

$t = t_0$ should disrupt the current through it.   We may assume that the entire current $i_L = I$ flows through the switch prior to t_0.   Therefore the current in L jumps from zero to I at $t = t_0$.   The voltage across L is given by

$$v_L(t) = L \frac{di_L(t)}{dt} = LI \, \delta(t - t_0) \tag{2-16}$$

Substitution of (2-16) into (2-15) yields

$$i_L(t_0^+) - i_L(t_0^-) = \frac{1}{L} \int_{t_0^-}^{t_0^+} LI \, \delta(\tau - t_0) \, d\tau = I$$

From this theoretical development we conclude that the current in an inductor can be discontinuous only if the voltage across it becomes infinite, i.e., the voltage is an impulse function.

Magnetic coupling (mutual inductance)

Not all passive electrical devices and phenomena can be described in terms of pure R, L, and C elements.   A well-known example of such a device is the transformer.   The basic transformer may feature two separate coils wound on a common iron core as shown in Fig. 2-10.   According to experimental results obtained by Faraday, which eventually were termed in Faraday's induction law, when a fluctuating current is sent through one of the coils, a voltage appears at the terminals of the other.   This is because an alternating current in one coil gives rise to a fluctuating flux

ϕ linking with the other coil, thus inducing an electromotive force (emf) across its terminals.   Usually, the coil connected to the source of excitation is referred to as the *primary* windings, and the coil connected to the load is the *secondary* side of the transformer.   Because of the inductive effects between two (or more) coils of a transformer, the mutual inductance M (henrys) is used to describe the relationship between the current in one coil and the induced voltage in the other.   This is in contrast to the self-inductance L which describes the current and voltage relationship in the same coil.   In general, when current varies in one coil, the polarity or direction of the induced voltage in the other coil depends upon two factors: the direction or polarity of the inducing current (or applied voltage) and the sense or orientation of the coil windings.   Referring to Fig. 2-10, when

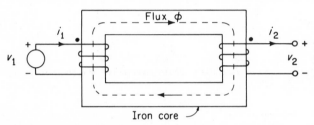

Fig. 2-10   Schematic of a transformer.

the instantaneous polarity of v_1 and the corresponding direction† of i_1 are as shown, the induced voltage v_2 in coil 2 has a positive instantaneous polarity at the top of the coil.   This is because the voltage v_2 is in the direction of producing a current (if the terminals of coil 2 were shorted) i_2 so as to oppose the flux ϕ produced by i_1.   However, if the orientation of one of the coils is reversed, with the direction of v_1 unaltered, the polarity of v_2 is reversed.   Therefore a "dot" convention[2,3] is used to indicate the way the coils are oriented, which eventually leads to the sign convention of the current-voltage relationships in coupled circuits.   The dot convention is described with reference to Fig. 2-10.   If we arbitrarily place a dot at the + terminal of v_1, a dot is also placed at the + terminal of the induced voltage v_2.

Just how does the dot convention contribute to the analysis of coupled circuits?   Once the orientation of the windings is described by the dot convention, the transformer schematics can be represented by the simple

---

† Since alternating currents are referred to here, the instantaneous *direction* of a current actually implies the instantaneous value of di/dt at a given instant.

model of Fig. 2-11.   Note that the resistances of the coils are neglected.
The voltage-current relationships of the transformer can now be described
mathematically by the equations

$$v_1(t) = L_1 \frac{di_1}{dt} + M \frac{di_2}{dt} \tag{2-17}$$

$$v_2(t) = M \frac{di_1}{dt} + L_2 \frac{di_2}{dt} \tag{2-18}$$

where M is the mutual inductance.   Although M is itself always a positive
quantity, the mutual-inductance terms in (2-17) and (2-18) may have a
positive or a negative sign, depending upon the location of the dots and the
current directions of the transformer.   Referring to the situation shown in
Fig. 2-11, the current i_1 flowing into the dot induces a voltage $M_1\, di_1/dt$

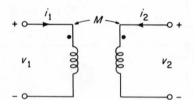

Fig. 2-11   Dot convention of a transformer.

which is positive at the dotted terminals in the secondary coil.   The current i_2, assumed to be also flowing into the dotted terminal, induces a
voltage $L_2\, di_2/dt$ in the secondary, which is also positive at the dotted end.
Thus the mutual term in (2-18) has a plus sign.   Similarly, the voltage
induced in the primary due to i_2 is positive at the dotted terminal; thus
the mutual term in (2-17) is also positive.   However, if the polarity of
v_2 is reversed from that of Fig. 2-11, i_2 flows out of the dotted terminal,
meaning that the instantaneous value of di_2/dt is negative; the mutual
terms in (2-17) and (2-18) will all be negative.   Using the same argument,
we conclude that *when both currents i_1 and i_2 enter or leave the dotted terminals, the mutual inductance M carries a positive sign; otherwise, M has a
negative sign.*   To clarify the signs of the induced voltages due to M, four
different possibilities of arrangements are illustrated in Fig. 2-12.   Only
the voltage-current relationships of the arrangement shown in Fig. 2-12a
are given.   The student should find the relationships for the other three
cases, as an exercise.
    The mutual inductance M is related to the self-inductances L_1 and L_2
by

$$M = k \sqrt{L_1 L_2} \tag{2-19}$$

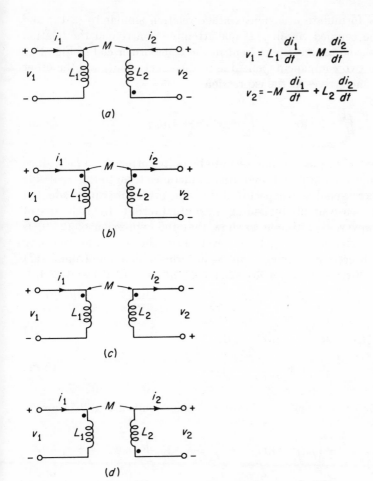

$$v_1 = L_1 \frac{di_1}{dt} - M \frac{di_2}{dt}$$

$$v_2 = -M \frac{di_1}{dt} + L_2 \frac{di_2}{dt}$$

(a)

(b)

(c)

(d)

Fig. 2-12 *Several different dot assignments and voltage-current signs in the transformer. The voltage-current relations of (b), (c), and (d) are to be filled in by the student.*

where k is a constant called the *coefficient of coupling*. The value of k, proportional to the tightness of the coupling, lies between zero and unity. Because of the existence of leakage flux, the coefficient of coupling is always less than unity for a practical transformer. In the ideal case, we may assume that k is unity, and the transformer is called a *perfect transformer*. A perfect transformer does not exist in reality, although a transformer with iron core which provides a low reluctance path for the flux may have a k very close to unity.

We now formulate a current-voltage relation similar to (2-12) and (2-13) for the coupled circuit. If one attempts to arrive at the relation simply by reasoning that the current in the transformer coil of Fig. 2-11 must contain two components, one due to the effect of $v_1(t)$ and the other due to $v_2(t)$, one arrives at the expression

$$i_1(t) = \frac{1}{L_1} \int_{t_0^-}^{t} v_1(\tau) \, d\tau + \frac{1}{M} \int_{t_0^-}^{t} v_2(\tau) \, d\tau + i_1(t_0^-) \tag{2-20}$$

At first glance this equation may seem to be quite correct. In fact, since (2-17) is obtained by adding the mutual-inductance term to the right side of (2-11), it is reasonable to expect that the same procedure can be adopted for the present case simply by adding the mutual term to the right side of (2-12). However, it is simple to show that the expression of (2-20) is incorrect for the circuit of Fig. 2-11. Evidently, the correct answer may be obtained directly by solving i_1 and i_2 in terms of v_1 and v_2 from (2-17) and (2-18). First solving for di_1/dt and di_2/dt from (2-17) and (2-18), we get

$$\frac{di_1}{dt} = \frac{L_2}{L_1 L_2 - M^2} v_1 - \frac{M}{L_1 L_2 - M^2} v_2 \tag{2-21}$$

$$\frac{di_2}{dt} = \frac{-M}{L_1 L_2 - M^2} v_1 + \frac{L_1}{L_1 L_2 - M^2} v_2 \tag{2-22}$$

Therefore the current-voltage relations for the circuit of Fig. 2-11 are

$$i_1(t) = \frac{L_2}{L_1 L_2 - M^2} \int_{t_0^-}^{t} v_1(\tau) \, d\tau - \frac{M}{L_1 L_2 - M^2} \int_{t_0^-}^{t} v_2(\tau) \, d\tau + i_1(t_0^-) \tag{2-23}$$

$$i_2(t) = - \frac{M}{L_1 L_2 - M^2} \int_{t_0^-}^{t} v_1(\tau) \, d\tau + \frac{L_1}{L_1 L_2 - M^2} \int_{t_0^-}^{t} v_2(\tau) \, d\tau + i_2(t_0^-) \tag{2-24}$$

Now, comparing (2-23) with (2-20), we notice that the two equations are the same, except for the constants in front of the two integrals. Let us clarify this situation by referring to the transformer circuit diagram of Fig. 2-11. When a voltage $v_1(t)$ is applied to the terminals of coil 1, with the terminals of coil 2 open, the voltage-current relation in coil 1 is

$$v_1(t) = L_1 \frac{di_1(t)}{dt}$$

and the induced voltage on the secondary windings is

$$v_2(t) = M \frac{di_1(t)}{dt}$$

These two expressions can be regarded as the definitions of L_1 and M, and we noticed that they are considered with the terminals of coil 2 *open*. Similarly, if a voltage $v_2(t)$ is applied across the terminals of coil 2, with coil 1 open, we have

$$v_2(t) = L_2 \frac{di_2(t)}{dt}$$

and

$$v_1(t) = M \frac{di_2(t)}{dt}$$

Note that the last four equations are written with the unexcited windings open. Had these windings been shorted, there would have been currents flowing in them, which would have contributed more terms to these expressions.

In order to obtain a current-voltage relation similar to (2-12), we must short-circuit the unexcited terminals of the transformer. Referring to Fig. 2-13a, we can write

$$i_1(t) = \Gamma_1 \int_{t_0^-}^{t} v_1(\tau) \, d\tau + i_1(t_0^-) \qquad v_2 = 0 \tag{2-25}$$

where Γ_1 is dimensionally an *inverse inductance*.[4] In general, Γ_1 is not equal to $1/L_1$ unless $M = 0$, since the conditions under which L_1 and Γ_1 are defined are basically different. Now since coil 2 is short-circuited, the current i_2 induced in the secondary windings is given by

$$i_2(t) = -\Gamma_M \int_{t_0^-}^{t} v_1(\tau) \, d\tau + i_2(t_0^-) \tag{2-26}$$

where Γ_M is called the *mutual-inverse inductance*. Since Γ_M and M are not defined under the same condition, Γ_M is not equal to $1/M$. A minus sign is placed in front of Γ_M in (2-26) since by definition the voltage induced in coil 2 is positive at the dotted end and thus the actual direction of the current i_2 is opposite to that shown in Fig. 2-13a. In a similar manner, if we short-circuit coil 1 and apply $v_2(t)$ to the secondary windings as shown

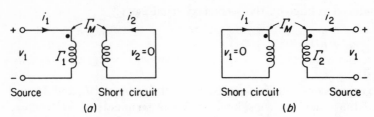

Fig. 2-13 Definitions of the inverse inductances.

in Fig. 2-13b, the following two equations are obtained:

$$i_1(t) = -\Gamma_M \int_{t_0^-}^{t} v_2(\tau)\, d\tau + i_1(t_0^-)\tag{2-27}$$

$$i_2(t) = \Gamma_2 \int_{t_0^-}^{t} v_2(\tau)\, d\tau + i_2(t_0^-)\tag{2-28}$$

Superposing the effects of v_1 and v_2, (2-25) and (2-27) can be combined to read

$$i_1(t) = \Gamma_1 \int_{t_0^-}^{t} v_1(\tau)\, d\tau - \Gamma_M \int_{t_0^-}^{t} v_2(\tau)\, d\tau + i_1(t_0^-)\tag{2-29}$$

Similarly, (2-26) and (2-28) can be combined to give

$$i_2(t) = -\Gamma_M \int_{t_0^-}^{t} v_1(\tau)\, d\tau + \Gamma_2 \int_{t_0^-}^{t} v_2(\tau)\, d\tau + i_2(t_0^-)\tag{2-30}$$

These expressions are now valid for the circuit shown in Fig. 2-11. It is important to note that the sign for M in the circuit of Fig. 2-11 is positive, but its mutual-inverse inductance Γ_M has a negative sign. This also means that when M has a negative sign, Γ_M will be positive.

The relationships between the inductances and the inverse inductances are established by simply comparing (2-29) and (2-30) with (2-23) and (2-24). Therefore

$$\Gamma_1 = \frac{L_2}{L_1 L_2 - M^2} = \text{self-inverse inductance in coil 1}\tag{2-31}$$

$$\Gamma_2 = \frac{L_1}{L_1 L_2 - M^2} = \text{self-inverse inductance in coil 2}\tag{2-32}$$

$$\Gamma_M = \frac{M}{L_1 L_2 - M^2} = \text{mutual-inverse inductance between coils 1 and 2}\tag{2-33}$$

It is apparent that Γ_1 and $1/L_1$ are the same only when M is zero.   Then (2-29) reverts to the form of (2-12), which is the expression of $i_1(t)$ in a single uncoupled inductor.

The equivalent circuits portraying the current-voltage relationships in (2-17), (2-18), (2-29), and (2-30) are shown in Fig. 2-14.

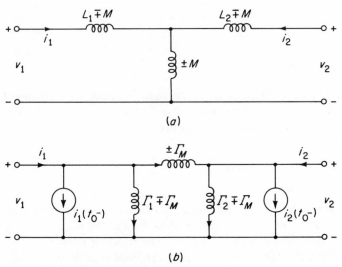

(a)

(b)

Fig. 2-14   Equivalent circuits portraying Eqs. (2-17), (2-18), (2-29), and (2-30).

The ideal transformer[3,5]

An idealized element often used in network analysis and synthesis is the *ideal transformer*.   The ideal transformer is basically different from a perfect transformer, and the two concepts should not be confused with each other.   To find the difference between these two types of transformers, let us refer to the symbolic representation of the ideal transformer shown in Fig. 2-15.   Note that the mutual inductance M is removed from the diagram, and the coupling of the two coils is indicated by the

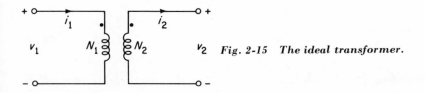

Fig. 2-15   The ideal transformer.

number of turns of the windings, N_1 and N_2.   In essence, the ideal transformer is a fictitious element used to represent certain current-voltage relationships in an electric network.   Specifically, the current and voltage relationships in the ideal transformer are defined as

$$N_1 i_1 - N_2 i_2 = 0 \qquad (2\text{-}34)$$

and

$$\frac{v_1}{v_2} = \frac{N_1}{N_2} \qquad (2\text{-}35)$$

Notice that in (2-34) i_2 carries a negative sign, because, with reference to Fig. 2-15, i_2 is assumed to flow out of the dotted terminal.   The two equations (2-34) and (2-35) may be combined to read

$$\frac{v_1}{v_2} = \frac{i_2}{i_1} = \frac{N_1}{N_2} = \text{turns ratio } n \qquad (2\text{-}36)$$

We can now conclude that a practical transformer is characterized by its winding resistances, self-inductances, and mutual inductances.   When the transformer is considered to be perfect, the winding resistances are neglected and the inductances must satisfy the condition $M = \sqrt{L_1 L_2}$. The ideal transformer, on the other hand, is characterized only by the turns ratio $n = N_1/N_2$, which defines the relationships between the currents and the voltages in the transformer.   A natural question is: Under what condition would a perfect transformer become the ideal transformer? To answer this question, we refer to the circuit diagram shown in Fig. 2-15. The voltage ratio of the device as a perfect transformer ($k = 1$) is

$$\frac{v_2}{v_1} = \frac{-\left(-M\dfrac{di_1}{dt} + L_2 \dfrac{di_2}{dt} \right)}{L_1 \dfrac{di_1}{dt} - M \dfrac{di_2}{dt}} = \frac{\sqrt{L_1 L_2}\, \dfrac{di_1}{dt} - L_2 \dfrac{di_2}{dt}}{L_1 \dfrac{di_1}{dt} - \sqrt{L_1 L_2}\, \dfrac{di_2}{dt}} \qquad (2\text{-}37)$$

Simplifying, (2-37) becomes

$$\frac{v_2}{v_1} = \sqrt{\frac{L_2}{L_1}} \qquad (2\text{-}38)$$

Comparing (2-38) with (2-36), we see that the ideal transformer will be identical with a perfect transformer if the following relationship holds:

$$n = \frac{N_1}{N_2} = \sqrt{\frac{L_1}{L_2}} \qquad (2\text{-}39)$$

Since it is well known that the inductance of a coil is directly proportional to the square of the number of turns, the relationship in (2-38) is expected. At this point it would seem that the two transformers were alike if L_1 and L_2 satisfy (2-39).   However, we still have to check the current relations in the two transformers.   Writing

$$v_1(t) = L_1 \frac{di_1}{dt} - M \frac{di_2}{dt} \qquad (2\text{-}40)$$

and integrating both sides from $-\infty$ to t, we have

$$\int_{-\infty}^{t} v_1(\tau)\, d\tau = L_1[i_1(t) - i_1(-\infty)] - M[i_2(t) - i_2(-\infty)]$$

Assuming that $i_1(-\infty)$ and $i_2(-\infty)$ are both zero and solving for $i_1(t)$ from the last expression, we get

$$i_1(t) = \frac{M}{L_1} i_2(t) + \frac{1}{L_1} \int_{-\infty}^{t} v_1(\tau)\, d\tau \qquad (2\text{-}41)$$

Since $M/L_1 = N_2/N_1$, (2-41) is written

$$i_1(t) = \frac{N_2}{N_1} i_2(t) + \frac{1}{L_1} \int_{-\infty}^{t} v_1(\tau)\, d\tau \qquad (2\text{-}42)$$

Comparing (2-42) with (2-36), we see that, for the two transformers to be alike, L_1 must approach infinity, since the integral on the right side of (2-42) is finite for $v_1 \neq 0$.   Similarly, with the relationship between v_2, i_1, and i_2, we can show that L_2 must also be infinite.   This means that the ideal transformer has an infinite number of winding turns ($N_1 = N_2 = \infty$), but the ratio N_1/N_2 is a constant.

    It is interesting to show that if the lower limit of integration in the derivation of (2-41) and (2-42) is changed from $-\infty$ to t_0, a more general current relationship for the ideal transformer is obtained.   This is

$$i_1(t) - i_1(t_0) = \frac{N_2}{N_1} [i_2(t) - i_2(t_0)] \qquad (2\text{-}43)$$

where $i_1(t_0)$ and $i_2(t_0)$ are the initial currents in the two windings at t_0.

BIBLIOGRAPHY

1   Harrington, R. F.: "Introduction to Electromagnetic Engineering," McGraw-Hill Book Company, New York, 1958.
2   Boast, W. B.: "Principles of Electric and Magnetic Circuits," Harper & Row, Publishers, Incorporated, New York, 1950.
3   Van Valkenburg, M. E.: "Network Analysis," 2d ed., Prentice-Hall, Inc., Englewood Cliffs, N.J., 1964.
4   Brenner, E., and M. Javid, "Analysis of Electric Circuits," McGraw-Hill Book Company, New York, 1959.
5   Gardner, M. F., and J. L. Barnes: "Transients in Linear Systems," John Wiley & Sons, Inc., New York, 1942.

THREE

ELEMENTARY MATRIX ALGEBRA

3-1 INTRODUCTION

In the study of modern network and system theory long and complicated equations are frequently encountered. To save time and space, it is often found desirable to use appropriate shorthand symbols to simplify the representation of these mathematical expressions. The simplified notation may not reduce the amount of work required to solve the equations, but it certainly makes the complex equations much easier to handle and to manipulate.

As a simple illustration, consider the following set of simultaneous algebraic equations:

$$a_{11}x_1 + a_{12}x_2 + a_{13}x_3 = y_1$$
$$a_{21}x_1 + a_{22}x_2 + a_{23}x_3 = y_2 \qquad (3\text{-}1)$$
$$a_{31}x_1 + a_{32}x_2 + a_{33}x_3 = y_3$$

A matrix equation,

$$\mathbf{AX} = \mathbf{Y} \tag{3-2}$$

may be defined as a simplified version of (3-1).   The symbols $\mathbf{A}$, $\mathbf{X}$, and $\mathbf{Y}$ are defined as matrices, which possess certain relations with the coefficients and the variables of the original equations.   Similarly to an ordinary algebraic equation, (3-2) can be interpreted as "the product of the matrices $\mathbf{A}$ and $\mathbf{X}$ is equal to the matrix $\mathbf{Y}$."   However, in order that (3-2) and (3-1) be identical, $\mathbf{A}$, $\mathbf{X}$, and $\mathbf{Y}$ must be defined as

$$\mathbf{A} = \begin{bmatrix} a_{11} & a_{12} & a_{13} \\ a_{21} & a_{22} & a_{23} \\ a_{31} & a_{32} & a_{33} \end{bmatrix} \quad \mathbf{X} = \begin{bmatrix} x_1 \\ x_2 \\ x_3 \end{bmatrix} \quad \mathbf{Y} = \begin{bmatrix} y_1 \\ y_2 \\ y_3 \end{bmatrix} \tag{3-3}$$

which are "bracketed arrays of coefficients (numbers) and variables." Thus, in detailed form, (3-2) is written

$$\begin{bmatrix} a_{11} & a_{12} & a_{13} \\ a_{21} & a_{22} & a_{23} \\ a_{31} & a_{32} & a_{33} \end{bmatrix} \begin{bmatrix} x_1 \\ x_2 \\ x_3 \end{bmatrix} = \begin{bmatrix} y_1 \\ y_2 \\ y_3 \end{bmatrix} \tag{3-4}$$

Now we notice that the left-hand side of (3-4) involves the product of two "arrays of numbers," and the operation is not defined by the ordinary laws of algebra.   Further, after the product of $\mathbf{A}$ and $\mathbf{X}$ is formed, what is meant by equating one array of numbers to another as shown in (3-4)? All this implies that in order that (3-2) and (3-4) be correct matrix representations of (3-1), new mathematical laws and a new kind of algebra must be defined to govern the manipulation of matrices.   Once the *matrix algebra* is established, it will be seen that the solutions of (3-1) can be obtained directly by solving the matrix equation (3-2) or (3-4).

3-2   NOTATION AND DEFINITIONS OF A MATRIX

Matrix   *A matrix is a collection of numbers or elements arranged in a rectangular or square array.*

The usual way of representing a matrix is to enclose the array of matrix elements, and some of the more frequently used forms are as follows:

$$\begin{bmatrix} 3 & 5 & 2 \\ 0 & 1 & 1 \end{bmatrix} \quad \begin{pmatrix} a_{11} & a_{12} & a_{13} \\ a_{21} & a_{22} & a_{23} \end{pmatrix} \quad \left\| \begin{matrix} x_1 \\ x_2 \\ x_3 \end{matrix} \right\|$$

Observe that throughout this text the square bracket is used.

One should not confuse a matrix with a determinant, although the latter is also a square array of numbers. A major difference between a determinant and a matrix is that the former has a value and the latter does not. A determinant is a square array; that is, it has the same number of rows and columns. A matrix does not have such a restriction; it can have any number of rows and columns. However, we show later that there is a relation between a matrix and a determinant in that it is possible to define the determinant of a square matrix.

Matrix elements   When a matrix is written

$$\mathbf{A} = \begin{bmatrix} a_{11} & a_{12} & a_{13} \\ a_{21} & a_{22} & a_{23} \end{bmatrix} \tag{3-5}$$

a_{ij} is called the element of the matrix in the ith row and the jth column.

Order of a matrix   The numbers of rows and columns of a matrix are designated by the *order* of the matrix. For instance, the matrix in (3-5) has two rows and three columns, and it is said to have an order of (2,3). In general, for a matrix with n rows and m columns, the order is (n,m).

Using the ideas of matrix elements and order, (3-5) can be written, simply,

$$\mathbf{A} = [a_{ij}]_{n,m} = [a_{ij}]_{2,3} \tag{3-6}$$

Square matrix   A square matrix is one that has an equal number of rows and columns; or in terms of the order, $n = m$. Examples of the square matrix are

$$[a_{ij}]_{2,2} = \begin{bmatrix} 3 & 2 \\ 1 & 0 \end{bmatrix} \qquad [b_{ij}]_{3,3} = \begin{bmatrix} 5 & 6 & 0 \\ 1 & 1 & 0 \\ 2 & 1 & 3 \end{bmatrix}$$

Column matrix   A column matrix is formed when the matrix order is $(n,1)$, and $n \neq 1$. A column matrix has only one column, but more than one row.

Example 3-1   *Column matrices*

$$\begin{bmatrix} \dfrac{dx}{dt} \\ \dfrac{dy}{dt} \end{bmatrix} \qquad \begin{bmatrix} 3 \\ 0 \\ -2 \end{bmatrix}$$

Row matrix   A row matrix is one that has an order $(1,m)$, with $m \neq 1$. A row matrix has only one row, but usually has more than one column.

Example 3-2   Row matrix

$$[4 \quad 10 \quad -2]$$

Diagonal matrix   A diagonal matrix is a square matrix with $a_{ij} = 0$ for all $i \neq j$.

Example 3-3   Diagonal matrices

$$\begin{bmatrix} a_{11} & 0 & 0 \\ 0 & a_{22} & 0 \\ 0 & 0 & a_{33} \end{bmatrix} \quad \begin{bmatrix} 1 & 0 \\ 0 & -1 \end{bmatrix}$$

Unit matrix (identity matrix)   A unit matrix is a diagonal matrix with $a_{ij} = 1$ for $i = j$. A unit matrix is often denoted by **I** or **U**.

Example 3-4   Unit, or identity, matrix

$$\mathbf{I} = \begin{bmatrix} 1 & 0 & 0 \\ 0 & 1 & 0 \\ 0 & 0 & 1 \end{bmatrix}$$

Null matrix   A null matrix is one in which all the elements are zero. Thus $a_{ij} = 0$ for all i and j.

Example 3-5   Null matrices

$$[\mathbf{0}] = \begin{bmatrix} 0 & 0 & 0 \\ 0 & 0 & 0 \end{bmatrix} \quad [0 \quad 0 \quad 0]$$

Symmetrical matrix   A square matrix is said to be symmetrical if its elements satisfy $a_{ij} = a_{ji}$ for all i, j. A symmetrical matrix has the property that, if its rows are interchanged with columns, the same matrix is obtained.

Example 3-6   Symmetrical matrices

$$\begin{bmatrix} 5 & 1 & 3 \\ 1 & -2 & 0 \\ 3 & 0 & 0 \end{bmatrix} \quad \begin{bmatrix} 4 & -1 \\ -1 & 5 \end{bmatrix}$$

Determinant of a matrix   With each square matrix a determinant having the same elements and order is associated. For instance, the determinant of the square matrix $\mathbf{A} = [a_{ij}]_{n,n}$ is designated by

$$\Delta_A = [a_{ij}]_{n,n} = |\mathbf{A}| \tag{3-7}$$

Example 3-7   *Determinant of a matrix*   Of the square matrix

$$\mathbf{A} = \begin{bmatrix} 3 & 0 & 1 \\ 3 & -1 & 2 \\ 0 & 1 & 1 \end{bmatrix}$$

its determinant is

$$\Delta_A = \begin{vmatrix} 3 & 0 & 1 \\ 3 & -1 & 2 \\ 0 & 1 & 1 \end{vmatrix} = -6$$

Singular matrix   A square matrix is said to be singular if the value of its determinant is zero. This condition usually implies that not all the rows or not all the columns of the matrix are independent of each other. As an illustration of the dependency of rows, consider the following set of equations:

$$\begin{aligned} x_1 + 3x_2 + 2x_3 &= 0 \\ 2x_1 - x_2 - x_3 &= 0 \\ 6x_1 + 4x_2 + 2x_3 &= 0 \end{aligned} \tag{3-8}$$

In matrix form, these equations are represented by

$$\mathbf{AX} = \mathbf{0}$$

where

$$\mathbf{A} = \begin{bmatrix} 1 & 3 & 2 \\ 2 & -1 & -1 \\ 6 & 4 & 2 \end{bmatrix} \quad \text{and} \quad \mathbf{X} = \begin{bmatrix} x_1 \\ x_2 \\ x_3 \end{bmatrix}$$

Since $\mathbf{A}$ is a square matrix, it has a determinant Δ_A, and

$$\Delta_A = \begin{vmatrix} 1 & 3 & 2 \\ 2 & -1 & -1 \\ 6 & 4 & 2 \end{vmatrix} = -2 - 18 + 16 + 12 - 12 + 4 = 0$$

Careful inspection reveals that the three equations in (3-8) are not entirely independent of each other. In other words, the last equation is equal to two times the sum of the first two equations.

In a similar way we see that the matrix

$$\mathbf{A} = \begin{bmatrix} 1 & 3 & 5 \\ 2 & -1 & -4 \\ 6 & 4 & 2 \end{bmatrix}$$

is singular because not all the columns of the matrix are independent of each other. In this case it is simple to show that the difference between the first and the second column is proportional to the difference between the first and the third column. Therefore the determinant of $\mathbf{A}$ is zero.

Nonsingular matrix   A square matrix whose determinant is nonzero is a nonsingular matrix.

Example 3-8   Nonsingular matrix

$$\mathbf{A} = \begin{bmatrix} 11 & -2 \\ 4 & 1 \end{bmatrix} \qquad \Delta_A = \begin{vmatrix} 11 & -2 \\ 4 & 1 \end{vmatrix} = 11 + 8 = 19$$

Therefore A is a nonsingular matrix.

Transposed matrix   The transpose of a matrix $\mathbf{A}$ is defined as the matrix obtained by interchanging the corresponding rows and columns in $\mathbf{A}$. If $\mathbf{A} = [a_{ij}]_{n,m}$, the transpose of $\mathbf{A}$, denoted by $\mathbf{A}'$, is given by

$$\mathbf{A}' = \text{transpose of } \mathbf{A} = [a_{ji}]_{m,n} \tag{3-9}$$

Notice that if the order of $\mathbf{A}$ is (n,m), the transposed matrix $\mathbf{A}'$ has an order (m,n).

Example 3-9   Transpose of a matrix   Given

$$\mathbf{A} = \begin{bmatrix} 1 & 3 \\ 2 & 4 \\ 0 & -1 \end{bmatrix}$$

the transpose of A is

$$\mathbf{A}' = \begin{bmatrix} 1 & 2 & 0 \\ 3 & 4 & -1 \end{bmatrix}$$

Adjoint matrix   Let $\mathbf{A} = [a_{ij}]_{n,n}$ be a square matrix.   The adjoint matrix of $\mathbf{A}$, denoted by adj $\mathbf{A}$, is defined as

$$\text{adj } \mathbf{A} = \text{adj } [a_{ij}]_{n,n} = [ij \text{ cofactor of } \Delta_A]' \tag{3-10}$$

We recall that the "ij cofactor of Δ_A" is the determinant obtained by omitting the ith row and the jth column of Δ_A and then multiplying by $(-1)^{i+j}$.

Example 3-10   Adjoint of a matrix   If $\mathbf{A} = [a_{ij}]_{3,3}$, the adjoint of $\mathbf{A}$ is given by

$$\text{adj } \mathbf{A} = \begin{bmatrix} \text{cofactor } a_{11} & \text{cofactor } a_{12} & \text{cofactor } a_{13} \\ \text{cofactor } a_{21} & \text{cofactor } a_{22} & \text{cofactor } a_{23} \\ \text{cofactor } a_{31} & \text{cofactor } a_{32} & \text{cofactor } a_{33} \end{bmatrix}'$$

$$= \begin{bmatrix} \text{cofactor } a_{11} & \text{cofactor } a_{21} & \text{cofactor } a_{31} \\ \text{cofactor } a_{12} & \text{cofactor } a_{22} & \text{cofactor } a_{32} \\ \text{cofactor } a_{13} & \text{cofactor } a_{23} & \text{cofactor } a_{33} \end{bmatrix}$$

Therefore

$$\text{adj } \mathbf{A}$$
$$= \begin{bmatrix} a_{22}a_{33} - a_{23}a_{32} & -(a_{12}a_{33} - a_{13}a_{32}) & a_{12}a_{23} - a_{13}a_{22} \\ -(a_{21}a_{33} - a_{23}a_{31}) & a_{11}a_{33} - a_{13}a_{31} & -(a_{11}a_{23} - a_{13}a_{21}) \\ a_{21}a_{32} - a_{22}a_{31} & -(a_{11}a_{32} - a_{12}a_{31}) & a_{11}a_{22} - a_{12}a_{21} \end{bmatrix}$$

Example 3-11   If

$$\mathbf{A} = \begin{bmatrix} 4 & 1 \\ -3 & 0 \end{bmatrix}$$

the adjoint of $\mathbf{A}$ is

$$\text{adj } \mathbf{A} = \begin{bmatrix} 0 & 3 \\ -1 & 4 \end{bmatrix}' = \begin{bmatrix} 0 & -1 \\ 3 & 4 \end{bmatrix}$$

Vector matrix

In general, a matrix $\mathbf{x}$ may be used to represent a group of scalar variables or a group of vectors.   In the scalar case, the elements of $\mathbf{x}$ will have only numbers attached to them.   A vector, on the other hand, has both magnitude and direction.   Displacement, velocity, acceleration, current, and voltage, all are well-known examples of vectors.   Vectors are usually represented in various types of coordinate systems.   For instance, a three-dimensional cartesian coordinate system with coordinates x_1, x_2, and x_3 is

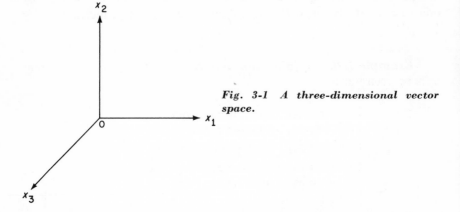

Fig. 3-1   A three-dimensional vector space.

shown in Fig. 3-1.   Normally, these variables are functions of the independent variable time.

A typical vector-matrix equation is given by

$$\mathbf{A}\mathbf{x}(t) = \mathbf{y}(t)$$

or

$$\frac{d\mathbf{x}(t)}{dt} = \mathbf{A}\mathbf{x}(t) + \mathbf{B}\mathbf{y}(t)$$

where $\mathbf{x}(t)$ and $\mathbf{y}(t)$ are both column matrices, and $\mathbf{A}$ and $\mathbf{B}$ are matrices.

In the most general case, a vector matrix $\mathbf{x}$ can only be a row matrix or a column matrix.   Whether it is a row matrix of order $(1,n)$ or a column matrix of order $(n,1)$, it is referred to as an *n vector*.

3-3   MATRIX ALGEBRA

In manipulating and solving matrix equations it is necessary to define such matrix operations as the addition, subtraction, multiplication, division, and others.   Some of these operations, as will be shown, have rules similar to those in the algebra for ordinary real numbers, but others may have entirely different meaning.

Equality of matrices

Two matrices **A** and **B** are said to be equal if and only if they satisfy the following two conditions:

1 They are of the same order.
2 $a_{ij} = b_{ij}$ for every i and j.

Example 3-12

$$\begin{bmatrix} a_{11} & a_{12} \\ a_{21} & a_{22} \end{bmatrix} = \begin{bmatrix} -1 & 2 \\ -3 & 0 \end{bmatrix}$$

implies that $a_{11} = -1$, $a_{12} = 2$, $a_{21} = -3$, and $a_{22} = 0$.
It is meaningless to write

$$\begin{bmatrix} x_1 \\ x_2 \\ x_3 \end{bmatrix} = \begin{bmatrix} 3 & 2 \\ 4 & 0 \\ -1 & 1 \end{bmatrix}$$

since the two matrices are not of the same order.

Matrix additions

Two matrices **A** and **B** can be added as **A** + **B** if they are of the same order.   Then

$$[a_{ij}]_{n,m} + [b_{ij}]_{n,m} = [c_{ij}]_{n,m} \tag{3-11}$$

where $c_{ij} = a_{ij} + b_{ij}$ for all i and j.   The order of the matrix is preserved after addition.

Example 3-13   Given

$$\mathbf{A} = \begin{bmatrix} 2 & 3 & 4 \\ -1 & -1 & 0 \end{bmatrix} \qquad \mathbf{B} = \begin{bmatrix} -2 & 0 & -1 \\ 1.5 & 3 & 0 \end{bmatrix}$$

Then

$$\mathbf{A} + \mathbf{B} = \begin{bmatrix} 2-2 & 3+0 & 4-1 \\ -1+1.5 & -1+3 & 0+0 \end{bmatrix} = \begin{bmatrix} 0 & 3 & 3 \\ 0.5 & 2 & 0 \end{bmatrix}$$

Matrix subtractions

Subtraction of matrices is treated as a special case of matrix addition; that is, if **A** and **B** are of the same order,

$$\mathbf{A} - \mathbf{B} = [a_{ij}]_{n,m} - [b_{ij}]_{n,m} = [a_{ij}]_{n,m} + [-b_{ij}]_{n,m}$$
$$= [c_{ij}]_{n,m} \tag{3-12}$$

Therefore $c_{ij} = a_{ij} - b_{ij}$ for all i and all j.

Associative and commutative laws

The associative law and the commutative law of real numbers still hold for the addition and subtraction of matrices. A comparison of the two situations is indicated in the following table:

	Real number	Matrix
Associative law	$(a + b) + c = a + (b + c)$	$(\mathbf{A} + \mathbf{B}) + \mathbf{C} = \mathbf{A} + (\mathbf{B} + \mathbf{C})$
Commutative law	$a + b + c = b + c + a$ $= c + a + b$	$\mathbf{A} + \mathbf{B} + \mathbf{C} = \mathbf{B} + \mathbf{C} + \mathbf{A}$ $= \mathbf{C} + \mathbf{A} + \mathbf{B}$

Matrix multiplication

To form the product **AB** for the matrices **A** and **B**, they must be *conformable;* i.e., the number of columns of **A** must equal the number of rows of **B**. In other words, if $\mathbf{A} = [a_{ij}]_{n,m}$ and $\mathbf{B} = [b_{ij}]_{p,q}$, **A** and **B** are conformable to produce the product

$$\mathbf{AB} = [a_{ij}]_{n,m} \times [b_{ij}]_{p,q} = [c_{ij}]_{n,q} \tag{3-13}$$

if and only if $m = p$. The product matrix **C** will have the same number of rows as **A** and the same number of columns as **B**. It is important to note that if **A** and **B** are conformable for **AB**, they may not be conformable for **BA**, unless in (3-13) n also equals q. This points out the fact that the commutative law is not generally valid for matrix multiplication.

The product **AB** is often referred to either as **B** *premultiplied by* **A** or as **A** *postmultiplied by* **B**.

The rule of matrix multiplication is given as follows: If

$$[a_{ij}]_{n,m} \times [b_{ij}]_{m,q} = [c_{ij}]_{n,q} \tag{3-14}$$

then

$$c_{ij} = \sum_{r=1}^{m} a_{ir}b_{rj} \quad \text{all } i, j \tag{3-15}$$

Example 3-14   Given

$$A = [a_{ij}]_{2,4} \quad \text{and} \quad B = [b_{ij}]_{4,2}$$

then

$$AB = \begin{bmatrix} a_{11} & a_{12} & a_{13} & a_{14} \\ a_{21} & a_{22} & a_{23} & a_{24} \end{bmatrix} \begin{bmatrix} b_{11} & b_{12} \\ b_{21} & b_{22} \\ b_{31} & b_{32} \\ b_{41} & b_{42} \end{bmatrix}$$

$$= \begin{bmatrix} a_{11}b_{11} + a_{12}b_{21} + a_{13}b_{31} + a_{14}b_{41} & a_{11}b_{12} + a_{12}b_{22} + a_{13}b_{32} + a_{14}b_{42} \\ a_{21}b_{11} + a_{22}b_{21} + a_{23}b_{31} + a_{24}b_{41} & a_{21}b_{12} + a_{22}b_{22} + a_{23}b_{32} + a_{24}b_{42} \end{bmatrix}$$

$$= \begin{bmatrix} c_{11} & c_{12} \\ c_{21} & c_{22} \end{bmatrix}$$

Example 3-15

$$AB = \begin{bmatrix} 3 & -4 & 2 \\ 1 & 0 & -1 \end{bmatrix} \begin{bmatrix} 5 & 0 \\ 1 & 2 \\ -3 & -1 \end{bmatrix}$$

$$= \begin{bmatrix} (3)(5) + (-4)(1) + (2)(-3) & (3)(0) + (-4)(2) + (2)(-1) \\ (1)(5) + (0)(1) + (-1)(-3) & (1)(0) + (0)(2) + (-1)(-1) \end{bmatrix}$$

$$= \begin{bmatrix} 5 & -10 \\ 8 & 1 \end{bmatrix}$$

$$BA = \begin{bmatrix} 5 & 0 \\ 1 & 2 \\ -3 & -1 \end{bmatrix} \begin{bmatrix} 3 & -4 & 2 \\ 1 & 0 & -1 \end{bmatrix} = \begin{bmatrix} 15 & -20 & 10 \\ 5 & -4 & 0 \\ -10 & 12 & -5 \end{bmatrix}$$

Therefore $AB \neq BA$, although both products are conformable.

Property of the unit matrix

The unit (identity) matrix I possesses the following property:

$$IA = AI = A \tag{3-16}$$

Advance of proof of this relationship is given as Prob. 3-11 at the end of this chapter.

Associative, Commutative, and Distributive Laws

We have shown above that the commutative law does not hold in general for matrix multiplication. However, the associative and the distributive laws are valid, and are demonstrated in the following relationship for matrix products.

Distributive	*Associative*
$A(B + C) = AB + AC$	$(AB)C = A(BC)$

Multiplication by a scalar k

Multiplication of a matrix A by a scalar k is effected by multiplying each element of A by k. In other words,

$$kA = [ka_{ij}]_{n,m} \tag{3-17}$$

Matrix division: matrix inversion

In the algebra for real numbers, $ax = y$ leads to $x = (1/a)y$, or $x = a^{-1}y$, where $1/a$, or a^{-1}, is called the inverse of a. In matrix algebra a similar relation exists; but a special interpretation must be made on the *inverse* of a matrix.

Let A be a square nonsingular matrix. Then "the inverse of A," denoted by A^{-1}, is defined as the adjoint matrix of A divided by the determinant of A, provided that A is nonsingular. In other words,

$$\text{Inverse of } A = A^{-1} = \frac{\text{adj } A}{|A|} \tag{3-18}$$

where A is a square nonsingular matrix.

Example 3-16   Given

$$A = \begin{bmatrix} 1 & 2 & -1 \\ 0 & -1 & 3 \\ 1 & 0 & 1 \end{bmatrix} \quad \text{adj } A = \begin{bmatrix} -1 & -2 & 5 \\ 3 & 2 & -3 \\ 1 & 2 & -1 \end{bmatrix}$$

Then

$$\mathbf{A}^{-1} = \frac{\text{adj } \mathbf{A}}{|\mathbf{A}|} = \frac{\text{adj } \mathbf{A}}{4} = \begin{bmatrix} -\frac{1}{4} & -\frac{1}{2} & \frac{5}{4} \\ \frac{3}{4} & \frac{1}{2} & -\frac{3}{4} \\ \frac{1}{4} & \frac{1}{2} & -\frac{1}{4} \end{bmatrix}$$

An important property of the matrix inverse is that

$$\mathbf{A}^{-1}\mathbf{A} = \mathbf{A}\mathbf{A}^{-1} = \mathbf{I} \tag{3-19}$$

where $\mathbf{A}$ is a square nonsingular matrix.

Using the identity in (3-19), the matrix equation in (3-2) can be solved in a straightforward manner. Premultiplying both sides of (3-2) by $\mathbf{A}^{-1}$ gives

$$\mathbf{A}^{-1}\mathbf{A}\mathbf{X} = \mathbf{A}^{-1}\mathbf{Y}$$

or

$$\mathbf{I}\mathbf{X} = \mathbf{X} = \mathbf{A}^{-1}\mathbf{Y}$$

where $\mathbf{A}$ must be square and nonsingular.

Partitioning a matrix

It is sometimes desirable to divide a matrix into a set of submatrices. The partitioning of a matrix can be regarded as a process of subdividing the matrix into a set of arrays of numbers so that each array can be treated as a matrix. As a simple example, the following matrix $\mathbf{A}$, which is a 3 $\times$ 4 matrix, is partitioned into a 1 $\times$ 3 matrix with elements $\mathbf{A}_{11}$, $\mathbf{A}_{12}$, $\mathbf{A}_{13}$.

$$\mathbf{A} = \begin{bmatrix} a_{11} & a_{12} & a_{13} & a_{14} \\ a_{21} & a_{22} & a_{23} & a_{24} \\ a_{31} & a_{32} & a_{33} & a_{34} \end{bmatrix} = [\mathbf{A}_{11} \; \vdots \; \mathbf{A}_{12} \; \vdots \; \mathbf{A}_{13}] \tag{3-20}$$

In this case, $\mathbf{A}_{11}$, $\mathbf{A}_{12}$, and $\mathbf{A}_{13}$ are also matrices with elements defined as follows:

$$\mathbf{A}_{11} = \begin{bmatrix} a_{11} \\ a_{21} \\ a_{31} \end{bmatrix} \qquad \mathbf{A}_{12} = \begin{bmatrix} a_{12} & a_{13} \\ a_{22} & a_{23} \\ a_{32} & a_{33} \end{bmatrix} \qquad \mathbf{A}_{13} = \begin{bmatrix} a_{14} \\ a_{24} \\ a_{34} \end{bmatrix}$$

In (3-20), dashed lines indicate the partitioning of the matrix.   In this example, the *column partitioning* is performed; i.e., the columns of **A** are partitioned into three individual matrices.   In general, simultaneous partitioning, identified as *row partitioning*, can be performed to the rows. For instance, the matrix **A** in (3-20) can be partitioned into the following form:

$$\mathbf{A} = \begin{bmatrix} a_{11} & a_{12} & a_{13} & a_{14} \\ a_{21} & a_{22} & a_{23} & a_{24} \\ a_{31} & a_{32} & a_{33} & a_{34} \end{bmatrix} = \begin{bmatrix} \mathbf{A}_{11} & \mathbf{A}_{12} & \mathbf{A}_{13} \\ \mathbf{A}_{21} & \mathbf{A}_{22} & \mathbf{A}_{23} \end{bmatrix}$$

where

$$\mathbf{A}_{11} = a_{11}$$

$$\mathbf{A}_{12} = [a_{12} \quad a_{13}]$$

$$\mathbf{A}_{13} = a_{14}$$

$$\mathbf{A}_{21} = \begin{bmatrix} a_{21} \\ a_{31} \end{bmatrix}$$

$$\mathbf{A}_{22} = \begin{bmatrix} a_{22} & a_{23} \\ a_{32} & a_{33} \end{bmatrix}$$

$$\mathbf{A}_{23} = \begin{bmatrix} a_{24} \\ a_{34} \end{bmatrix}$$

When we have an isolated matrix such as **A** in (3-20), we can partition it in any way we wish.   But once the matrix is associated with other matrices in a matrix equation, the partitioning of the matrices necessarily has restrictions.   Since the operations involved in a matrix equation are usually in the form of addition (subtraction), multiplication, and equality, we are concerned with the rules of partitioning matrices in connection with these basic operations.   It should be pointed out, however, that matrix partitioning simply subdivides matrices into smaller matrices; the operation does not alter the end results of a matrix manipulation.

Addition and subtraction   Consider the addition (or subtraction) of two matrices **A** and **B** to form

$$\mathbf{A} + \mathbf{B} = \mathbf{C} \qquad \text{or} \qquad \mathbf{A} - \mathbf{B} = \mathbf{C}$$

Then the row partitioning of **A** and **B** must be the same, and the column partitioning of **A** and **B** must be the same.   In other words, since **A** and **B** in this case must be of the same order (same number of rows and same number of columns), they must be partitioned in the same way.

Example 3-17   Given

$$\mathbf{A} = \begin{bmatrix} a_{11} & a_{12} & a_{13} \\ a_{21} & a_{22} & a_{23} \end{bmatrix} \quad \text{and} \quad \mathbf{B} = \begin{bmatrix} b_{11} & b_{12} & b_{13} \\ b_{21} & b_{22} & b_{23} \end{bmatrix}$$

If **A** is partitioned as

$$\mathbf{A} = \left[\begin{array}{c:cc} a_{11} & a_{12} & a_{13} \\ \hdashline a_{21} & a_{22} & a_{23} \end{array}\right] = \begin{bmatrix} \mathbf{A}_{11} & \mathbf{A}_{12} \\ \mathbf{A}_{21} & \mathbf{A}_{22} \end{bmatrix}$$

then, to form $\mathbf{A} + \mathbf{B}$ or $\mathbf{A} - \mathbf{B}$, **B** must be partitioned in the same way as **A** so that

$$\begin{aligned}
\mathbf{A} \pm \mathbf{B} &= \left[\begin{array}{c:cc} a_{11} & a_{12} & a_{13} \\ \hdashline a_{21} & a_{22} & a_{23} \end{array}\right] \pm \left[\begin{array}{c:cc} b_{11} & b_{12} & b_{13} \\ \hdashline b_{21} & b_{22} & b_{23} \end{array}\right] \\
&= \left[\begin{array}{c:c} \mathbf{A}_{11} & \mathbf{A}_{12} \\ \hdashline \mathbf{A}_{21} & \mathbf{A}_{22} \end{array}\right] \pm \left[\begin{array}{c:c} \mathbf{B}_{11} & \mathbf{B}_{12} \\ \hdashline \mathbf{B}_{21} & \mathbf{B}_{22} \end{array}\right] \\
&= \left[\begin{array}{c:cc} a_{11} \pm b_{11} & a_{12} \pm b_{12} & a_{13} \pm b_{13} \\ \hdashline a_{21} \pm b_{21} & a_{22} \pm b_{22} & a_{23} \pm b_{23} \end{array}\right] \\
&= \left[\begin{array}{c:c} \mathbf{A}_{11} \pm \mathbf{B}_{11} & \mathbf{A}_{12} \pm \mathbf{B}_{12} \\ \hdashline \mathbf{A}_{21} \pm \mathbf{B}_{21} & \mathbf{A}_{22} \pm \mathbf{B}_{22} \end{array}\right] \quad (3\text{-}21)
\end{aligned}$$

Multiplication   When two matrices **A** and **B** (conformable for multiplication) are multiplied to form the product $\mathbf{AB} = \mathbf{C}$, the following rules in regard to the partitioning of **A** and **B** should be observed:

1   The rows of **A** and the columns of **B** may be partitioned arbitrarily.
2   The column partitioning of **A** must be identical with the row partitioning of **B**.

   In other words, in order that the submatrices of **A** be still conformable to the submatrices of **B** after partitioning, the columns of **A** must be partitioned the same way as the rows of **B**.

Example 3-18   Consider the two matrices **A** and **B** given below, which are conformable for the product **AB**:

$$\mathbf{A} = \begin{bmatrix} a_{11} & a_{12} & a_{13} \\ a_{21} & a_{22} & a_{23} \end{bmatrix} \quad \mathbf{B} = \begin{bmatrix} b_{11} & b_{12} \\ b_{21} & b_{22} \\ b_{31} & b_{32} \end{bmatrix}$$

and

$$\mathbf{AB} = \begin{bmatrix} a_{11}b_{11} + a_{12}b_{21} + a_{13}b_{31} & a_{11}b_{12} + a_{12}b_{22} + a_{13}b_{32} \\ a_{21}b_{11} + a_{22}b_{21} + a_{23}b_{31} & a_{21}b_{12} + a_{22}b_{22} + a_{23}b_{32} \end{bmatrix} \quad (3\text{-}22)$$

Let us assume that the matrix $\mathbf{A}$ is partitioned in the following manner:

$$\mathbf{A} = \left[\begin{array}{cc|c} a_{11} & a_{12} & a_{13} \\ \hline a_{21} & a_{22} & a_{23} \end{array}\right] = \left[\begin{array}{c|c} \mathbf{A}_{11} & \mathbf{A}_{12} \\ \hline \mathbf{A}_{21} & \mathbf{A}_{22} \end{array}\right]$$

Then, in order that $\mathbf{A}$ be still conformable to $\mathbf{B}$, we must partition $\mathbf{B}$ in the following fashion:

$$\mathbf{B} = \left[\begin{array}{c|c} b_{11} & b_{12} \\ b_{21} & b_{22} \\ \hline b_{31} & b_{32} \end{array}\right] = \left[\begin{array}{c|c} \mathbf{B}_{11} & \mathbf{B}_{12} \\ \hline \mathbf{B}_{21} & \mathbf{B}_{22} \end{array}\right] \quad \text{or} \quad \mathbf{B} = \left[\begin{array}{cc} b_{11} & b_{12} \\ b_{21} & b_{22} \\ \hline b_{31} & b_{32} \end{array}\right] = \left[\begin{array}{c} \mathbf{C}_{11} \\ \hline \mathbf{C}_{21} \end{array}\right]$$

Then the product of $\mathbf{A}$ and $\mathbf{B}$ is

$$\mathbf{AB} = \left[\begin{array}{c|c} \mathbf{A}_{11} & \mathbf{A}_{12} \\ \hline \mathbf{A}_{21} & \mathbf{A}_{22} \end{array}\right] \left[\begin{array}{c|c} \mathbf{B}_{11} & \mathbf{B}_{12} \\ \hline \mathbf{B}_{21} & \mathbf{B}_{22} \end{array}\right]$$

$$= \left[\begin{array}{c|c} \mathbf{A}_{11}\mathbf{B}_{11} + \mathbf{A}_{12}\mathbf{B}_{21} & \mathbf{A}_{11}\mathbf{B}_{12} + \mathbf{A}_{12}\mathbf{B}_{22} \\ \hline \mathbf{A}_{21}\mathbf{B}_{11} + \mathbf{A}_{22}\mathbf{B}_{21} & \mathbf{A}_{21}\mathbf{B}_{12} + \mathbf{A}_{22}\mathbf{B}_{22} \end{array}\right]$$

or

$$\mathbf{AB} = \left[\begin{array}{c|c} \mathbf{A}_{11} & \mathbf{A}_{12} \\ \hline \mathbf{A}_{21} & \mathbf{A}_{22} \end{array}\right] \left[\begin{array}{c} \mathbf{C}_{11} \\ \mathbf{C}_{21} \end{array}\right] = \left[\begin{array}{c} \mathbf{A}_{11}\mathbf{C}_{11} + \mathbf{A}_{12}\mathbf{C}_{21} \\ \mathbf{A}_{21}\mathbf{C}_{11} + \mathbf{A}_{22}\mathbf{C}_{21} \end{array}\right]$$

or

$$\mathbf{AB} = \left[\begin{array}{c|c} [a_{11} \quad a_{12}]\begin{bmatrix} b_{11} \\ b_{21} \end{bmatrix} + a_{13}b_{31} & [a_{11} \quad a_{12}]\begin{bmatrix} b_{12} \\ b_{22} \end{bmatrix} + a_{13}b_{32} \\ \hline [a_{21} \quad a_{22}]\begin{bmatrix} b_{11} \\ b_{21} \end{bmatrix} + a_{23}b_{31} & [a_{21} \quad a_{22}]\begin{bmatrix} b_{12} \\ b_{22} \end{bmatrix} + a_{23}b_{32} \end{array}\right]$$

$$= \left[\begin{array}{c} [a_{11} \quad a_{12}]\begin{bmatrix} b_{11} & b_{12} \\ b_{21} & b_{22} \end{bmatrix} + a_{13}[b_{31} \quad b_{32}] \\ [a_{21} \quad a_{22}]\begin{bmatrix} b_{11} & b_{12} \\ b_{21} & b_{22} \end{bmatrix} + a_{23}[b_{31} \quad b_{32}] \end{array}\right]$$

$$= \left[\begin{array}{c|c} a_{11}b_{11} + a_{12}b_{21} + a_{13}b_{31} & a_{11}b_{12} + a_{12}b_{22} + a_{13}b_{32} \\ \hline a_{21}b_{11} + a_{22}b_{21} + a_{23}b_{31} & a_{21}b_{12} + a_{22}b_{22} + a_{23}b_{32} \end{array}\right] \quad (3\text{-}23)$$

which is identical with the result in (3-22).

3-4 POWERS AND SERIES OF MATRICES

Power of a matrix

If $\mathbf{A}$ is a square matrix of order (n,n), its kth continued product, $\mathbf{AA} \cdots \mathbf{A}$, can be written as the kth power of $\mathbf{A}$. Therefore

$$\underbrace{\mathbf{AA} \cdots \mathbf{A}}_{k} = \mathbf{A}^k \tag{3-24}$$

where $k = 0, 1, 2, \ldots$. In particular, when $k = 0$, $\mathbf{A}^0$ is defined as the unit matrix $\mathbf{I}$.

Polynomial of a matrix and matrix polynomials

A polynomial of order n of a scalar variable x can be written

$$f(x) = a_n x^n + a_{n-1} x^{n-1} + \cdots + a_1 x + a_0 \tag{3-25}$$

Similarly, if $\mathbf{A}$ denotes a square matrix of any order with constant elements, a polynomial of matrix of order n can be defined for $\mathbf{A}$ as

$$\mathbf{f}(\mathbf{A}) = a_n \mathbf{A}^n + a_{n-1} \mathbf{A}^{n-1} + \cdots + a_1 \mathbf{A} + a_0 \mathbf{I} \tag{3-26}$$

where $a_n, a_{n-1}, \ldots, a_1, a_0$ are scalar quantities.

Since a matrix equation is used primarily for the purpose of representing a set of polynomials or equations with scalar variables, a *matrix polynomial* can be defined as

$$\mathbf{F}(x) = \mathbf{A}_n x^n + \mathbf{A}_{n-1} x^{n-1} + \cdots + \mathbf{A}_1 x + \mathbf{A}_0 \tag{3-27}$$

where $\mathbf{A}_n, \mathbf{A}_{n-1}, \ldots, \mathbf{A}_1, \mathbf{A}_0$ are diagonal matrices of the same order.

If the $\mathbf{A}$ matrices in (3-27) are of the order k, the matrix polynomial is equivalent to k polynomials, each of which is described by the scalar polynomial of (3-25).

For instance, consider the following polynomials:

$$f_1(x_1) = x_1^2 + 3x_1 + 2$$
$$f_2(x_2) = 9x_2^2 + 9x_2 + 2$$

These equations can be represented by one matrix polynomial as

$$\mathbf{F(x)} = \mathbf{A}_2\mathbf{x}^2 + \mathbf{A}_1\mathbf{x} + \mathbf{A}_0$$

$$= \begin{bmatrix} 1 & 0 \\ 0 & 9 \end{bmatrix}\mathbf{x}^2 + \begin{bmatrix} 3 & 0 \\ 0 & 9 \end{bmatrix}\mathbf{x} + \begin{bmatrix} 2 & 0 \\ 0 & 2 \end{bmatrix}$$

Therefore

$$\mathbf{F}(x) = \begin{bmatrix} f_1 \\ f_2 \end{bmatrix} \qquad \mathbf{A}_2 = \begin{bmatrix} 1 & 0 \\ 0 & 9 \end{bmatrix} \qquad \mathbf{A}_1 = \begin{bmatrix} 3 & 0 \\ 0 & 9 \end{bmatrix}$$

$$\mathbf{A}_0 = \begin{bmatrix} 2 & 0 \\ 0 & 2 \end{bmatrix} \qquad \text{and} \qquad \mathbf{x} = \begin{bmatrix} x_1 \\ x_2 \end{bmatrix}$$

If the scalar equation $f(x) = 0$ has the distinct roots $x = \lambda_1, \lambda_2, \ldots,$ λ_n, the polynomial of (3-25) can be factored as

$$f(x) = a_n(x - \lambda_1)(x - \lambda_2) \cdots (x - \lambda_n) \tag{3-28}$$

Similarly, if $\mathbf{A} = \lambda_i\mathbf{I}$, $i = 1, 2, \ldots, n$, satisfies the matrix equation $\mathbf{F(A)} = 0$, the polynomial of matrix (3-26) can also be factored as

$$f(\mathbf{A}) = a_n(\mathbf{A} - \lambda_1\mathbf{I})(\mathbf{A} - \lambda_2\mathbf{I}) \ldots (\mathbf{A} - \lambda_n\mathbf{I}) \tag{3-29}$$

Example 3-19 Consider the polynomial of matrix $\mathbf{A}$,

$$f(\mathbf{A}) = \mathbf{A}^2 + 3\mathbf{A} + 2\mathbf{I} \tag{3-30}$$

where

$$\mathbf{A} = \begin{bmatrix} 1 & -1 \\ 0 & 3 \end{bmatrix}$$

Then

$$\mathbf{A}^2 = \begin{bmatrix} 1 & -1 \\ 0 & 3 \end{bmatrix}^2 = \begin{bmatrix} 1 & -1 \\ 0 & 3 \end{bmatrix}\begin{bmatrix} 1 & -1 \\ 0 & 3 \end{bmatrix} = \begin{bmatrix} 1 & -4 \\ 0 & 9 \end{bmatrix}$$

and (3-30) becomes

$$f(\mathbf{A}) = \begin{bmatrix} 1 & -4 \\ 0 & 9 \end{bmatrix} + 3\begin{bmatrix} 1 & -1 \\ 0 & 3 \end{bmatrix} + \begin{bmatrix} 2 & 0 \\ 0 & 2 \end{bmatrix} = \begin{bmatrix} 6 & -7 \\ 0 & 20 \end{bmatrix} \tag{3-31}$$

Factoring (3-30) according to (3-29), we get

$$f(\mathbf{A}) = (\mathbf{A} + \mathbf{I})(\mathbf{A} + 2\mathbf{I})$$

or

$$\mathbf{f(A)} = \begin{bmatrix} 1 & -1 \\ 0 & 3 \end{bmatrix} + \begin{bmatrix} 1 & 0 \\ 0 & 1 \end{bmatrix} \begin{bmatrix} 1 & -1 \\ 0 & 3 \end{bmatrix} + \begin{bmatrix} 2 & 0 \\ 0 & 2 \end{bmatrix}$$

$$= \begin{bmatrix} 2 & -1 \\ 0 & 4 \end{bmatrix} \begin{bmatrix} 3 & -1 \\ 0 & 5 \end{bmatrix} = \begin{bmatrix} 6 & -7 \\ 0 & 20 \end{bmatrix}$$

which agrees with the result obtained in (3-31).

Example 3-20   Consider the matrix equation

$$\mathbf{F}(x) = \mathbf{A}^2 x^2 + 3\mathbf{A}x + 2\mathbf{I} = 0$$

where

$$\mathbf{A} = \begin{bmatrix} 3 & 0 \\ 0 & 1 \end{bmatrix}$$

and x is a scalar variable. This matrix equation can be solved by factoring it as

$$(\mathbf{A}x + 2\mathbf{I})(\mathbf{A}x + \mathbf{I}) = 0$$

from which we get

$$\mathbf{A}x = -2\mathbf{I}$$

or

$$3x = -2 \qquad x = -2 \qquad \mathbf{A}x = -\mathbf{I}$$

Therefore

$$3x = -1 \qquad \text{and} \qquad x = -1$$

The two sets of solutions of x for the two original scalar equations are

$$x_1 = -\tfrac{2}{3} \qquad x_2 = -\tfrac{1}{3}$$

and

$$x_1 = -2 \qquad x_2 = -1$$

The exponential function of a matrix

The exponential function of a scalar x is defined by

$$e^x = \exp x = 1 + x + \frac{x^2}{2!} + \frac{x^3}{3!} + \cdots \tag{3-32}$$

The exponential function of a square matrix is defined in the same way; i.e.,

$$e^{\mathbf{A}} = \exp \mathbf{A} = \mathbf{I} + \mathbf{A} + \frac{\mathbf{A}^2}{2!} + \frac{\mathbf{A}^3}{3!} + \cdots \tag{3-33}$$

where $\mathbf{A}$ is a square matrix.   Also, if x is a scalar variable,

$$e^{\mathbf{A}x} = \exp \mathbf{A}x = \mathbf{I} + \mathbf{A}x + \frac{(\mathbf{A}x)^2}{2!} + \frac{(\mathbf{A}x)^3}{3!} + \cdots \tag{3-34}$$

PROBLEMS

3-1   Find the transpose of the following matrices:

$$\mathbf{A} = \begin{bmatrix} 1 & 0 & 3 & 2 \\ 5 & 7 & 0 & 6 \end{bmatrix} \qquad \mathbf{A} = \begin{bmatrix} 1 & s \\ s^2 & 3 \\ 2 & 0 \end{bmatrix}$$

3-2   Prove that $(\mathbf{A} + \mathbf{B})' = \mathbf{A}' + \mathbf{B}'$.

3-3   Prove that $(\mathbf{AB})' = \mathbf{B}'\mathbf{A}'$.

3-4   Find the adjoint of the following matrices:

$$\mathbf{A} = \begin{bmatrix} 1 & 3 \\ 2 & 4 \end{bmatrix} \qquad \mathbf{A} = \begin{bmatrix} 1 & 3 & 2 \\ 0 & 1 & -1 \\ 4 & 0 & 1 \end{bmatrix}$$

3-5   Find the inverses (if they exist) of the following matrices.   If the inverse does not exist, explain why.

$$(a) \quad \mathbf{A} = \begin{bmatrix} 1 & 3 & -5 \\ 6 & 0 & 5 \\ 2 & 1 & -1 \end{bmatrix} \qquad (d) \quad \mathbf{A} = \begin{bmatrix} 7 \\ 5 \\ 6 \end{bmatrix}$$

$$(b) \quad \mathbf{A} = \begin{bmatrix} 10 & 1.5 \\ 2.5 & 4 \end{bmatrix} \qquad (e) \quad \mathbf{A} = \begin{bmatrix} 1 & 2 & -3 \\ 6 & 12 & 5 \\ 2 & 4 & 0 \end{bmatrix}$$

$$(c) \quad \mathbf{A} = \begin{bmatrix} s(s+1) & s \\ s & 2 \end{bmatrix} \qquad (f) \quad \mathbf{A} = \begin{bmatrix} 1 & 0 & 1 \\ 3 & 2 & 4 \\ 5 & 4 & 7 \end{bmatrix}$$

3-6 Evaluate the following matrix sums and differences:

(a) $\begin{bmatrix} 6 & 3 \\ 2 & -1 \end{bmatrix} + \begin{bmatrix} 0 & 3 \\ -2 & 4 \end{bmatrix}$

(c) $\begin{bmatrix} \dfrac{1}{s+1} & \dfrac{1}{s} \\[2mm] \dfrac{1}{s} & \dfrac{1}{s(s+2)} \end{bmatrix} + \begin{bmatrix} 3 & \dfrac{1}{s} \\[2mm] -1 & 1 \\ \dfrac{}{s} & \end{bmatrix}$

(b) $[-1 \quad 0 \quad 5] - [13 \quad 1 \quad 10]$

(d) $\begin{bmatrix} 2s & 0 & 1 \\ 11 & -s & 3s^2 \end{bmatrix} + \begin{bmatrix} s^2 & -4 & s \\ 0 & 3s & 2 \end{bmatrix}$

3-7 Find out if the following matrices are conformable for the product **AB** and **BA**. Find the products.

(a) $\mathbf{A} = \begin{bmatrix} 1 & 0 & 3 \\ 2 & 10 & 6 \end{bmatrix}$ $\mathbf{B} = \begin{bmatrix} 2 & 3 \\ 7 & 0 \end{bmatrix}$

(b) $\mathbf{A} = \begin{bmatrix} 2 & -3 \\ 1 & 0 \end{bmatrix}$ $\mathbf{B} = \begin{bmatrix} 12 & 0 & 5 \\ -6 & 3 & 1 \end{bmatrix}$

(c) $\mathbf{A} = [1 \quad 5 \quad -2]$ $\mathbf{B} = \begin{bmatrix} 4 \\ 6 \\ 0 \end{bmatrix}$

(d) $\mathbf{A} = \begin{bmatrix} 3s & 5 \\ 0 & -1 \\ 20 & 0 \end{bmatrix}$ $\mathbf{B} = [4 \quad 9 \quad -2]$

3-8 Find out if the following matrices are conformable for the products **ABC**, **BAC**, **BCA**, **CAB**, **CBA**. Find the valid products.

$$\mathbf{A} = \begin{bmatrix} 1 & 1 \\ 2 & 5 \end{bmatrix} \qquad \mathbf{B} = \begin{bmatrix} 2 \\ 3 \end{bmatrix} \qquad \mathbf{C} = [6 \quad 1]$$

3-9 Give a numerical example showing that **AB** = **AC** but **B** ≠ **C**.

3-10 Give a numerical example showing that **AB** = **0** but **A** ≠ **0**, **B** ≠ **0**.

3-11 Prove that

$$\mathbf{IA} = \mathbf{AI} = \mathbf{A}$$

where **I** is a unit matrix.

3-12 Explain why $(\mathbf{A} - \mathbf{B})^2 = \mathbf{A}^2 - 2\mathbf{AB} + \mathbf{B}^2$ is not necessarily true in matrix algebra. What should be the correct matrix relationship?

3-13 Express the following algebraic equations in matrix form:

$$3x_1 + 5x_2 + \ x_3 = 1$$
$$x_1 - 2x_2 - \ x_3 = 0$$
$$-x_1 + 3x_2 + 4x_3 = -1$$

3-14 Express the following differential equations in matrix form:

$$\frac{dx_1}{dt} = 4x_1 + 3x_2 - x_3$$

$$\frac{dx_2}{dt} = -x_1 - x_2 + 2$$

$$\frac{dx_3}{dt} = 3x_1 + x_2 - x_3 + 5$$

3-15 The partitions on the matrix **A** are given below.   Complete the partitioning on the matrix **B** and **C** and carry out the indicated matrix manipulations.

(a) $\mathbf{A} + \mathbf{B} = \begin{bmatrix} 0 & 4 \\ 2 & 6 \\ \hline 1 & 0 \end{bmatrix} + \begin{bmatrix} 3 & 1 \\ -2 & -1 \\ 0 & 4 \end{bmatrix}$

(b) $\mathbf{AB} = \begin{bmatrix} 2 & 1 & 4 & -7 \\ \hline 6 & 0 & 1 & -1 \end{bmatrix} \begin{bmatrix} 1 \\ 4 \\ 0 \\ -1 \end{bmatrix}$

(c) $\mathbf{ABC} = \begin{bmatrix} 0 & 4 \\ \hline 3 & 1 \\ \hline -1 & 0 \\ -2 & 3 \end{bmatrix} \begin{bmatrix} 4 & 10 & 0 & -5 \\ 1 & 0 & 1 & -1 \end{bmatrix} \begin{bmatrix} 1 & 2 \\ 0 & 1 \\ -1 & 6 \\ 0 & 2 \end{bmatrix}$

BIBLIOGRAPHY

Bellman, R.: "Introduction to Matrix Analysis," McGraw-Hill Book Company, New York, 1960.

Frazer, R. A., W. J. Duncan, and A. R. Collar: "Elementary Matrices," Cambridge University Press, New York, 1938.

Reed, M. B., and G. B. Reed: "Mathematical Methods in Electrical Engineering," Harper & Row, Publishers, Incorporated, New York, 1951.

FOUR

NETWORK ANALYSIS

4-1 INTRODUCTION

The main objective of network analysis is the determination of the currents and voltages at various points of a network. For instance, referring to the network shown in Fig. 4-1, it may be desirable, from the network-analysis viewpoint, to determine the voltage across and the current in each of the network elements as functions of the input source voltage and the independent variable time. The unknown voltages and currents are generally regarded as the dependent variables; and in this example they are v_1, v_2, v_3, v_4 and i_1, i_2, i_3, i_4. The basic problem, essentially, involves the formulation of the independent network equations from which these voltages and currents may be solved. It is apparent, however, that we do not need eight variables to describe this simple network. In fact, it is easy to see that some of the currents and voltages assigned are dependent on each other. With the help of some fundamental knowledge of network analysis it is not difficult to see that a minimum of two equations are necessary to solve the network of Fig. 4-1.   Therefore the network-analysis problem can be stated simply as:

1   To establish the minimum number of variables which completely describe the behavior of the network.
2   To formulate a minimum number of independent network equations relating the variables chosen in step 1.
3   To solve the network equations formulated in step 2.

In this text we discuss two major ways of formulating network equations.   The method discussed in this chapter is essentially the conventional loop-and-node analysis; the state-variable approach is taken up in the next chapter.

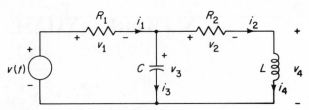

Fig. 4-1   An electric network.

The conventional network analysis concentrates to a great extent on the topology of the network itself.   In other words, the ways and means by which the dependent variables and the number of independent network equations are established depend mostly upon the topology of the network.   The nature of the network elements affects only the form of the equations in accordance with the mathematical descriptions of each element.   In other words, the number of equations needed to solve the network of Fig. 4-1 is obtained by consideration of how the network elements are connected rather than what the network elements are.   Therefore the conventional network analysis is really built on the foundation of network topology.   The emphasis is slightly different with the state-variable method.   In the state-variable approach, the dependent variables (state variables) and the number of network equations (state equations) depend essentially on the number of inductors and capacitors and other energy-storage devices contained in the network.

4-2   LOOP AND NODE EQUATIONS OF ELECTRIC NETWORKS

The conventional network analysis is based on the writing of loop equations and node equations of a network.   These equations are usually obtained by applying Kirchhoff's† voltage and current laws.

Kirchhoff's voltage law governs the voltage relationships in a network and is the foundation of loop analysis.   The law states: *At any given instant of time, the algebraic sum of the voltages around a loop of an electric network is zero.   Or the sum of the voltage rises is equal to the sum of the voltage drops around a loop.*   A loop is defined as a closed contour formed by a collection of network elements.

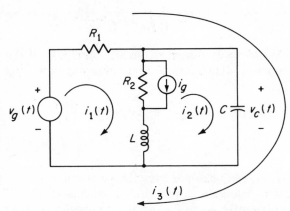

Fig. 4-2   *An electric network with two independent loops.*

In an analogous way, Kirchhoff's current law governs the current relationships in a network and is the basis of node analysis.   The current law states: *At any given instant of time, the algebraic sum of the currents at a node is equal to zero.   Or the net current flowing into a node is zero.*   A node is defined as a junction, or intersection, of two or more network elements.

As an illustration of the loop analysis, let us refer to the network shown in Fig. 4-2.   It is apparent that three different loops can be selected for this network configuration.   The three loop currents are designated

† It is assumed that the reader is already familiar with Kirchhoff's laws and their applications.   Therefore no detailed explanation of the laws is given here.   The fundamentals of writing loop and node equations are covered in many standard textbooks, some of which are listed at the end of this chapter.

as i_1, i_2, and i_3. It is clear, however, that only two of these three loop currents are independent; e.g., $i_3 = i_1 + i_2$. Therefore there are only two independent loop equations for this network. Choosing i_1 and i_2 arbitrarily and assuming that the initial voltage on the capacitor is $v_c(t_0^+)$, the two loop equations for $t \geq t_0$ are written†

Loop 1:

$$v_g(t) + R_2 i_g(t) = (R_1 + R_2)i_1(t) + L\frac{di_1(t)}{dt} - R_2 i_2(t) - L\frac{di_2(t)}{dt}$$

$$(4\text{-}1)$$

Loop 2:

$$-R_2 i_g(t) = -R_2 i_1(t) - L\frac{di_1(t)}{dt} + R_2 i_2(t) + L\frac{di_2(t)}{dt}$$
$$+ \frac{1}{C}\int_{t_0^+}^{t} i_2(\tau)\,d\tau + v_c(t_0^+) \quad (4\text{-}2)$$

The initial voltage $v_c(t_0^+)$ is ordinarily placed on the left-hand side of the equation with the input sources. Therefore an alternative way of writing (4-2) is

$$-R_2 i_g(t) - v_c(t_0^+) = -R_2 i_1(t) - L\frac{di_1(t)}{dt} + R_2 i_2(t) + L\frac{di_2(t)}{dt}$$
$$+ \frac{1}{C}\int_{t_0^+}^{t} i_2(\tau)\,d\tau$$

The two currents i_1 and i_2 can be solved from these two simultaneous integral-differential equations, using standard techniques such as the classical method of solving differential equations or the Laplace-transform method. Since the purpose of this section is to review the writing of loop and node equations, we do not attempt to carry out the solutions of (4-1) and (4-2).

In general, it is possible to systematize the loop analysis by writing loop equations in the form of general network equations. For a network with L loops, its loop equations may be written

$$v_k(t) = \sum_{j=1}^{L} z_{kj} i_j(t) \qquad k = 1, 2, \ldots, L \tag{4-3}$$

where

$$z_{kj} = R_{kj} + L_{kj}\frac{d}{dt} + \frac{1}{C_{kj}}\int_{t_0^+}^{t} d\tau \tag{4-4}$$

† In this case it is not necessary to assign a loop current in the loop formed by R_2 and i_g. The current in R_2, when writing the loop equation for loop 1, is $i_1 - i_2 - i_g$.

and $v_k(t)$ represents the effects of the current and voltage sources and the initial capacitor voltages in the kth loop.   For $k \neq j$,

R_{kj} = total resistance common to loops k and j
L_{kj} = total inductance (including mutual inductance) common to loops k and j
C_{kj} = total capacitance common to loops k and j

For $k = j$, z_{kk} represents the total self-impedance† in loop k.   All self-impedances z_{kk} carry positive signs.   The common impedance z_{kj} ($k \neq j$) carries a positive sign if i_k and i_j are assumed to be in the same direction in the elements common to both loops; otherwise it has a negative sign. The expression in (4-4) is simplified if we let p be the differential operator, denoting d/dt, and $1/p$ be the integral operator, denoting $\int_{t_0^+}^{t} d\tau$.   Then (4-4) becomes

$$z_{kj} = R_{kj} + L_{kj}p + \frac{1}{C_{kj}p} \tag{4-5}$$

The loop equations in (4-3) can also be expressed in matrix form,

$$\mathbf{v}_l = \mathbf{Z}_l \mathbf{i}_l \tag{4-6}$$

where $\mathbf{v}_l$ and $\mathbf{i}_l$ are $L \times 1$ vector matrices, and $\mathbf{Z}_l$ is an $L \times L$ impedance matrix.   For example, the loop equations in (4-1) and (4-2) can be written

$$\begin{bmatrix} v_g(t) + R_2 i_g(t) \\ -v_c(t_0^+) - R_2 i_g(t) \end{bmatrix} = \begin{bmatrix} R_1 + R_2 + Lp & -(R_2 + Lp) \\ -(R_2 + Lp) & R_2 + Lp + \dfrac{1}{Cp} \end{bmatrix} \begin{bmatrix} i_1(t) \\ i_2(t) \end{bmatrix}$$

$$\tag{4-7}$$

An alternative way of analyzing the network in Fig. 4-2 is by node analysis, using Kirchhoff's current law.   The nodes are selected as shown in Fig. 4-3.   The reference node is also chosen arbitrarily as shown.   Since there is a total of only three nodes, there can only be two independent node pairs.   Therefore two node equations are needed for this network: Node 1:

$$\frac{v_g(t)}{R_1} - i_g(t) = \frac{v_1(t)}{R_1} + \frac{v_1(t)}{R_2} + C\frac{dv_1(t)}{dt} - \frac{v_2(t)}{R_2} \tag{4-8}$$

---

† Impedance is usually defined for sinusoidal steady-state conditions.   In this case, impedance is used merely to identify z_{kj}, which is defined by (4-4).

Node 2:

$$-i_L(t_0^+) + i_g(t) = -\frac{v_1(t)}{R_2} + \frac{1}{L}\int_{t_0^+}^{t} v_2(\tau)\, d\tau + \frac{v_2(t)}{R_2} \tag{4-9}$$

where $i_L(t_0^+)$ is the initial current in the inductor.

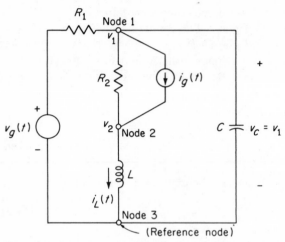

Fig. 4-3   Network shown in Fig. 4-2 for node analysis.

In general, for a network with N nodes, a total of $N - 1$ independent node-pair voltages can be defined, and the $N - 1$ node equations are written

$$i_k(t) = \sum_{j=1}^{N-1} y_{kj}v_j(t) \qquad k = 1, 2, \ldots, N - 1 \tag{4-10}$$

where $y_{kj} = 1/R_{kj} + C_{kj}p + 1/L_{kj}p$; i_k represents the effective current sources due to current sources and voltage sources and the initial inductor currents at node k. For $k \neq j$, y_{kj} is the total admittance connected between node j and node k, and y_{kj} is negative. For $k = j$, y_{kk} becomes the sum of all admittances connected to node k and is always positive.

In matrix form, (4-10) is written as

$$\mathbf{i}_n = \mathbf{Y}_n\mathbf{v}_n \tag{4-11}$$

where i_n and v_n are $(N - 1) \times 1$ vector matrices, and Y_n is an $(N - 1) \times (N - 1)$ admittance matrix. For the network of Fig.4-2,

$$
i_n = \begin{bmatrix} \dfrac{v_g(t)}{R_1} - i_g(t) \\[2ex] -i_L(t_0^+) + i_g(t) \end{bmatrix}
\qquad
Y_n = \begin{bmatrix} \dfrac{1}{R_1} + \dfrac{1}{R_2} + Cp & -\dfrac{1}{R_2} \\[2ex] -\dfrac{1}{R_2} & \dfrac{1}{R_2} + \dfrac{1}{Lp} \end{bmatrix}
$$

and

$$
v_n = \begin{bmatrix} v_1(t) \\ v_2(t) \end{bmatrix}
$$

Networks with mutual inductances

Loop-and-node analysis of electric networks which contain transformers or mutual inductances need special attention. Shown in Fig. 4-4 is a

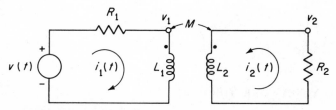

Fig. 4-4   A network with a transformer.

network with a transformer. The two currents are assumed to be flowing into the dotted terminals; therefore M has a positive sign. The two loop equations are written in the usual fashion:

$$
v(t) = R_1 i_1(t) + L_1 \frac{di_1(t)}{dt} + M \frac{di_2(t)}{dt} \qquad \text{primary side} \qquad (4\text{-}12)
$$

$$
0 = R_2 i_2(t) + L_2 \frac{di_2(t)}{dt} + M \frac{di_1(t)}{dt} \qquad \text{secondary side} \qquad (4\text{-}13)
$$

When applying node analysis to magnetically coupled networks, the inverse inductances defined in Sec. 2-2 and the current-voltage relationships in Eqs. (2-23) and (2-24) should be used. The node model of the

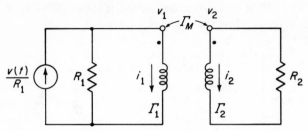

Fig. 4-5   Node-analysis model for the network in Fig. 4-4.

network in Fig. 4-4 is drawn in Fig. 4-5.   Applying Kirchhoff's current law to the two nodes, we get

Node 1:

$$\frac{v(t)}{R_1} = \frac{v_1(t)}{R_1} + \Gamma_1 \int_{t_0^+}^t v_1(\tau)\, d\tau - \Gamma_M \int_{t_0^+}^t v_2(\tau)\, d\tau + i_1(t_0^+) \tag{4-14}$$

Node 2:

$$0 = \frac{v_2(t)}{R_2} + \Gamma_2 \int_{t_0^+}^t v_2(\tau)\, d\tau - \Gamma_M \int_{t_0^+}^t v_1(\tau)\, d\tau + i_2(t_0^+) \tag{4-15}$$

4-3   ELEMENTARY NETWORK TOPOLOGY

The purpose of this section is to establish the definition and terminology of a linear-network graph from which the variables and the number of independent network equations can be established.

Terminology and definitions

Since the graphical structure of a network plays a dominant role in network analysis, we study the topological properties of a linear network by replacing all its elements by simple line segments.   The configuration thus obtained is called the *graph* of the linear network.   More specifically, a graph is a collection of *nodes* and *branches*, which in turn are defined as follows:

   Branch   A branch is a line segment which represents a network element or a combination of elements connected between two points.   A branch is sometimes also called an *edge* in the literature.

Node   A node is a junction of two or more network elements. A node is sometimes also called a *vertex*.

In general, a branch may represent a single resistor R, an inductor L, or a capacitor C or any other network element; or it may represent a combination of these elements.   The flexibility of choosing branches and nodes with respect to network elements is illustrated in Fig. 4-6.   For instance, the parallel combination of RC elements shown in Fig. 4-6e and d can be regarded as either a single branch connected between two nodes or as two parallel branches.   The series RL elements shown in Fig. 4-6c are considered as one branch, or they may be regarded as two branches as shown in Fig. 4-6f.

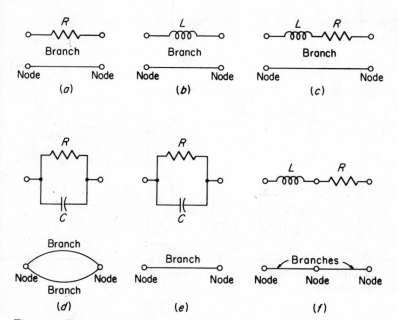

Fig. 4-6   Examples of branches and nodes.

In constructing the graph of a linear network, special attention should be placed on the active elements.   For a network with ideal sources, the ideal voltage source should first be replaced by a short circuit and the ideal current source should be replaced by an open circuit.   Examples of graphs of networks with ideal sources are shown in Fig. 4-7.

Oriented graph   A graph is *oriented* when all its nodes and branches are numbered, and arbitrary directions are assigned to the branches.   An example of the oriented graph is shown in Fig. 4-8.

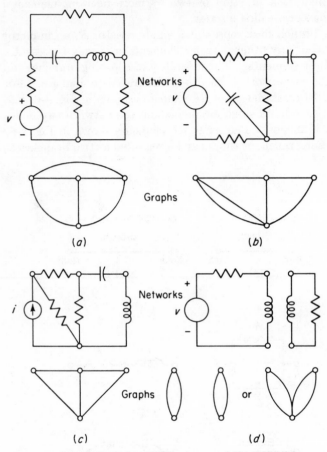

Fig. 4-7   Examples of graphs of networks with voltage and current sources.

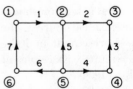

Fig. 4-8   An oriented graph.

The following definitions are necessary when studying the properties of a graph:

Loop   A loop is a collection of branches in a graph (oriented or unoriented) which form a closed path.   Examples of the loops of a graph are shown in Figs. 4-9 and 4-10.

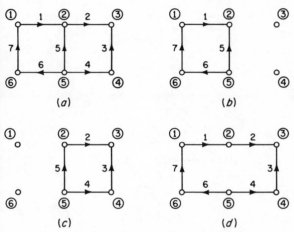

Fig. 4-9   (a) *Oriented graph.*   (b)–(d) *loops.*

Tree   A tree is a "subgraph" of a graph which satisfies the following three conditions:

1   All the nodes of the original graph must be included.
2   All the nodes must be connected by branches called the tree branches.
3   The tree branches must not form any loop in the subgraph.

Tree branch   A branch of a tree is called a tree branch.
Link branch   A link branch is a branch of the graph which does not belong to the particular tree under consideration.
Since a graph may have many different trees, the link branches of a graph will depend on the selection of a particular tree.   Once the tree branches of a graph are specified, the remaining branches become link branches.   An example of the selections of trees and the associated link branches of a graph is given in Fig. 4-11.   It should be noted that even a graph as simple as that of Fig. 4-11 usually has many different trees; only a few of the trees are shown in the figure.

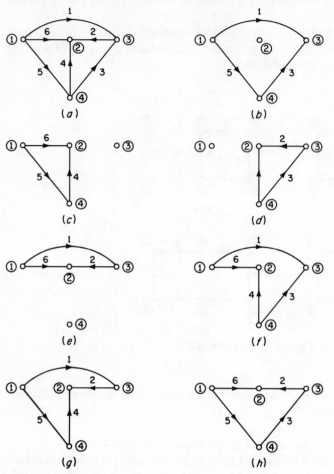

Fig. 4-10 (*a*) *Graph.* (*b*)–(*h*) *Loops.*

Let us denote the number of nodes and the number of branches of a graph by the following symbols:

N = number of nodes of a graph
B = number of branches of a graph

Then the definitions of tree and link branches easily lead us to the fact that there are a total of $N - 1$ tree branches in a particular tree; and therefore there must be a total of $B - (N - 1)$ link branches in a graph.

For instance, for the graph shown in Fig. 4-11, $N = 6$, $B = 7$; therefore there are $N - 1 = 5$ tree branches in each tree and two link branches.

Since the trees are formed with the maximum number of branches in a graph just short of forming a loop, the significance of the link branches is that a tree plus any one of its associated link branches will always form a loop (see Fig. 4-11, for example).

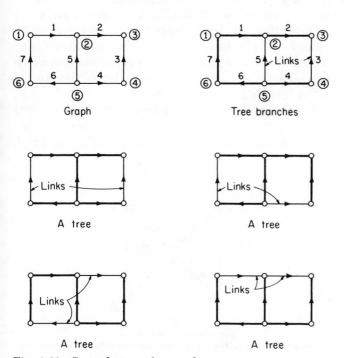

Fig. 4-11   Several trees of a graph.

In the following discussion we show that the concepts of trees and links actually form the foundation for the node-and-loop analysis.

4-4   NODE EQUATIONS

As mentioned earlier, our main objective in network analysis is to establish the independent branch-voltage and branch-current equations from which the independent loop and node equations can be determined. In the following discussion we show that the study of the *cut-set* of a graph allows the systematic selection of a set of independent voltages called the *node-pair voltages*.

Cut-set   A cut-set of a graph is a collection of branches and nodes such that, if these branches are removed from the graph, the graph will be divided into two separate parts.   Restoring any one of these branches will destroy the separation property of the two parts.   Since a tree includes the branches that connect all the nodes of a graph without forming a loop, it is easy to see that, given a particular tree, a cut-set can be formed by cutting one tree branch at a time, and the remaining elements in the cut-set are link branches.   From this relationship we conclude that, given a particular tree configuration, the total number of cut-sets is equal to the number of tree branches.   For the convenience of defining the polarity of the node-pair voltage, a cut-set is illustrated as a closed contour which cuts a particular tree branch.   As a simple example, let us refer to the graph of Fig. 4-12a.   A particular tree is selected as shown in Fig. 4-12b, with the tree branches drawn in heavy solid lines.   The four cut-sets associated with the tree are shown in Fig. 4-12c.   Observe that each cut-set cuts only one tree branch at a time, and it separates the entire graph

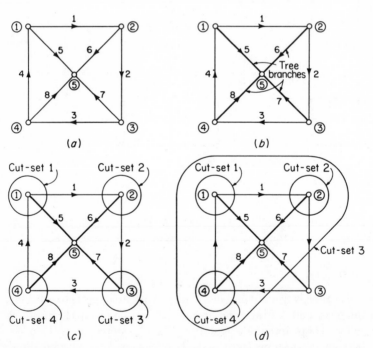

Fig. 4-12 (a) *a graph.* (b) *A tree.* (c), (d) *Cut-sets associated with the tree in* (b). *The tree branches are in heavy lines, and the link branches are in light lines.*

into two parts, so that restoring any one branch of the cut-set will destroy this separation property. We have also arbitrarily chosen the cut-set contours to enclose the nodes 1, 2, 3, 4, one at a time   However, the same cut-sets can also be drawn as shown in Fig. 4-12d.   The difference between the configurations in Fig. 4-12c and d lies only in the enclosure property of cut-set 3, which eventually affects only the reference polarity of the node-pair voltage for this cut-set.

It is apparent that the graph shown in Fig. 4-12 also has many other cut-sets, but they will be associated with different trees.   For instance, if a different tree is chosen as shown in Fig. 4-13a, the cut-sets are formed as shown in Fig. 4-13b.

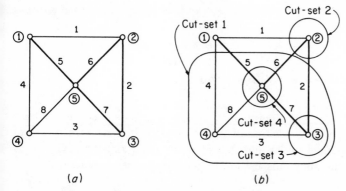

Fig. 4-13   (a) A tree of the graph in Fig. 4-12a formed by branches 1, 3, 4, and 8.   (b) Cut-sets associated with the tree in (a).

Node-pair voltage

The node-pair voltage is defined as the voltage difference between the two parts of a graph that are separated by a cut-set.   The polarity of the node-pair voltage is defined according to the way the cut-set contour is drawn, with the positive end placed at the enclosed side of the cut-set. For instance, cut-set 1 of Fig. 4-12c is repeated in Fig. 4-14a.   The node-pair voltage v_1 is measured along tree branch 5, which is cut by the cut-set 1.   The positive side of v_1 is near node 1, which is enclosed by the cut-set. Similarly, the node-pair voltages for the other three cut-sets of the graph in Fig. 4-12c are defined and shown in Fig. 4-14b.

The node-pair-voltage concept should help clarify the motivation of defining trees.   Since a tree never has any loops, the voltages across the tree branches, being the node-pair voltages, also form an independent set of voltages in the graph.   It is apparent that once the node-pair voltages are independently specified, the voltages across the link branches can always be expressed as linear combinations of the node-pair voltages. Referring to the graph of Fig. 4-14b, it is interesting to note that the

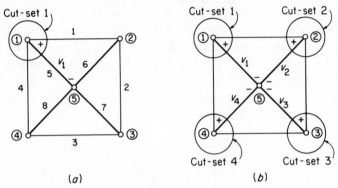

(a) (b)

Fig. 4-14   Illustration of node-pair voltages.

particular tree selection is equivalent to assigning node 5 as the reference (tandem) node, and v_1, v_2, v_3, and v_4 are the node voltages between each of the four independent nodes and the reference node, respectively.

Based on the above discussion, in general, we can conclude that

$$\text{Number of node-pair voltages} = \text{number of tree branches}$$
$$= \text{number of cut-sets}$$
$$= N - 1 \qquad\qquad (4\text{-}16)$$

where N is the number of nodes of the graph.

Cut-set matrix

The independent branch-current relationships of a network can be obtained using the oriented graph and the cut-set ideas.   Let us regard the directions of the branches of an oriented graph as current directions.   Also, the current is assumed positive when it is directed away from a cut-set under consideration, and negative when it is directed toward the cut-set. Thus a set of current equations can be written for each cut-set by use of Kirchhoff's current law.   Let us consider the oriented graph shown in Fig. 4-15a and the particular tree and cut-sets shown in Fig. 4-15b.   Applying Kirchhoff's current law to each of the four cut-sets and using the

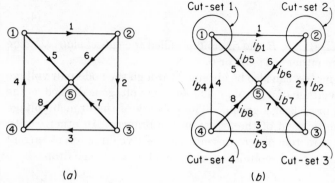

Fig. 4-15 (a) A graph. (b) Tree and cut-sets.

reference direction of currents defined above, we get

Cut-set 1:

$$i_{b1} - i_{b4} + i_{b5} = 0$$

Cut-set 2:

$$-i_{b1} + i_{b2} + i_{b6} = 0$$

(4-17)

Cut-set 3:

$$-i_{b2} + i_{b3} + i_{b7} = 0$$

Cut-set 4:

$$-i_{b3} + i_{b4} + i_{b8} = 0$$

Observe that the total number of independent cut-set equations is equal to the number of trees or cut-sets.   In matrix form, (4-17) becomes

$$
\begin{bmatrix}
1 & 0 & 0 & -1 & 1 & 0 & 0 & 0 \\
-1 & 1 & 0 & 0 & 0 & 1 & 0 & 0 \\
0 & -1 & 1 & 0 & 0 & 0 & 1 & 0 \\
0 & 0 & -1 & 1 & 0 & 0 & 0 & 1
\end{bmatrix}
\begin{bmatrix}
i_{b1} \\
i_{b2} \\
i_{b3} \\
i_{b4} \\
i_{b5} \\
i_{b6} \\
i_{b7} \\
i_{b8}
\end{bmatrix}
$$

(4-18)

or

$$\mathbf{A}\mathbf{i}_b = 0 \tag{4-19}$$

where $\mathbf{A}$ is an $(N-1) \times B$ matrix, and is called the *cut-set matrix*. The elements of $\mathbf{A}$ are either $+1, -1$, or 0.

The cut-set matrix can also be obtained through the node-pair voltage and the branch voltage of a graph. The branch voltage is defined as the voltage across a branch of a graph. The polarity of the branch voltage is positive at the tail end of the arrow on the branch. In other words, since the branch direction also represents the positive direction of current in the branch, the branch voltage is interpreted as a voltage drop.

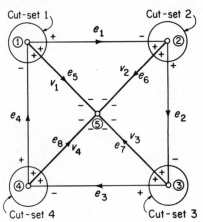

Fig. 4-16   Node-pair voltages and branch voltages.

The node-pair and branch voltages of the graph in Fig. 4-15 are assigned as shown in Fig. 4-16. The relations between the branch voltages and the node-pair voltages are written

$$e_1 = v_1 - v_2$$

$$e_2 = v_2 - v_3$$

$$e_3 = v_3 - v_4$$

$$e_4 = v_4 - v_1$$

$$e_5 = v_1 \tag{4-20}$$

$$e_6 = v_2$$

$$e_7 = v_3$$

$$e_8 = v_4$$

In matrix form, (4-20) becomes

$$
\mathbf{e}_b =
\begin{bmatrix}
1 & -1 & 0 & 0 \\
0 & 1 & -1 & 0 \\
0 & 0 & 1 & -1 \\
-1 & 0 & 0 & 1 \\
1 & 0 & 0 & 0 \\
0 & 1 & 0 & 0 \\
0 & 0 & 1 & 0 \\
0 & 0 & 0 & 1
\end{bmatrix}
\mathbf{v}_n
\qquad (4\text{-}21)
$$

Comparing (4-21) with (4-18), it is apparent that the right side of (4-21) is $\mathbf{A}'\mathbf{v}_n$, where $\mathbf{A}$ is the cut-set matrix. Therefore (4-21) becomes

$$
\mathbf{e}_b = \mathbf{A}'\mathbf{v}_n
\qquad (4\text{-}22)
$$

which is often referred to as the *node-transformation equation*.

Now we have established the relationships between the tree, the cut-set, and the node-pair voltages. In node analysis it is the node-pair voltages that are to be obtained, since, once they are determined, all the branch voltages are automatically found. However, in order to solve for $\mathbf{v}_n$, we need a set of equations relating the branch currents to the branch voltages through the network elements. Let us represent a general branch

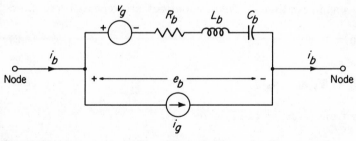

Fig. 4-17   *A general configuration of a branch of a network.*

of a network by the configuration shown in Fig. 4-17, with the network parameters defined as

R_b = total resistance in branch
L_b = total inductance in branch
C_b = total capacitance in branch

v_g = total series voltage source in branch†
i_g = total current source across branch‡
e_b = branch voltage
i_b = branch current

Then the voltage-current relation for the branch can be written

$$e_b = \left(R_b + L_b \frac{d}{dt} + \frac{1}{C_b} \int_{t_0^+}^t d\tau \right) (i_b - i_g) + v_g \tag{4-23}$$

$$i_b = \left(G_b + C_b \frac{d}{dt} + \frac{1}{L_b} \int_{t_0^+}^t d\tau \right) (e_b - v_g) + i_g \tag{4-24}$$

For a network with many branches, (4-23) and (4-24) can be written in matrix form:

$$\mathbf{e}_b = \mathbf{v}_g + \mathbf{Z}_b(\mathbf{i}_b - \mathbf{i}_g) \tag{4-25}$$

$$\mathbf{i}_b = \mathbf{i}_g + \mathbf{Y}_b(\mathbf{e}_b - \mathbf{v}_g) \tag{4-26}$$

where $\mathbf{e}_b$, $\mathbf{v}_g$, $\mathbf{i}_b$, and $\mathbf{i}_g$ are $B \times 1$ matrices, and $\mathbf{Z}_b$ and $\mathbf{Y}_b$ are the branch impedance and the branch admittance, respectively, and are $B \times B$ diagonal matrices (if the network does not have transformers and magnetic coupling). The (k,k) element on the main diagonal of $\mathbf{Z}_b$ represents the total impedance found in branch k of the network. A similar statement can also be made for $\mathbf{Y}_b$ in terms of the total admittance of a branch.

The Kirchhoff current-law equations, the node-transformation equations, and the branch voltage-current equations (4-26) are now combined to form the node equations. These equations are repeated as follows:

$$\mathbf{Ai}_b = 0 \tag{4-27}$$

$$\mathbf{e}_b = \mathbf{A'v}_n \tag{4-28}$$

$$\mathbf{i}_b = \mathbf{i}_g + \mathbf{Y}_b(\mathbf{e}_b - \mathbf{v}_g) \tag{4-29}$$

Substituting from (4-29) in (4-27) gives

$$\mathbf{Ai}_g + \mathbf{AY}_b(\mathbf{e}_b - \mathbf{v}_g) = 0 \tag{4-30}$$

Now substituting from (4-28) in (4-30) gives, after rearranging,

$$\mathbf{AY}_b\mathbf{v}_g - \mathbf{Ai}_g = \mathbf{AY}_b\mathbf{A'v}_n \tag{4-31}$$

† v_g also includes the initial capacitor voltages in loop analysis.
‡ i_g also includes the initial inductor currents in node analysis.

It is interesting to note that (4-31) is of the same form as the node equation in (4-11).   In fact, if we let

$$\mathbf{A}\mathbf{Y}_b\mathbf{v}_g - \mathbf{A}\mathbf{i}_g = \mathbf{i}_n \tag{4-32}$$

and

$$\mathbf{A}\mathbf{Y}_b\mathbf{A}' = \mathbf{Y}_n \tag{4-33}$$

(4-31) also becomes

$$\mathbf{i}_n = \mathbf{Y}_n\mathbf{v}_n \tag{4-34}$$

where $\mathbf{Y}_n$ is called the *node-admittance matrix*.   Equation (4-34) represents a set of $N - 1$ independent node equations of a network with N nodes. The node-pair voltages are obtained by solving $\mathbf{v}_n$ from (4-34).   Therefore

$$\mathbf{v}_n = \mathbf{Y}_n^{-1}\mathbf{i}_n \tag{4-35}$$

if $\mathbf{Y}_n$ is nonsingular.

The foregoing method presented may seem quite laborious at first glance.   Indeed, when the network under study is a simple one, the admittance matrices $\mathbf{Y}_n$ and $\mathbf{i}_n$ can be written out by mere inspection.   However, the method using the cut-set matrix and branch-impedance matrix is foolproof, allowing a systematic analysis of a complex network configuration.

Example 4-1   Write the node equations for the network shown in Fig. 4-2, using (4-32) to (4-34).   The network and its graph are shown in Fig. 4-18.   Observe that the ideal voltage source is replaced by a

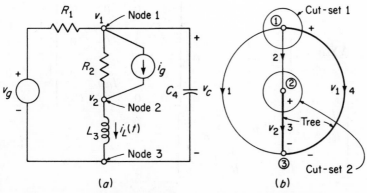

Fig. 4-18   (a) Network in Fig. 4-2.   (b) The oriented graph.

short circuit, and the ideal current source is replaced by an open circuit in the graph.

In order to compare the results with those obtained in Sec. 4-2, we choose the tree and the corresponding cut-sets as shown in Fig. 4-18b. In this way, the node number 3 is considered as the reference node, since the node-pair voltages measured across the two tree branches are essentially v_1 and v_2.

The cut-set matrix for the network is written by inspection from the oriented graph

$$\mathbf{A} = \begin{bmatrix} 1 & 1 & 0 & 1 \\ 0 & -1 & 1 & 0 \end{bmatrix}$$

The branch-admittance matrix $\mathbf{Y}_b$ is obtained by filling the positions on its main diagonal with admittances of the corresponding branch and with zeros everywhere else. We have

$$\mathbf{Y}_b = \begin{bmatrix} \dfrac{1}{R_1} & 0 & 0 & 0 \\ 0 & \dfrac{1}{R_2} & 0 & 0 \\ 0 & 0 & \dfrac{1}{L_3 p} & 0 \\ 0 & 0 & 0 & C_4 p \end{bmatrix}$$

where $1/p$ is the integral operator and p is the differential operator as defined earlier.

From (4-33), the node-admittance matrix is

$$\mathbf{Y}_n = \mathbf{A}\mathbf{Y}_b\mathbf{A}' = \begin{bmatrix} 1 & 1 & 0 & 1 \\ 0 & -1 & 1 & 0 \end{bmatrix} \begin{bmatrix} \dfrac{1}{R_1} & 0 & 0 & 0 \\ 0 & \dfrac{1}{R_2} & 0 & 0 \\ 0 & 0 & \dfrac{1}{L_3 p} & 0 \\ 0 & 0 & 0 & C_4 p \end{bmatrix} \begin{bmatrix} 1 & 0 \\ 1 & -1 \\ 0 & 1 \\ 1 & 0 \end{bmatrix}$$

$$= \begin{bmatrix} \dfrac{1}{R_1} + \dfrac{1}{R_2} + C_4 p & -\dfrac{1}{R_2} \\ -\dfrac{1}{R_2} & \dfrac{1}{R_2} + \dfrac{1}{L_3 p} \end{bmatrix} \tag{4-36}$$

which agrees with the result obtained earlier in Sec. 4-2.

The input matrix $\mathbf{i}_n$ is obtained from (4-32); therefore

$$\mathbf{i}_n = \mathbf{A}\mathbf{Y}_b\mathbf{v}_g - \mathbf{A}\mathbf{i}_g$$

$$= \begin{bmatrix} \dfrac{1}{R_1} & \dfrac{1}{R_2} & 0 & C_4p \\ 0 & -\dfrac{1}{R_2} & \dfrac{1}{L_3p} & 0 \end{bmatrix} \begin{bmatrix} v_g \\ 0 \\ 0 \\ 0 \end{bmatrix} - \begin{bmatrix} 1 & 1 & 0 & 1 \\ 0 & -1 & 1 & 0 \end{bmatrix} \begin{bmatrix} 0 \\ i_g \\ i_L(t_0^+) \\ 0 \end{bmatrix}$$

$$= \begin{bmatrix} \dfrac{v_g}{R_1} - i_g \\ -i_L(t_0^+) + i_g \end{bmatrix}$$

Observe that $\mathbf{v}_g$ and $\mathbf{i}_g$ can also be interpreted as

$$\mathbf{v}_g = \begin{bmatrix} \text{voltage sources in branch 1} \\ \text{voltage sources in branch 2} \\ \text{voltage sources in branch 3} \\ \text{voltage sources in branch 4} \end{bmatrix} = \begin{bmatrix} v_g \\ 0 \\ 0 \\ 0 \end{bmatrix}$$

$$\mathbf{i}_g = \begin{bmatrix} \text{current sources across branch 1} \\ \text{current sources across branch 2} \\ \text{current sources across branch 3} \\ \text{current sources across branch 4} \end{bmatrix} = \begin{bmatrix} 0 \\ i_g \\ i_L(t_0^+) \\ 0 \end{bmatrix}$$

The signs of v_g and i_g in the last two matrices are fixed according to the convention established by Figs. 4-16 and 4-17; that is, i_g has a positive sign if it is in the same direction as the assumed branch current, and v_g has a positive sign if its plus side is at the tail end of the branch arrow.

Now the node equations of the network are

$$\begin{bmatrix} \dfrac{v_g}{R_1} - i_g \\ -i_L(t_0^+) + i_g \end{bmatrix} = \begin{bmatrix} \dfrac{1}{R_1} + \dfrac{1}{R_2} + C_4p & -\dfrac{1}{R_2} \\ -\dfrac{1}{R_2} & \dfrac{1}{R_2} + \dfrac{1}{L_3p} \end{bmatrix} \begin{bmatrix} v_1 \\ v_2 \end{bmatrix}$$

Example 4-2   A network with magnetic coupling is shown in Fig. 4-19a. The network is considered to have three nodes and four branches. The node equations of the network are to be written using the method described in this section. The oriented graph of the network, a tree, and the corresponding cut-sets of the tree are shown in Fig. 4-19b. The cut-set matrix is written by inspection.

$$\mathbf{A} = \begin{bmatrix} 1 & 1 & 0 & 0 \\ 0 & -1 & 1 & 1 \end{bmatrix} \tag{4-37}$$

Since the network now has mutual inductance, the branch-admittance matrix is no longer a diagonal matrix. The (2,3) and (3,2) positions of the admittance matrix $\mathbf{Y}_b$ are occupied by the mutual-inverse inductance Γ_M term. Therefore

$$\mathbf{Y}_b = \begin{bmatrix} \dfrac{1}{R_1} & 0 & 0 & 0 \\ 0 & \dfrac{\Gamma_2}{s} & -\dfrac{\Gamma_M}{s} & 0 \\ 0 & -\dfrac{\Gamma_M}{s} & \dfrac{\Gamma_3}{s} & 0 \\ 0 & 0 & 0 & \dfrac{1}{R_4} \end{bmatrix} \tag{4-38}$$

Since the branch currents in branches 2 and 3 are assumed to be all flowing into the dotted ends of the coils, according to the discussion in Sec. 2-2, the mutual-inverse inductance Γ_M carries a negative sign. From (4-32),

$$\mathbf{i}_n = \mathbf{A}\mathbf{Y}_b\mathbf{v}_g - \mathbf{A}\mathbf{i}_g$$

$$= \begin{bmatrix} 1 & 1 & 0 & 0 \\ 0 & -1 & 1 & 1 \end{bmatrix} \begin{bmatrix} \dfrac{1}{R_1} & 0 & 0 & 0 \\ 0 & \dfrac{\Gamma_2}{p} & -\dfrac{\Gamma_M}{p} & 0 \\ 0 & -\dfrac{\Gamma_M}{p} & \dfrac{\Gamma_3}{p} & 0 \\ 0 & 0 & 0 & \dfrac{1}{R_4} \end{bmatrix} \begin{bmatrix} v_g \\ 0 \\ 0 \\ 0 \end{bmatrix}$$

$$- \begin{bmatrix} 1 & 1 & 0 & 0 \\ 0 & -1 & 1 & 1 \end{bmatrix} \begin{bmatrix} 0 \\ i_{L2}(t_0^+) \\ i_{L3}(t_0^+) \\ 0 \end{bmatrix}$$

$$= \begin{bmatrix} \dfrac{v_g}{R_1} - i_{L2}(t_0^+) \\ i_{L2}(t_0^+) - i_{L3}(t_0^+) \end{bmatrix} \tag{4-39}$$

From (4-33), we get

$$\mathbf{Y}_n = \mathbf{A}\mathbf{Y}_b\mathbf{A}' = \begin{bmatrix} \dfrac{1}{R_1} + \dfrac{\Gamma_2}{p} & -\dfrac{\Gamma_2 + \Gamma_M}{p} \\ -\dfrac{\Gamma_2 + \Gamma_M}{p} & \dfrac{\Gamma_3 - \Gamma_M}{p} + \dfrac{1}{R_4} \end{bmatrix} \begin{bmatrix} v_1 \\ v_2 \end{bmatrix} \tag{4-40}$$

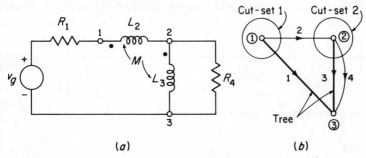

Fig. 4-19   (a) *Network for Example 4-2.*   (b) *The oriented graph.*

Substituting from (4-39) and (4-40) in (4-34), the node equations of the network are written

$$
\begin{bmatrix} \dfrac{v_g}{R_1} - i_{L2}(t_0^+) \\[2mm] i_{L2}(t_0^+) - i_{L3}(t_0^+) \end{bmatrix} =
\begin{bmatrix} \dfrac{1}{R_1} + \dfrac{\Gamma_2}{p} & -\dfrac{\Gamma_2 + \Gamma_M}{p} \\[3mm] -\dfrac{\Gamma_2 + \Gamma_M}{p} & \dfrac{\Gamma_3 - \Gamma_M}{p} + \dfrac{1}{R_4} \end{bmatrix}
\begin{bmatrix} v_1 \\[2mm] v_2 \end{bmatrix} \qquad (4\text{-}41)
$$

Example 4-3   A network with a dependent voltage source is shown in Fig. 4-20a.   We shall show that the admittance $\mathbf{Y}_n$ of this type of network will not be a symmetrical matrix.

The tree is chosen as shown in Fig. 4-20b so that the node-pair voltages defined by the three cut-sets are also the node voltages v_1, v_2, and v_3, as shown in Fig. 4-20a.   This particular scheme is chosen simply because it will enable us to check the result by the conventional means of writing node equations.

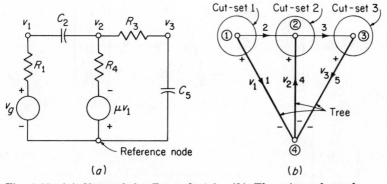

Fig. 4-20   (a) *Network for Example 4-3.*   (b) *The oriented graph.*

The cut-set matrix is obtained by inspection of the oriented graph

$$\mathbf{A} = \begin{bmatrix} 1 & 1 & 0 & 0 & 0 \\ 0 & -1 & 1 & -1 & 0 \\ 0 & 0 & -1 & 0 & 1 \end{bmatrix} \tag{4-42}$$

and the branch-admittance matrix is

$$\mathbf{Y}_b = \begin{bmatrix} \dfrac{1}{R_1} & 0 & 0 & 0 & 0 \\ 0 & pC_2 & 0 & 0 & 0 \\ 0 & 0 & \dfrac{1}{R_3} & 0 & 0 \\ 0 & 0 & 0 & \dfrac{1}{R_4} & 0 \\ 0 & 0 & 0 & 0 & pC_5 \end{bmatrix} \tag{4-43}$$

Therefore

$$\mathbf{AY}_b\mathbf{A}' = \begin{bmatrix} \dfrac{1}{R_1} + pC_2 & -pC_2 & 0 \\ -pC_2 & pC_2 + \dfrac{1}{R_4} + \dfrac{1}{R_3} & -\dfrac{1}{R_3} \\ 0 & -\dfrac{1}{R_3} & \dfrac{1}{R_3} + pC_5 \end{bmatrix} \tag{4-44}$$

and

$$\mathbf{i}_n = \mathbf{AY}_b\mathbf{v}_g = \begin{bmatrix} \dfrac{1}{R_1} & pC_2 & 0 & 0 & 0 \\ 0 & -pC_2 & \dfrac{1}{R_3} & -\dfrac{1}{R_4} & 0 \\ 0 & 0 & -\dfrac{1}{R_3} & 0 & pC_5 \end{bmatrix} \begin{bmatrix} v_g \\ 0 \\ 0 \\ \mu v_1 \\ 0 \end{bmatrix}$$

$$= \begin{bmatrix} \dfrac{v_g}{R_1} \\ -\dfrac{\mu v_1}{R_4} \\ 0 \end{bmatrix} \tag{4-45}$$

Substituting from (4-44) and (4-45) in (4-34), we get

$$
\begin{bmatrix} \dfrac{v_g}{R_1} \\[2mm] -\dfrac{\mu v_1}{R_4} \\[2mm] 0 \end{bmatrix} = \begin{bmatrix} \dfrac{1}{R_1} + pC_2 & -pC_2 & 0 \\[2mm] -pC_2 & pC_2 + \dfrac{1}{R_4} + \dfrac{1}{R_3} & -\dfrac{1}{R_3} \\[2mm] 0 & -\dfrac{1}{R_3} & \dfrac{1}{R_3} + pC_5 \end{bmatrix} \begin{bmatrix} v_1 \\ v_2 \\ v_3 \end{bmatrix} \qquad (4\text{-}46)
$$

However, since the input matrix i_n contains the dependent variable v_1, (4-46) should be written with the term $-\mu v_1/R_4$ moved to the right-hand side of the equation. Therefore (4-46) becomes

$$
\begin{bmatrix} \dfrac{v_g}{R_1} \\[2mm] 0 \\[2mm] 0 \end{bmatrix} = \begin{bmatrix} \dfrac{1}{R_1} + pC_2 & -pC_2 & 0 \\[2mm] -pC_2 + \dfrac{\mu}{R_2} & pC_2 + \dfrac{1}{R_4} + \dfrac{1}{R_3} & -\dfrac{1}{R_3} \\[2mm] 0 & -\dfrac{1}{R_3} & \dfrac{1}{R_3} + pC_5 \end{bmatrix} \begin{bmatrix} v_1 \\ v_2 \\ v_3 \end{bmatrix} \qquad (4\text{-}47)
$$

From these illustrative examples, we can draw the following conclusions concerning the branch- and node-admittance matrices of a network:

1 The branch-admittance matrix $\mathbf{Y}_b$ of a network without mutual couplings is a diagonal matrix.
2 The branch-admittance matrix of a network with mutual couplings is not a diagonal matrix, but it is symmetrical if the network is passive.
3 The node-admittance matrix $\mathbf{Y}_n$ of a passive network is symmetrical.
4 The node-admittance matrix $\mathbf{Y}_n$ of an active network is not symmetrical.

4-5 LOOP EQUATIONS

Tie-set

The independent loop equations of a network may be established from the idea of *tie-sets*, or simply, *loops*. Let us consider the linear graph in Fig. 4-21, which has the tree chosen arbitrarily as shown. The branches that do not belong to the tree are known as link branches. Notice that, if we start with just the tree branches of the graph, and any link branch is added to the tree, a loop (closed contour) or a so-called tie-set is formed.

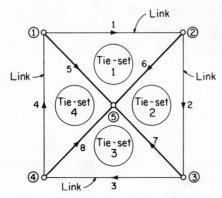

Fig. 4-21   Illustration of tie-sets.

Therefore a tie-set is defined as a collection of branches which form a loop, and the loop can always be interpreted as containing only one link branch, and the remaining ones are tree branches. As shown in Fig. 4-21, four tie-sets are formed when all the links are added to the tree configuration one at a time.

As a different example, a different tree is selected as shown in Fig. 4-22. When link branch 1 is restored, it and tree branches 4, 6, and 8 form a tie-set. Similarly, link branch 7 and tree branches 3 and 8 form another tie-set. The remaining two tie-sets are clearly shown in Fig. 4-22 also.

According to the definition of the tie-set just given, it is easy to see that the total number of tie-sets of a graph is equal to the number of

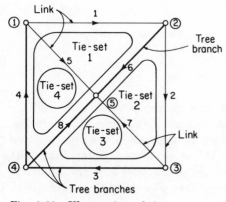

Fig. 4-22   Illustration of tie-sets.

link branches.   Since it has been established in Sec. 4-3 that the number of links of a graph is equal to $B - (N - 1)$, where B is the number of branches and N is the number of nodes, we can conclude that

Number of tie-sets $= B - N + 1$

Just how do we associate the tie-sets with the independent number of loops of a graph?   Since each tie-set is defined with a new link branch, the tie-sets naturally are independent of each other.   Now if we define a loop current in each of the tie-sets, these loop currents are necessarily independent of each other, since each loop has a new branch which is not in any other loop.   Therefore we conclude that the number of independent loop currents is equal to the number of tie-sets, and is given by the preceding equation.   However, when a graph has S separate parts, such as a network with transformers or magnetic coupling, the equation should be modified to read

$L = $ number of independent loop currents

$\quad = $ number of tie-sets $= B - N + S$

Tie-set matrix

The tie-set matrix of an oriented graph is obtained by applying Kirchhoff's voltage law to the tie-sets of the graph.   Since each branch of a graph is assigned with a branch voltage with the positive side located at the tail end of the arrow, a voltage equation can be written for each tie-set (independent loop) in terms of the branch voltages.   Let us consider the oriented graph of Fig. 4-23, with the tree and the corresponding four tie-sets selected as shown.   As described earlier, the positive direction of the tie-set current is defined to be in the same direction as that of the link branch.   Therefore, applying Kirchhoff's voltage law to tie-set 1 gives

Tie-set 1:

$$e_1 - e_5 + e_6 = 0$$

Similarly, for the other three tie-sets,

Tie-set 2:

$$e_2 - e_6 + e_7 = 0$$

Tie-set 3:

$$e_3 - e_7 + e_8 = 0$$

Tie-set 4:

$$e_4 + e_5 - e_8 = 0$$

In matrix form, these four voltage equations become

$$\begin{bmatrix} 1 & 0 & 0 & 0 & -1 & 1 & 0 & 0 \\ 0 & 1 & 0 & 0 & 0 & -1 & 1 & 0 \\ 0 & 0 & 1 & 0 & 0 & 0 & -1 & 1 \\ 0 & 0 & 0 & 1 & 1 & 0 & 0 & -1 \end{bmatrix} \begin{bmatrix} e_1 \\ e_2 \\ e_3 \\ e_4 \\ e_5 \\ e_6 \\ e_7 \\ e_8 \end{bmatrix} = 0 \qquad (4\text{-}48)$$

or simply,

$$\mathbf{B}e_b = 0 \qquad (4\text{-}49)$$

where $\mathbf{B}$ is a $(B - N + 1) \times B$ matrix, and is called the *tie-set matrix*. The elements of $\mathbf{B}$ are either $+1$, -1, or 0.

The tie-set matrix $\mathbf{B}$ can also be obtained from the relation between the loop currents and the branch currents in the tie-sets. The branch currents are assigned in the usual manner to the oriented graph as shown in Fig. 4-23, and the loop currents are designated as i_1, i_2, i_3, and i_4.

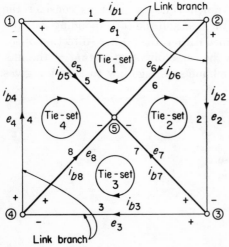

Fig. 4-23   *Relations between loop currents and branch currents.*

Then the loop currents are related to the branch currents by the following relations:

$$
\begin{aligned}
i_{b1} &= i_1 \\
i_{b2} &= i_2 \\
i_{b3} &= i_3 \\
i_{b4} &= i_4 \\
i_{b5} &= i_4 - i_1 \\
i_{b6} &= i_1 - i_2 \\
i_{b7} &= i_2 - i_3 \\
i_{b8} &= i_3 - i_4
\end{aligned}
\tag{4-50}
$$

In matrix form (4-50) becomes

$$
\mathbf{i}_b =
\begin{bmatrix}
i_{b1} \\
i_{b2} \\
i_{b3} \\
i_{b4} \\
i_{b5} \\
i_{b6} \\
i_{b7} \\
i_{b8}
\end{bmatrix}
=
\begin{bmatrix}
1 & 0 & 0 & 0 \\
0 & 1 & 0 & 0 \\
0 & 0 & 1 & 0 \\
0 & 0 & 0 & 1 \\
-1 & 0 & 0 & 1 \\
1 & -1 & 0 & 0 \\
0 & 1 & -1 & 0 \\
0 & 0 & 1 & -1
\end{bmatrix}
\begin{bmatrix}
i_1 \\
i_2 \\
i_3 \\
i_4
\end{bmatrix}
\tag{4-51}
$$

Comparing (4-51) with (4-48), it is apparent that (4-51) can be written

$$
\mathbf{i}_b = \mathbf{B}'\mathbf{i}_l = \mathbf{B}'
\begin{bmatrix}
i_1 \\
i_2 \\
i_3 \\
i_4
\end{bmatrix}
\tag{4-52}
$$

Equation (4-52) is often referred to as the *loop-transformation equation*.

Now Kirchhoff's voltage-law equation (4-49), the loop-transformation equation (4-52), and the branch voltage-current equations (4-25) can be combined to form the loop equations. These equations are repeated as follows:

$$
\mathbf{B}\mathbf{e}_b = \mathbf{0}
\tag{4-53}
$$

$$
\mathbf{i}_b = \mathbf{B}'\mathbf{i}_l
\tag{4-54}
$$

$$
\mathbf{e}_b = \mathbf{v}_g + \mathbf{Z}_b(\mathbf{i}_b - \mathbf{i}_g)
\tag{4-55}
$$

Substituting from (4-55) in (4-53) gives

$$
\mathbf{B}\mathbf{v}_g + \mathbf{B}\mathbf{Z}_b(\mathbf{i}_b - \mathbf{i}_g) = \mathbf{0}
\tag{4-56}
$$

Now substituting from (4-54) in (4-56) and rearranging gives

$$\mathbf{B}\mathbf{Z}_b\mathbf{i}_g - \mathbf{B}\mathbf{v}_g = \mathbf{B}\mathbf{Z}_b\mathbf{B}'\mathbf{i}_l \qquad (4\text{-}57)$$

Letting

$$\mathbf{v}_l = \mathbf{B}\mathbf{Z}_b\mathbf{i}_g - \mathbf{B}\mathbf{v}_g \qquad (4\text{-}58)$$

and

$$\mathbf{Z}_l = \mathbf{B}\mathbf{Z}_b\mathbf{B}' \qquad (4\text{-}59)$$

(4-57) becomes

$$\mathbf{v}_l = \mathbf{Z}_l\mathbf{i}_l \qquad (4\text{-}60)$$

which is the loop equation in matrix form.   It is necessary to repeat here that now the source matrix $\mathbf{v}_g$ includes the initial capacitor voltages but $\mathbf{i}_g$ does not include the initial inductor currents.

In general, $\mathbf{v}_l$ is a $B - N + S$ column matrix which contains the voltage and current sources.   Furthermore, the kth row of $\mathbf{v}_l$ contains the element

$$[v_l]_{k,1} = \text{sum of all effects of voltage and current sources found in} \atop \text{tie-set (loop) } k \quad (4\text{-}61)$$

$\mathbf{Z}_l$ is the *loop-impedance matrix* and is $(B - N + S) \times (B - N + S)$.   It can be shown that the elements in $\mathbf{Z}_l$ are described by z_{kj} in (4-4).

Example 4-4   Let us consider the network used in Example 4-1 (Fig. 4-18).   The network is repeated in Fig. 4-24a.   The oriented graph,

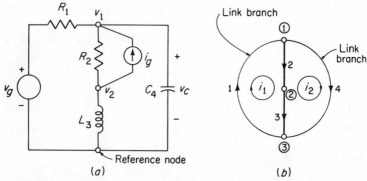

Fig. 4-24   (a) *Network for Example 4-4.*   (b) *The oriented graph and tie-sets.*

a tree and its corresponding tie-sets, is shown in Fig. 4-24b. For this network, $N = 3$, $B = 4$, and $S = 1$ (there is only one connected part); therefore $B - N + 1 = 2$, meaning that there are two independent loop currents.   The directions of the loop currents are defined as the same as those of the link-branch currents.

The tie-set matrix **B** can ordinarily be written by inspection of the oriented graph.   However, as our first illustrative example on loop equations, we first write Kirchhoff's voltage equations:

Loop 1:

$$e_1 + e_2 + e_3 = 0$$

Loop 2:

$$-e_2 - e_3 + e_4 = 0$$

from which we get

$$\mathbf{B} = \begin{bmatrix} 1 & 1 & 1 & 0 \\ 0 & -1 & -1 & 1 \end{bmatrix}$$

The branch-impedance matrix $\mathbf{Z}_b$ is obtained by filling the positions on its main diagonal with impedances of the corresponding branch of the network and with zeros everywhere else.   Thus

$$\mathbf{Z}_b = \begin{bmatrix} R_1 & 0 & 0 & 0 \\ 0 & R_2 & 0 & 0 \\ 0 & 0 & L_3 p & 0 \\ 0 & 0 & 0 & \dfrac{1}{C_4 p} \end{bmatrix}$$

Observe that $\mathbf{Z}_b$ can also be obtained by taking the inverse of the branch admittance $\mathbf{Y}_b$, which is obtained in Example 4-1.

From (4-59), the loop-impedance matrix is written

$$\mathbf{Z}_l = \mathbf{B}\mathbf{Z}_b\mathbf{B}' = \begin{bmatrix} 1 & 1 & 1 & 0 \\ 0 & -1 & -1 & 1 \end{bmatrix} \begin{bmatrix} R_1 & 0 & 0 & 0 \\ 0 & R_2 & 0 & 0 \\ 0 & 0 & L_3 p & 0 \\ 0 & 0 & 0 & \dfrac{1}{C_4 p} \end{bmatrix} \begin{bmatrix} 1 & 0 \\ 1 & -1 \\ 1 & -1 \\ 0 & 1 \end{bmatrix}$$

$$= \begin{bmatrix} R_1 + L_3 p + R_2 & -(R_2 + L_3 p) \\ -(R_2 + L_3 p) & R_2 + L_3 p + \dfrac{1}{C_4 p} \end{bmatrix} \qquad (4\text{-}62)$$

It is apparent that the elements of $\mathbf{Z}_l$ could also be determined by inspection of the network, using the method described in Sec. 4-2, and that (4-62) agrees with the result obtained earlier in (4-7).

The input matrix $\mathbf{v}_l$ is obtained from (4-58); that is,

$$\mathbf{v}_l = \mathbf{B}\mathbf{Z}_b\mathbf{i}_g - \mathbf{B}\mathbf{v}_g$$

$$= \begin{bmatrix} R_1 & R_2 & L_3p & 0 \\ 0 & -R_2 & -L_3p & \dfrac{1}{C_4p} \end{bmatrix} \begin{bmatrix} 0 \\ i_g \\ 0 \\ 0 \end{bmatrix} - \begin{bmatrix} 1 & 1 & 1 & 0 \\ 0 & -1 & -1 & 1 \end{bmatrix} \begin{bmatrix} -v_g \\ 0 \\ 0 \\ v_c(t_0^+) \end{bmatrix}$$

Therefore

$$\mathbf{v}_l = \begin{bmatrix} R_2 i_g \\ -R_2 i_g \end{bmatrix} - \begin{bmatrix} -v_g \\ v_c(t_0^+) \end{bmatrix} = \begin{bmatrix} R_2 i_g + v_g \\ -v_c(t_0^+) - R_2 i_g \end{bmatrix}$$

which agrees with the left-hand side of (4-7). Substituting $\mathbf{v}_l$ and $\mathbf{Z}_l$ into (4-60), the loop equation is obtained as

$$\begin{bmatrix} R_2 i_g + v_g \\ -v_c(t_0^+) - R_2 i_g \end{bmatrix} = \begin{bmatrix} R_1 + R_2 + L_3p & -(R_2 + L_3p) \\ -(R_2 + L_3p) & R_2 + L_3p + \dfrac{1}{C_4p} \end{bmatrix} \begin{bmatrix} i_1 \\ i_2 \end{bmatrix}$$

which agrees with (4-7).

Example 4-5   The network with magnetic coupling in Fig. 4-19a is reconsidered for loop analysis. The oriented graph of the network, a tree, and the corresponding tie-sets are shown in Fig. 4-25b.

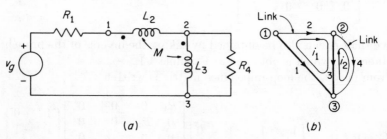

(a) (b)

Fig. 4-25   (a) Network for Example 4-5.   (b) The oriented graph and tie-sets.

The tie-set matrix of the graph in Fig. 4-25b is written by inspection.

$$\mathbf{B} = \begin{bmatrix} -1 & 1 & 1 & 0 \\ 0 & 0 & -1 & 1 \end{bmatrix}$$

The branch-impedance matrix $\mathbf{Z}_b$ is

$$\mathbf{Z}_b = \begin{bmatrix} R_1 & 0 & 0 & 0 \\ 0 & L_2p & Mp & 0 \\ 0 & Mp & L_3p & 0 \\ 0 & 0 & 0 & R_4 \end{bmatrix} \tag{4-63}$$

The mutual-inductance terms are positive since the branch currents i_{b2} and i_{b3} are assumed to be flowing into the dots of the coils (Fig. 4-25b). It can be shown that $\mathbf{Z}_b$ of (4-63) is the matrix inverse of the $\mathbf{Y}_b$ in (4-38). From (4-58), we get

$$\mathbf{v}_l = \mathbf{B}\mathbf{Z}_b\mathbf{i}_g - \mathbf{B}\mathbf{v}_g = -\mathbf{B}\mathbf{v}_g = -\begin{bmatrix} -1 & 1 & 1 & 0 \\ 0 & 0 & -1 & 1 \end{bmatrix}\begin{bmatrix} v_g \\ 0 \\ 0 \\ 0 \end{bmatrix}$$

where

$$\mathbf{v}_l = \begin{bmatrix} v_g \\ 0 \end{bmatrix}$$

Using (4-59), the loop-impedance matrix is found to be

$$\mathbf{Z}_l = \mathbf{B}\mathbf{Z}_b\mathbf{B}' = \begin{bmatrix} R_1 + (L_2 + L_3 + 2M)p & -(M + L_3)p \\ -(M + L_3)p & R_4 + L_3p \end{bmatrix}$$

Thus the loop equation is

$$\begin{bmatrix} v_g \\ 0 \end{bmatrix} = \begin{bmatrix} R_1 + (L_2 + L_3 + 2M)p & -(M + L_3)p \\ -(M + L_3)p & R_4 + L_3p \end{bmatrix}\begin{bmatrix} i_1 \\ i_2 \end{bmatrix}$$

For a network with dependent sources, the loop impedance matrix $\mathbf{Z}_l$ will no longer be symmetric, as in the passive case. The student should carry out the loop analysis for the network in Example 4-3 as an exercise.

4-6 THE E SHIFT AND THE I SHIFT

The illustrative examples in the preceding sections all have one common feature in that all the branches of the networks satisfy the basic configuration shown in Fig. 4-17. Quite often, however, in more complex situations, we find a current generator connected across several branches or a voltage generator connected in series with several branches.   Therefore the basic branch configuration shown in Fig. 4-17 does not apply directly to these situations.   Illustrative examples of these conditions are shown in Fig. 4-26.   In Fig. 4-26a, the ideal voltage source v_g is connected to a node which is a junction of two other branches.   Figure 4-26b shows a situation where a current source is connected across two branches.

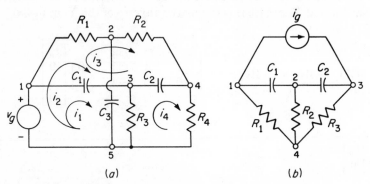

Fig. 4-26   Situations where Fig. 4-17 does not apply.

The ideal voltage source itself, without a series impedance of any kind, is a short circuit and therefore does not form any branch on the oriented graph.   In order to identify v_g with a particular branch or branches, it is necessary to perform an operation called the *E shift*.   It is possible to shift the voltage generator v_g to the branches that are connected in series with it without changing the characteristic of the network. In Fig. 4-27a the voltage source v_g is shifted to the two branches that are connected to node 1.   The network is essentially not affected by this shift in v_g since the loop equations of the four loops shown in Figs. 4-26a and 4-27a will be identical.   The ideal voltage source v_g can also be shifted "backward" into the three branches that are connected to its negative side as shown in Fig. 4-27b.   It is apparent that this shift again will not affect any one of the loop equations.

The difficulty with the current source shown in Fig. 4-26b can be circumvented by an *I shift*, which effectively places the current source i_g in parallel with each of the branches that form a closed loop with i_g.

The I shift of the current source i_g of Fig. 4-26b results in the network of Fig. 4-28a or b.   In these two modified networks, since the net current

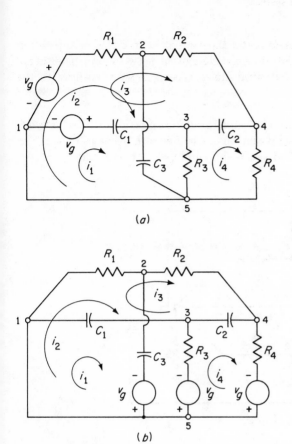

(a)

(b)

Fig. 4-27   The E shift.

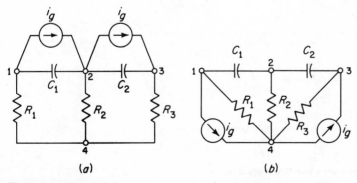

(a)   (b)

Fig. 4-28   The I shift.

flowing in or out of any node is still the same as that of the corresponding node in Fig. 4-26b, the I shift does not change the network properties at all.

Let us consider the following illustrative example treating with the E shift and the I shift.

Example 4-6   The loop and the node equations of the network shown in Fig. 4-29a are to be written.   The network becomes that of Fig. 4-29b after we have applied the E-shift and I-shift operations.

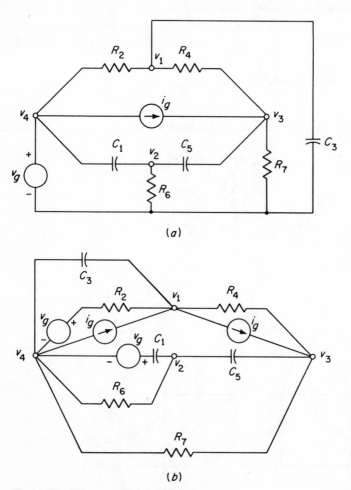

Fig. 4-29   *Networks for Example 4-6.*

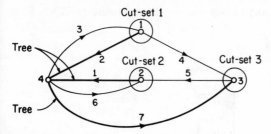

Fig. 4-30   Graph and tree of the network shown in Fig. 4-29.

The oriented graph, a tree, and the corresponding cut-set are shown in Fig. 4-30. Since $N = 4$, $B = 7$, there should be three cut-sets and four tie-sets. The cut-set matrix is

$$\mathbf{A} = \begin{bmatrix} 0 & 1 & -1 & 1 & 0 & 0 & 0 \\ 1 & 0 & 0 & 0 & -1 & -1 & 0 \\ 0 & 0 & 0 & -1 & 1 & 0 & -1 \end{bmatrix}$$

The branch-admittance matrix is

$$\mathbf{Y}_b = \begin{bmatrix} C_1 p & 0 & 0 & 0 & 0 & 0 & 0 \\ 0 & \dfrac{1}{R_2} & 0 & 0 & 0 & 0 & 0 \\ 0 & 0 & C_3 p & 0 & 0 & 0 & 0 \\ 0 & 0 & 0 & \dfrac{1}{R_4} & 0 & 0 & 0 \\ 0 & 0 & 0 & 0 & C_5 p & 0 & 0 \\ 0 & 0 & 0 & 0 & 0 & \dfrac{1}{R_6} & 0 \\ 0 & 0 & 0 & 0 & 0 & 0 & \dfrac{1}{R_7} \end{bmatrix}$$

Therefore

$$\mathbf{Y}_n = \mathbf{A}\mathbf{Y}_b\mathbf{A}' = \begin{bmatrix} \dfrac{1}{R_2} + \dfrac{1}{R_4} + C_3 p & 0 & -\dfrac{1}{R_4} \\ 0 & C_1 p + C_5 p + \dfrac{1}{R_6} & -C_5 p \\ -\dfrac{1}{R_4} & -C_5 p & \dfrac{1}{R_4} + \dfrac{1}{R_7} + C_5 p \end{bmatrix}$$

The input matrix $\mathbf{i}_n$ is obtained from Fig. 4-29b and using (4-32).   Thus

$$\mathbf{i}_n = \mathbf{A}\mathbf{Y}_b\mathbf{v}_g - \mathbf{A}\mathbf{i}_g$$

where

$$\mathbf{v}_g = \begin{bmatrix} v_g \\ v_g \\ 0 \\ 0 \\ 0 \\ 0 \\ 0 \end{bmatrix} \quad \text{and} \quad \mathbf{i}_g = \begin{bmatrix} 0 \\ -i_g \\ 0 \\ i_g \\ 0 \\ 0 \\ 0 \end{bmatrix}$$

Then

$$\mathbf{i}_n = \begin{bmatrix} \dfrac{v_g}{R_2} \\ C_1 p v_g \\ 0 \end{bmatrix} - \begin{bmatrix} 0 \\ 0 \\ -i_g \end{bmatrix} = \begin{bmatrix} \dfrac{v_g}{R_2} \\ C_1 p v_g \\ i_g \end{bmatrix}$$

and the node equation becomes

$$\begin{bmatrix} \dfrac{v_g}{R_2} \\ C_1 p v_g \\ i_g \end{bmatrix} = \begin{bmatrix} \dfrac{1}{R_2} + \dfrac{1}{R_4} + C_3 p & 0 & -\dfrac{1}{R_4} \\ 0 & C_1 p + C_5 p + \dfrac{1}{R_6} & -C_5 p \\ -\dfrac{1}{R_4} & -C_5 p & \dfrac{1}{R_4} + \dfrac{1}{R_7} + C_5 p \end{bmatrix} \begin{bmatrix} v_1 \\ v_2 \\ v_3 \end{bmatrix}$$

For loop analysis, the four tie-sets that correspond to the tree chosen in Fig. 4-30 are shown in Fig. 4-31.

The loop-impedance matrix $\mathbf{Z}_l$ is obtained either by inspection of the impedances found in the tie-sets or by use of (4-59).   Therefore

$$\mathbf{Z}_l = \begin{bmatrix} R_2 + \dfrac{1}{C_3 p} & 0 & -R_2 & 0 \\ 0 & \dfrac{1}{C_1 p} + R_6 & 0 & \dfrac{1}{C_1 p} \\ -R_2 & 0 & R_2 + R_4 + R_7 & -R_7 \\ 0 & \dfrac{1}{C_1 p} & -R_7 & R_7 + \dfrac{1}{C_1 p} + \dfrac{1}{C_5 p} \end{bmatrix}$$

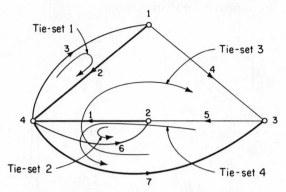

Fig. 4-31   Tie-sets for the tree chosen in Fig. 4-30.

The input matrix $\mathbf{v}_l$ is given by

$$\mathbf{v}_l = \mathbf{B}\mathbf{Z}_b\mathbf{i}_g - \mathbf{B}\mathbf{v}_g = \begin{bmatrix} 0 & R_2 & \dfrac{1}{C_3 p} & 0 & 0 & 0 & 0 \\[2mm] \dfrac{1}{C_1 p} & 0 & 0 & 0 & 0 & R_6 & 0 \\[2mm] 0 & -R_2 & 0 & R_4 & 0 & 0 & -R_7 \\[2mm] \dfrac{1}{C_1 p} & 0 & 0 & 0 & \dfrac{1}{C_5 p} & 0 & R_7 \end{bmatrix} \begin{bmatrix} 0 \\ -i_g \\ 0 \\ i_g \\ 0 \\ 0 \\ 0 \end{bmatrix}$$

$$-\begin{bmatrix} 0 & 1 & 1 & 0 & 0 & 0 & 0 \\ 1 & 0 & 0 & 0 & 0 & 1 & 0 \\ 0 & -1 & 0 & 1 & 0 & 0 & -1 \\ 1 & 0 & 0 & 0 & 1 & 0 & 1 \end{bmatrix} \begin{bmatrix} v_g + v_{c1}(t_0^+) \\ v_g \\ v_{c3}(t_0^+) \\ v_{c5}(t_0^+) \\ 0 \\ 0 \end{bmatrix}$$

or

$$\mathbf{v}_l = \begin{bmatrix} -R_2 i_g \\ 0 \\ R_2 i_g + R_4 i_g \\ 0 \end{bmatrix} - \begin{bmatrix} v_g + v_{c3}(t_0^+) \\ v_g + v_{c1}(t_0^+) \\ -v_g \\ v_g + v_{c1}(t_0^+) + v_{c5}(t_0^+) \end{bmatrix}$$

The four loop equations in matrix form are written

$$
\begin{bmatrix}
v_g + v_{c3}(t_0^+) - R_2 i_g \\
-v_g - v_{c1}(t_0^+) \\
v_g + (R_2 + R_4) i_g \\
-v_g - v_{c1}(t_0^+) - v_{c5}(t_0^+)
\end{bmatrix}
$$

$$
=
\begin{bmatrix}
R_2 + \dfrac{1}{C_3 p} & 0 & -R_2 & 0 \\[2mm]
0 & R_6 + \dfrac{1}{C_1 p} & 0 & \dfrac{1}{C_1 p} \\[2mm]
-R_2 & 0 & R_2 + R_4 + R_7 & -R_7 \\[2mm]
0 & \dfrac{1}{C_1 p} & -R_7 & R_7 + \dfrac{1}{C_1 p} + \dfrac{1}{C_5 p}
\end{bmatrix}
\begin{bmatrix}
i_1 \\ i_2 \\ i_3 \\ i_4
\end{bmatrix}
$$

PROBLEMS

4-1 Draw several trees for each of the networks shown in Fig. P4-1.

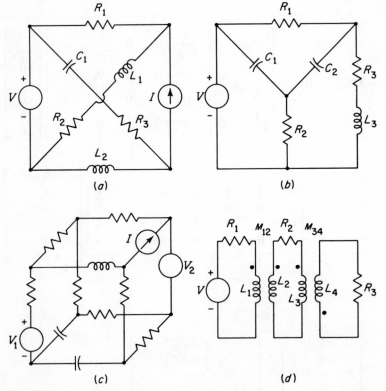

Fig. P4-1

4-2 For the networks shown in Fig. P4-1, determine the number of independent loop and node equations in each network.

4-3 Write a tie-set matrix for each of the networks shown in Fig. P4-1.

4-4 Write a cut-set matrix for each of the networks shown in Fig. P4-1.

4-5 Write loop equations for the networks shown in Fig. P4-2 by assigning independent loop currents to the networks.

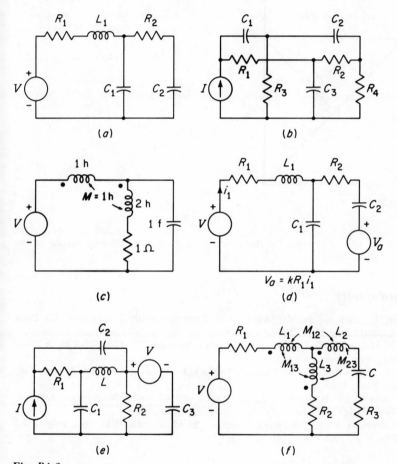

Fig. P4-2

4-6 Write node equations for the networks shown in Fig. P4-2 by assigning independent node voltages to the networks.

4-7 Write loop equations for the networks shown in Fig. P4-2, using the tie-set method discussed in Sec. 4-5.

4-8 Write node equations for the networks shown in Fig. P4-2, using the cut-set method discussed in Sec. 4-4.

4-9 Write loop equations for the network shown in Fig. P4-3 by means of the tie-set method.

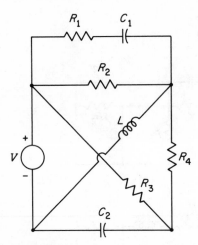

Fig. P4-3

4-10 Write node equations for the network shown in Fig. P4-3 by means of the cut-set method.

BIBLIOGRAPHY

Brenner, E., and M. Javid: "Analysis of Electric Circuits," McGraw-Hill Book Company, New York, 1959.

Reza, F. M., and S. Seely: "Modern Network Analysis," McGraw-Hill Book Company, New York, 1959.

Seshu, S., and N. Balabanian: "Linear Network Analysis," John Wiley & Sons, Inc., New York, 1959.

Seshu, S., and M. B. Reed: "Linear Graphs and Electrical Networks," Addison-Wesley Publishing Company, Inc., Reading, Mass., 1961.

Van Valkenburg, M. E.: "Network Analysis," 2d ed., Prentice-Hall, Inc., Englewood Cliffs, N.J., 1964.

FIVE

STATE-VARIABLE TECHNIQUES

5-1 THE CONCEPT OF STATES

Although the term *state variables* is relatively new, the concept of *states* has been in existence for many years. In electrical engineering, the interest in the state-variable concept originated in control-systems theory. The phase-plane method,[1] known to physicists and control-system engineers for many years, is basically a state-variable method. Recently, with the advent of self-optimizing control, adaptive control, computer control, and other sophisticated aspects of feedback-control-systems theory, interest in the state-variable technique has become more widespread.

The application of the state-variable concept is by no means restricted to problems in control systems. In general, problems in the physical world tend to follow certain cause-and-effect relationships. The future course of an event usually depends upon its past history and the excitation. For example, the prospect in earnings of a corporation over the next six

105

months depends upon the effort spent by the company on expansion in facilities, product and market improvements, etc., in the past, as well as on the present backlog, business condition, and volume of incoming orders over the period. In terms of physical systems, it can be stated that the output of the system depends upon the past history of the system as well as the present input.

To characterize the dynamic behavior of the system, a set of physical or mathematical variables, called state variables, are devised. These state variables, in general, contain as much information about the past history of the system as is required for the calculation of the future behavior of the system.

In systems and network theory, the state-variable method has definite advantages over some of the more conventional methods. One of the distinct features of the state method is that it decomposes a complex system into a set of interacting systems, which are then solved one at a time. In network analysis, the state-variable characterization has the advantage over the conventional loop-and-node analysis in that information about the past history of the network is represented directly by state variables. In control systems, the concept of state allows the study of complex control-system problems, and thus opened the door to modern control theory. Perhaps one of the greatest contributions of the state-variable method is that it permits problems in network and systems to be treated in a unified manner; it allows the engineer to set up a problem in such a way that it may be solved either manually or by means of a computer.

Let us introduce the concept of state[2] and state variables by means of a very simple and well-known network problem. Shown in Fig. 5-1a is an RC network whose input voltage is labeled $v(t)$ and the output is the voltage $v_c(t)$ across the capacitor. We assume that a d-c voltage of V_1 volts has been applied at the input terminals for a long time so that the voltage across the capacitor is virtually V_1. Now, at a given time t_0, the input voltage is made to jump abruptly from V_1 to V_2 volts. It is easy to show that the output voltage $v_c(t)$ for $t \geq t_0$ is described by

$$v_c(t) = [V_2 - v_c(t_0)][1 - e^{-(t-t_0)/RC}] + v_c(t_0) \qquad t \geq t_0 \qquad (5\text{-}1)$$

or

$$v_c(t) = (V_2 - V_1)[1 - e^{-(t-t_0)/RC}] + V_1 \qquad t \geq t_0 \qquad (5\text{-}2)$$

If we regard the application of $v(t)$ at $t = t_0$ as an independent event, we may consider t_0 as a time reference. Then $v_c(t_0)$ is the initial voltage across the capacitor. Equation (5-2) indicates that, regardless of what the input voltage was prior to t_0, the output voltage $v_c(t)$ for $t \geq t_0$ is

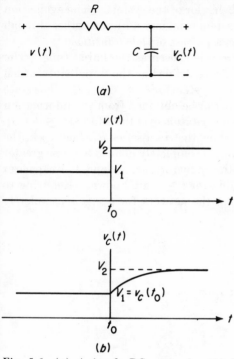

Fig. 5-1   *(a) A simple RC network.*   *(b) Input and output voltages of the RC network.*

completely defined by the following two factors:

1   The initial condition of the network, $v_c(t_0)$
2   The input voltage for $t \geq t_0$

In other words, the knowledge of the initial voltage and the input signal over the interval (t_0, t) is all that is necessary to determine the output voltage for t greater than t_0. The output and the input voltages of the RC network are now shown in Fig. 5-1b.

We can now regard the initial value of $v_c(t)$ at $t = t_0$ as a quantity which describes the complete *history* of the network up to the time t_0. Thus $v_c(t_0)$ defines the *initial state* of the network. The state of the RC network for time greater than t_0 is completely described by the expression of $v_c(t)$ in (5-2), and $v_c(t)$ is called the state variable of the network.

In general, the state of a network or a system is described by a set of numbers or variables called state variables. These variables usually contain as much information about the past history of the system as is required for the calculation of the future behavior of the system.   The evaluation of the response of a network or system from one state to another through time may be visualized simply as a process of *state transition*.

Usually, a reference time $t = t_0$ is chosen as the initial time.   The state variables evaluated at $t = t_0$ are defined as the initial state which describes the complete history of the system for $-\infty < t \leq t_0$.   The state of the system for any time $t_1 > t_0$ can be obtained from the information about the initial state and the input excitation over the interval $t_0 \leq t < t_1$.

In a similar manner we can show that in a series RLC network, the response or the state of the network is completely defined for time greater than t_0 if the initial values of the inductor current and the capacitor voltage at $t = t_0$ and the excitation for $t \geq t_0$ are known.   Referring to the circuit of Fig. 5-2, the state of the network for $t > t_0$ is completely

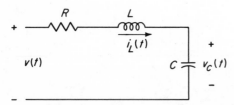

Fig. 5-2   A series RLC network.

defined by $i_L(t)$ and $v_c(t)$, which are chosen as the state variables, and the input voltage $v(t)$ for $t \geq t_0$.   We should mention at this point, however, that, in general, the choice of state variables in a given physical system is sometimes arbitrary.   It is not difficult to see that in network problems, if the state variables are chosen to be the currents in the inductors and the voltages across the capacitors, the initial conditions of the network may be applied directly to the solution of the problem.   This is why, in the last two illustrative examples, $i_L(t)$ and $v_c(t)$ were chosen as the state variables. However, it is apparent that we can also select, if we wish, some linear combination such as $v_c(t) + i_L(t)$ and $v_c(t) - i_L(t)$ as the state variables for the network shown in Fig. 5-2.

In terms of the state variables $i_L(t)$ and $v_c(t)$, the RLC network can be described by the following two first-order differential equations, called state equations:

$$L \frac{di_L(t)}{dt} = v(t) - Ri_L(t) - v_c(t) \tag{5-3}$$

$$C \frac{dv_c(t)}{dt} = i_L(t) \tag{5-4}$$

The first equation is obtained by equating the voltage across the inductor as a linear function of the input variable and the state variables. The second equation describes the current in the capacitor. It is interesting to note that, if we regard $i_L(t)$ as the loop current in the conventional loop analysis, (5-3) and (5-4) are equivalent to the loop equation

$$v(t) = L\frac{di_L(t)}{dt} + Ri_L(t) + \frac{1}{C}\int_{t_0^+}^{t} i_L(\tau)\,d\tau + v_c(t_0^+) \tag{5-5}$$

Assuming that $v(t) = u(t)$, a unit step voltage, and $v_c(t_0^+) = i_L(t_0^+) = 0$ at $t = t_0^+ = 0$, the solutions of (5-3) and (5-4), or of (5-5), are

$$i_L(t) = e^{-t} - e^{-2t} \tag{5-6}$$

and

$$v_c(t) = 1 - 2e^{-t} + e^{-2t} \tag{5-7}$$

for $t \geq 0$. The waveforms of $i_L(t)$ and $v_c(t)$ are sketched in Fig. 5-3.

The two plots in Fig. 5-3 can be described by just one plot as shown in Fig. 5-4. In this figure, the inductor current i_L is plotted against the capacitor voltage v_c, using t as an explicit parameter on the curve. This i_L versus v_c plot is generally known as a phase-plane diagram[1] of a second-order system. For higher-order systems, a multidimensional *phase space* has to be envisioned. The curve in the phase plane is called a *phase-plane trajectory;* each point on the phase-plane trajectory is asso-

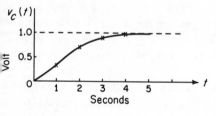

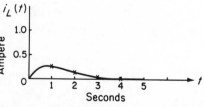

Fig. 5-3 *Capacitor voltage and inductor current as functions of time of the RLC network in Fig. 5-2.*

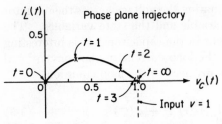

Fig. 5-4   *Phase-plane diagram of the RLC network in Fig. 5-2.*

ciated with a specific time $t_1 \geq t_0$, and the coordinates $[i_L(t_1),v_c(t_1)]$ of the point specify the values of i_L and v_c at $t = t_1$.   The point $[i_L(t_0),v_c(t_0)]$ on the phase-plane trajectory represents the initial state of the system. In this case, since the initial conditions are assumed to be zero, the initial-state point is located at the origin of the phase plane.   Finally, when time approaches infinity, $[i_L(\infty),v_c(\infty)]$ denotes the *final state* of the system.

Although the phase-space diagram gives a clear picture of the transition of state of a physical system as time progresses, it is usually difficult to visualize and to construct for systems with order higher than 2.

5-2   STATE EQUATIONS OF DYNAMIC SYSTEMS WITH CONTINUOUS SIGNALS

In the foregoing section the concept of state is introduced qualitatively by means of two practical examples.   In a more formal manner, the state variables of a dynamic system may be defined as *a minimal set of numbers, $x_1(t)$, $x_2(t)$, . . . , $x_n(t)$, of which, if values are specified at any time t_0, together with knowledge of the input to the system for $t_0 \leq \tau \leq t$, the evolution of the state and the output of the system for $t_0 \leq \tau \leq t$ are completely defined.* This statement also serves as a criterion for selecting state variables for a dynamic system.

Let us consider the block diagram of a dynamic system with m inputs and p outputs as shown in Fig. 5-5.   We assume that the signals in the

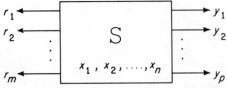

Fig. 5-5   *Block diagram of a dynamic system which has m inputs, p outputs, and n state variables.*

system are all functions of the continuous time variable t, so that the system can be represented by a set of n first-order differential equations.

$$\frac{dx_i(t)}{dt} = f_i[x_1(t),x_2(t), \ . \ . \ . \ ,x_n(t),r_1(t),r_2(t), \ . \ . \ . \ ,r_m(t),t] \qquad (5\text{-}8)$$

where $i = 1, 2, \ . \ . \ . \ , n; x_1(t), x_2(t), \ . \ . \ . \ , x_n(t)$ are the state variables of the system; $r_1(t), r_2(t), \ . \ . \ . \ , r_m(t)$ are the input variables of the system; and f_i denotes the functional relationships.

A simple example of this representation of a dynamic system by first-order differential equations, called state equations, was cited in the description of the RLC network of Fig. 5-3 by Eqs. (5-3) and (5-4). In this specific example, the state variables are chosen to be $v_c(t)$ and $i_L(t)$, and there is only one input in $v(t)$. In general, we may regard any one or all of the state variables, or the voltage across R or L, as the output variables. Therefore it is necessary, in Fig. 5-5, to denote the state variables by x and the system outputs by another set of variables, y. However, since the state variables completely define the dynamic behavior of the system, it should be possible to express the outputs of the system in Fig. 5-5 as

$$y_k(t) = g_k[x_1(t),x_2(t), \ . \ . \ . \ ,x_n(t),r_1(t),r_2(t), \ . \ . \ . \ ,r_m(t),t] \qquad (5\text{-}9)$$

where $k = 1, 2, \ . \ . \ . \ , p$ for p output variables.

The state equations (5-8) and the output equations (5-9) are together called the *dynamic equations* of the system. The equations are expressed in general form so that they can be nonlinear or linear explicit functions of time. The equations are said to be nonlinear if f_i and g_k are nonlinear functions of x or r or both; otherwise they are linear. If f_i and g_k do not contain explicit functions of time t, the equations are said to be *time-invariant;* otherwise they are *time-variant*. The following examples illustrate the ideas of linearity and time variancy, using state equations:

$$\frac{dx_i(t)}{dt} = f_i[x_i(t),r_j(t)] \qquad \text{time-invariant}$$

$$\frac{dx(t)}{dt} = 2[x(t)]^{1/2} + 3tr(t) \qquad \text{nonlinear and time-variant}$$

$$\frac{dx(t)}{dt} = 2[x(t)]^2 + 3r(t) \qquad \text{nonlinear and time-invariant}$$

$$\frac{dx(t)}{dt} = 2tx(t) + 3r(t) \qquad \text{linear and time-variant}$$

Our interest, however, is centered on dynamic systems that are linear and time-invariant. Then (5-8) and (5-9) can be expressed as

$$\frac{dx_i(t)}{dt} = \sum_{j=1}^{n} a_{ij}x_{,}(t) + \sum_{h=1}^{m} b_{ih}r_h(t) \qquad i = 1, 2, \ldots, n \qquad (5\text{-}10)$$

and

$$y_k(t) = \sum_{j=1}^{n} c_{kj}x_j(t) + \sum_{h=1}^{m} d_{kh}r_h(t) \qquad k = 1, 2, \ldots, p \qquad (5\text{-}11)$$

where a_{ij}, b_{ik}, c_{kj}, and d_{kh} are all constants. The analytical solutions of these state equations can be carried out by either the classical methods or the Laplace-transform method.

Matrix representation

Using matrix notations, the dynamic equations (5-10) and (5-11) can be expressed by the following compact vector-matrix equation forms:

$$\frac{d\mathbf{x}(t)}{dt} = \mathbf{f}(\mathbf{x},\mathbf{r},t) \qquad (5\text{-}12)$$

and

$$\mathbf{y}(t) = \mathbf{g}(\mathbf{x},\mathbf{r},t) \qquad (5\text{-}13)$$

where $\mathbf{f}$ and $\mathbf{g}$ are vector-valued functions. In the linear and time-invariant case, these equations become

$$\frac{d\mathbf{x}(t)}{dt} = \mathbf{A}\mathbf{x}(t) + \mathbf{B}\mathbf{r}(t) \qquad (5\text{-}14)$$

$$\mathbf{y}(t) = \mathbf{C}\mathbf{x}(t) + \mathbf{D}\mathbf{r}(t) \qquad (5\text{-}15)$$

Equation (5-14) is termed the *normal-form* vector-matrix equation of a linear time-invariant system. We use the term *vector* to represent the column (or row) matrices for the variables x_i, y_k, and r_j since they are all functions of time, and these elements comprise the coordinates of a point determining a changing-position vector in time space. In contrast, the $\mathbf{A}$,

B, C, and **D** matrices are all constant matrices and therefore are not vectors.

For a linear time-invariant system with n state variables, m inputs, and p outputs, **x** is an $n \times 1$ column matrix; i.e.,

$$\mathbf{x} = \begin{bmatrix} x_1 \\ x_2 \\ \cdot \\ \cdot \\ \cdot \\ x_n \end{bmatrix} \tag{5-16}$$

The vector **x** is often referred to as the *state vector*. The *input vector* **r** is an $m \times 1$ matrix, and the "output vector" **y** is a $p \times 1$ matrix. These are expressed as

$$\mathbf{r} = \begin{bmatrix} r_1 \\ r_2 \\ \cdot \\ \cdot \\ \cdot \\ r_m \end{bmatrix} \qquad \mathbf{y} = \begin{bmatrix} y_1 \\ y_2 \\ \cdot \\ \cdot \\ \cdot \\ y_p \end{bmatrix}$$

A is an $n \times n$ matrix whose elements are denoted by a_{ij}; **B** is an $n \times m$ matrix, and its elements are given by b_{ih}. **C** is a $p \times n$ matrix, and D is a $p \times m$ matrix. These are summarized as follows:

$$\mathbf{A} = [a_{ij}]_{n,n}$$
$$\mathbf{B} = [b_{ih}]_{n,m}$$
$$\mathbf{C} = [c_{kj}]_{p,n}$$
$$\mathbf{D} = [d_{kh}]_{p,m}$$

To illustrate writing state equations in vector-matrix form, let us rewrite (5-3) and (5-4) in the following form:

$$\frac{di_L(t)}{dt} = -\frac{R}{L}\, i_L(t) - \frac{1}{L}\, v_c(t) + \frac{1}{L}\, v(t) \tag{5-17}$$

$$\frac{dv_c(t)}{dt} = \frac{1}{C}\, i_L(t) \tag{5-18}$$

These two state equations can be expressed as a vector-matrix equation

$$\begin{bmatrix} \dfrac{di_L(t)}{dt} \\[2ex] \dfrac{dv_c(t)}{dt} \end{bmatrix} = \begin{bmatrix} -\dfrac{R}{L} & -\dfrac{1}{L} \\[2ex] \dfrac{1}{C} & 0 \end{bmatrix} \begin{bmatrix} i_L(t) \\[1ex] v_c(t) \end{bmatrix} + \begin{bmatrix} \dfrac{1}{L} \\[1ex] 0 \end{bmatrix} [v(t)] \tag{5-19}$$

which is of the same form as (5-14).

If we are interested in the values of the state variables v_c and i_L, we can regard these as the output variables. Then the output equation is simply

$$\mathbf{y}(t) = \begin{bmatrix} y_1(t) \\ y_2(t) \end{bmatrix} = \begin{bmatrix} 1 & 0 \\ 0 & 1 \end{bmatrix} \begin{bmatrix} i_L(t) \\ v_c(t) \end{bmatrix} \tag{5-20}$$

Referring to (5-15), we notice that $\mathbf{D}$ is a null matrix and

$$\mathbf{C} = \begin{bmatrix} 1 & 0 \\ 0 & 1 \end{bmatrix} \tag{5-21}$$

However, if in addition to i_L and v_c we are interested in the voltages across R and L in the circuit of Fig. 5-2, we should regard all these as the output variables also. In fact, these variables provide us with all the information we can get about the circuit. Letting $y_1 = i_L$, $y_2 = v_c$, $y_3 = Ri_L$, and $y_4 = L\, di_L/dt = v - Ri_L - v_c$, the output matrix equation is written

$$\mathbf{y} = \begin{bmatrix} y_1 \\ y_2 \\ y_3 \\ y_4 \end{bmatrix} = \begin{bmatrix} 1 & 0 \\ 0 & 1 \\ R & 0 \\ -R & -1 \end{bmatrix} \begin{bmatrix} i_L \\ v_c \end{bmatrix} + \begin{bmatrix} 0 \\ 0 \\ 0 \\ 1 \end{bmatrix} [v] \tag{5-22}$$

Therefore

$$\mathbf{C} = \begin{bmatrix} 1 & 0 \\ 0 & 1 \\ R & 0 \\ -R & -1 \end{bmatrix} \qquad \mathbf{D} = \begin{bmatrix} 0 \\ 0 \\ 0 \\ 1 \end{bmatrix}$$

5-3 CONTINUOUS - DATA STATE EQUATIONS OF GENERAL HIGHER - ORDER SYSTEMS

The state equations in vector-matrix form can also be applied to the representation of any high-order linear differential equations.   Let us consider the third-order differential equation

$$\frac{d^3y}{dt^3} + 4\frac{d^2y}{dt^2} + 3\frac{dy}{dt} + 2y = r(t) \tag{5-23}$$

In order to express this differential equation as a set of state equations, we must first define the three (the order of the differential equation) state variables.   A natural choice of the state variables is

$$x_1 = y \tag{5-24}$$

$$x_2 = \frac{dy}{dt} = \frac{dx_1}{dt} \tag{5-25}$$

$$x_3 = \frac{d^2y}{dt^2} = \frac{dx_2}{dt} \tag{5-26}$$

Hence the state-variable vector is denoted by

$$\mathbf{x} = \begin{bmatrix} x_1 \\ x_2 \\ x_3 \end{bmatrix} = \begin{bmatrix} y \\ \dfrac{dy}{dt} \\ \dfrac{d^2y}{dt^2} \end{bmatrix} \tag{5-27}$$

Solving for the highest-order derivative term in (5-23), we obtain

$$\frac{d^3y}{dt^3} = -2y - 3\frac{dy}{dt} - 4\frac{d^2y}{dt^2} + r \tag{5-28}$$

Equation (5-23) may now be represented by a set of three state equations:

$$\frac{dx_1}{dt} = x_2 \tag{5-29}$$

$$\frac{dx_2}{dt} = x_3 \tag{5-30}$$

$$\frac{dx_3}{dt} = -2x_1 - 3x_2 - 4x_3 + r \tag{5-31}$$

We notice that the first two state equations are merely the defining equations of the state variables. The third state equation is obtained from the original differential equation by replacing y and its derivatives by their corresponding state-variable equivalents.

In matrix form, the state equations are

$$\begin{bmatrix} \dfrac{dx_1}{dt} \\[2mm] \dfrac{dx_2}{dt} \\[2mm] \dfrac{dx_3}{dt} \end{bmatrix} = \begin{bmatrix} 0 & 1 & 0 \\ 0 & 0 & 1 \\ -2 & -3 & -4 \end{bmatrix} \begin{bmatrix} x_1 \\ x_2 \\ x_3 \end{bmatrix} + \begin{bmatrix} 0 \\ 0 \\ 1 \end{bmatrix} [r] \tag{5-32}$$

which is recognized as the matrix equation

$$\frac{dx}{dt} = \mathbf{A}x + \mathbf{B}r \tag{5-33}$$

In general, the nth-order differential equation

$$\frac{d^n y}{dt^n} + a_1 \frac{d^{n-1}y}{dt^{n-1}} + a_2 \frac{d^{n-2}y}{dt^{n-2}} + \cdots + a_{n-1}\frac{dy}{dt} + a_n y = r \tag{5-34}$$

may be represented by n first-order state equations. We define

$$\mathbf{x} = \begin{bmatrix} x_1 \\ x_2 \\ \cdot \\ \cdot \\ \cdot \\ x_n \end{bmatrix} = \begin{bmatrix} y \\[1mm] \dfrac{dy}{dt} \\[1mm] \cdot \\ \cdot \\ \cdot \\ \dfrac{d^{n-1}y}{dt^{n-1}} \end{bmatrix} \tag{5-35}$$

Solving for the highest-order derivative in (5-34) and using the state variables defined above, (5-34) becomes

$$\frac{d^n x}{dt^n} = -a_n x_1 - a_{n-1}x_2 - \cdots - a_2 x_{n-1} - a_1 x_n + r$$

The state equations are now

$$\frac{dx_1}{dt} = x_2$$

$$\frac{dx_2}{dt} = x_3$$

. . . . .

$$\frac{dx_{n-1}}{dt} = x_n$$

$$\frac{dx_n}{dt} = -a_n x_1 - a_{n-1} x_2 - \cdots - a_2 x_{n-1} - a_1 x_n + r$$

where the first $n - 1$ equations are merely the definitions of the state variables. These state equations can again be written in the vector-matrix form, with

$$\mathbf{A} = \begin{bmatrix} 0 & 1 & 0 & 0 & 0 & \cdots & 0 \\ 0 & 0 & 1 & 0 & 0 & \cdots & 0 \\ 0 & 0 & 0 & 1 & 0 & \cdots & 0 \\ \cdots & \cdots & \cdots & \cdots & \cdots & \cdots & \cdots \\ 0 & 0 & 0 & 0 & 0 & \cdots & 1 \\ -a_n & -a_{n-1} & -a_{n-2} & -a_{n-3} & -a_{n-4} & \cdots & -a_1 \end{bmatrix}$$

$$(n \times n \text{ matrix})$$

$$\mathbf{B} = \begin{bmatrix} 0 \\ 0 \\ 0 \\ \cdot \\ \cdot \\ \cdot \\ 1 \end{bmatrix} \qquad (n \times 1 \text{ matrix})$$

Now let us consider the situation where the right-hand side of a differential equation includes derivatives of the input r. In general, for instance, given the differential equation

$$\frac{d^2y}{dt^2} + a_1 \frac{dy}{dt} + a_2 y = b_0 \frac{d^2r}{dt^2} + b_1 \frac{dr}{dt} + b_2 r \tag{5-36}$$

how should the state variables be defined so that the equation can be represented by two first-order state equations? We realize that the main sources of difficulty in defining the state variables for this differential equation are the derivative terms on the right-hand side of the equation. The state variables are to be so defined that somehow they absorb these derivative terms.   The method described here illustrates the elimination of these derivative terms one at a time.

Starting with the d^2r/dt^2 term, we write (5-36) as

$$\frac{d^2y}{dt^2} - b_0 \frac{d^2r}{dt^2} + a_1 \frac{dy}{dt} + a_2 y = b_1 \frac{dr}{dt} + b_2 r \tag{5-37}$$

Letting

$$x_1 = y - b_0 r \tag{5-38}$$

we have

$$y = x_1 + b_0 r \tag{5-39}$$

Substituting (5-39) in (5-37) and rearranging, we get

$$\frac{d^2 x_1}{dt^2} + a_1 \frac{dx_1}{dt} + a_2 x_1 = (b_1 - a_1 b_0) \frac{dr}{dt} + (b_2 - a_2 b_0) r \tag{5-40}$$

Therefore, by defining the first state variable x_1 according to (5-38), we have eliminated the d^2r/dt^2 term from the right-hand side of (5-36). Next, we let

$$x_2 = \frac{dx_1}{dt} - (b - a_1 b_0) r \tag{5-41}$$

or

$$\frac{dx_1}{dt} = x_2 + (b_1 - a_1 b_0) r \tag{5-42}$$

Substituting (5-41) and (5-42) in (5-40) and simplifying, we get

$$\frac{dx_2}{dt} = -a_2 x_1 - a_1 x_2 + [(b_2 - a_2 b_0) - a_1 (b_1 - a_1 b_0)] r \tag{5-43}$$

The two state equations for (5-36) are now given by (5-42) and (5-43). In matrix form the state equations in (5-42) and (5-43) are written

$$
\begin{bmatrix} \dfrac{dx_1}{dt} \\ \dfrac{dx_2}{dt} \end{bmatrix} = \begin{bmatrix} 0 & 1 \\ -a_2 & -a_1 \end{bmatrix} \begin{bmatrix} x_1 \\ x_2 \end{bmatrix} + \begin{bmatrix} b_1 - a_1 b_0 \\ (b_2 - a_2 b_0) - a_1(b_1 - a_1 b_0) \end{bmatrix} r
$$

$$(5\text{-}44)$$

The relation between the original dependent variable y and the state variables is given by (5-39).

The elimination procedure described above can be extended to higher-order differential equations of the general form

$$
\frac{d^n y}{dt^n} + a_1 \frac{d^{n-1}y}{dt^{n-1}} + a_2 \frac{d^{n-2}y}{dt^{n-2}} + \cdots + a_{n-1} \frac{dy}{dt} + a_n y
$$

$$
= b_0 \frac{d^n r}{dt^n} + b_1 \frac{d^{n-1}r}{dt^{n-1}} + \cdots + b_{n-1} \frac{dr}{dt} + b_n r \quad (5\text{-}45)
$$

For example, when $n = 3$ in (5-45), the state variables may be defined as

$$x_1 = x - b_0 r \tag{5-46}$$

$$x_2 = \frac{dx_1}{dt} - (b_1 - a_1 b_0)r \tag{5-47}$$

$$x_3 = \frac{dx_2}{dt} - [(b_2 - a_2 b_0) - a_1(b_1 - a_1 b_0)]r \tag{5-48}$$

and the state equations become

$$
\begin{bmatrix} \dfrac{dx_1}{dt} \\ \dfrac{dx_2}{dt} \\ \dfrac{dx_3}{dt} \end{bmatrix} = \begin{bmatrix} 0 & 1 & 0 \\ 0 & 0 & 1 \\ -a_3 & -a_2 & -a_1 \end{bmatrix} \begin{bmatrix} x_1 \\ x_2 \\ x_3 \end{bmatrix}
$$

$$
+ \begin{bmatrix} b_1 - a_1 b_0 \\ (b_2 - a_2 b_0) - a_1(b_1 - a_1 b_0) \\ (b_3 - a_3 b_0) - a_1(b_2 - a_2 b_0) - a_1(b_1 - a_1 b_0) \end{bmatrix} r \quad (5\text{-}49)
$$

For $n = 4$, in addition to the state variables defined in (5-46) to (5-48), we must let

$$x_4 = \frac{dx_3}{dt} - \{(b_3 - a_3b_0) - a_1[(b_2 - a_2b_0) - a_1(b_1 - a_1b_0)]\}r \quad (5\text{-}50)$$

It is not difficult to see that the illustrative examples indicate a general pattern for higher-order differential equations. Thus, for the nth-order differential equation (5-45), the state equations in matrix form can be written

$$
\begin{bmatrix}
\dfrac{dx_1}{dt} \\[2mm]
\dfrac{dx_2}{dt} \\[2mm]
\dfrac{dx_3}{dt} \\[1mm]
\cdot \\ \cdot \\ \cdot \\
\dfrac{dx_n}{dt}
\end{bmatrix}
=
\begin{bmatrix}
0 & 1 & 0 & 0 & \cdots & 0 \\
0 & 0 & 1 & 0 & \cdots & 0 \\
0 & 0 & 0 & 1 & \cdots & 0 \\
\cdot & \cdot & \cdot & \cdot & & \cdot \\
& & & & & \\
-a_n & -a_{n-1} & -a_{n-2} & -a_{n-3} & \cdots & -a_1
\end{bmatrix}
\begin{bmatrix}
x_1 \\ x_2 \\ x_3 \\ \cdot \\ \cdot \\ \cdot \\ x_n
\end{bmatrix}
+
\begin{bmatrix}
h_1 \\ h_2 \\ h_3 \\ \cdot \\ \cdot \\ \cdot \\ h_n
\end{bmatrix}
r
$$

$$(5\text{-}51)$$

where

$$
\begin{aligned}
h_1 &= b_1 - a_1b_0 \\
h_2 &= (b_2 - a_2b_0) - a_1h_1 \\
h_3 &= (b_3 - a_3b_0) - a_2h_1 - a_1h_2 \\
&\cdots\cdots\cdots\cdots\cdots\cdots\cdots \\
h_n &= (b_n - a_nb_0) - a_{n-1}h_1 - a_{n-2}h_2 - \cdots - a_2h_{n-2} - a_1h_{n-1}
\end{aligned}
\quad (5\text{-}52)
$$

and

$$y = x_1 + b_0r$$

We notice that, using this method of representing (5-45) by state equations, the **A** matrix is essentially the same as in the homogeneous-equation case. The derivatives on the right-hand side of (5-45) affect only the elements of the **B** matrix. Furthermore, if y is denoted as the output variable, the output equation is always of the form

$$y = [1 \quad 0 \quad 0 \quad \cdots \quad 0]\begin{bmatrix} x_1 \\ x_2 \\ x_3 \\ \cdot \\ \cdot \\ \cdot \\ x_n \end{bmatrix} + [b_0]r \qquad (5\text{-}53)$$

Another approach to the state-equation representation of the differential equation (5-45) is to eliminate the derivative terms on the right-hand side of the equation in one operation. The method is best described with the use of Laplace transformation and signal flow graphs; hence it is reserved for Chap. 12.

5-4 THE STATE - TRANSITION MATRIX AND THE STATE - TRANSITION EQUATION (CONTINUOUS - DATA SYSTEMS)

In this section we seek the general solution of the state equations introduced in the preceding sections. Let us consider that the dynamics of an nth-order linear time-invariant system with continuous data are represented by the vector-matrix state equation

$$\frac{d\mathbf{x}(t)}{dt} = \mathbf{A}\mathbf{x}(t) + \mathbf{B}\mathbf{r}(t) \qquad (5\text{-}54)$$

where

$$\mathbf{x}(t) = \begin{bmatrix} x_1(t) \\ x_2(t) \\ \cdot \\ \cdot \\ \cdot \\ x_n(t) \end{bmatrix} = \begin{bmatrix} y(t) \\ \dfrac{dy(t)}{dt} \\ \cdot \\ \cdot \\ \cdot \\ \dfrac{d^{n-1}y(t)}{dt^{n-1}} \end{bmatrix} \qquad (5\text{-}55)$$

$$\mathbf{r}(t) = \begin{bmatrix} r_1(t) \\ r_2(t) \\ \cdot \\ \cdot \\ \cdot \\ r_m(t) \end{bmatrix} \qquad (5\text{-}56)$$

$y(t)$ denotes the output, and $r_1(t)$, $r_2(t)$, . . . , $r_m(t)$ are the m inputs of the system. $\mathbf{A}$ is an $n \times n$ square matrix, and $\mathbf{B}$ is an $n \times n$ matrix. The initial state of the system at $t = t_0$ is represented by $\mathbf{x}(t_0)$.

Given the initial state $\mathbf{x}(t_0)$ and the input vector $\mathbf{r}(t)$ for $t \geq t_0$, the solution of (5-54) for $t > t_0$, expressed as a function of $\mathbf{x}(t_0)$ and $\mathbf{r}(t)$, is defined as the *state-transition equation* of the system for $t > t_0$.

Solution of the homogeneous state equation

First, we consider the solution of (5-54) when $\mathbf{r}(t) = \mathbf{0}$.   The homogeneous state equation is

$$\frac{d\mathbf{x}(t)}{dt} = \mathbf{A}\mathbf{x}(t) \tag{5-57}$$

It is observed that this vector-matrix differential equation is analogous to the scalar equation

$$\frac{dx(t)}{dt} = ax(t) \tag{5-58}$$

whose solution may be obtained by the method of separation of variables. Rearranging (5-58) in the form

$$\frac{dx(t)}{x(t)} = a \, dt \tag{5-59}$$

and integrating both sides, we get

$$\ln x(t) = at + \ln k \tag{5-60}$$

where $\ln k$ is a constant.   Equation (5-60) can also be written

$$\ln x(t) = \ln e^{at} + \ln k$$
$$= \ln ke^{at} \tag{5-61}$$

Therefore

$$x(t) = ke^{at} \tag{5-62}$$

To determine the value of k, we let $t = 0$; then (5-62) gives

$$x(0) = k \tag{5-63}$$

Thus the solution of (5-58), giving $x(0)$, is

$$x(t) = e^{at}x(0) \tag{5-64}$$

For any initial time $t = t_0$, the initial value of $x(t)$ is $x(t_0)$. From (5-64) we have

$$x(0) = e^{-at_0}x(t_0) \tag{5-65}$$

Now substituting (5-65) in (5-64) yields

$$x(t) = e^{a(t-t_0)}x(t_0) \tag{5-66}$$

which is the solution of (5-58) for any initial condition $x(t_0)$.

In view of the analogy between (5-57) and (5-58), it is reasonable to assume that the solution of (5-57) is of the form

$$\mathbf{x}(t) = e^{\mathbf{A}(t-t_0)}\mathbf{x}(t_0) \tag{5-67}$$

However, it is necessary to point out that $e^{\mathbf{A}(t-t_0)}$ does not have the same meaning as $e^{a(t-t_0)}$, which is a scalar function of time. From the definition of the exponential function of a matrix given by (3-34), we have

$$e^{\mathbf{A}(t-t_0)} = \exp \mathbf{A}(t - t_0)$$

$$= \mathbf{I} + \mathbf{A}(t - t_0) + \frac{\mathbf{A}^2(t - t_0)^2}{2!} + \cdots + \frac{\mathbf{A}^n(t - t_0)^n}{n!} + \cdots \tag{5-68}$$

or

$$e^{\mathbf{A}(t-t_0)} = \sum_{k=0}^{\infty} \mathbf{A}^k \frac{(t - t_0)^k}{k!} \tag{5-69}$$

To show that (5-67) is a solution of the vector-matrix state equation of (5-57), we take the derivative on both sides of (5-67) with respect to t. Therefore

$$\frac{d\mathbf{x}(t)}{dt} = \frac{d}{dt}\left[\mathbf{I} + \mathbf{A}(t - t_0) + \frac{\mathbf{A}^2(t - t_0)^2}{2!} + \cdots\right]\mathbf{x}(t_0)$$

$$= \mathbf{A}\left[\mathbf{I} + \mathbf{A}(t - t_0) + \frac{\mathbf{A}^2(t - t_0)}{2!} + \cdots\right]\mathbf{x}(t_0)$$

$$= \mathbf{A}\exp\left[\mathbf{A}(t - t_0)\right]\mathbf{x}(t_0)$$

$$= \mathbf{A}\mathbf{x}(t) \tag{5-70}$$

which verifies that (5-67) does satisfy (5-57).

For convenience, the matrix exp $[\mathbf{A}t]$ is denoted by

$$\mathbf{\Phi}(t) = \exp[\mathbf{A}t] = e^{\mathbf{A}t} \tag{5-71}$$

and is called the *fundamental matrix*, or the *state-transition matrix, of the matrix* $\mathbf{A}$.

Using the notation of the state-transition matrix, (5-67) is written

$$\mathbf{x}(t) = \mathbf{\Phi}(t - t_0)\mathbf{x}(t_0) \tag{5-72}$$

Before obtaining the solution of the nonhomogeneous state equation in (5-54), it is important to present some of the important properties of the state-transition matrix $\mathbf{\Phi}(t)$.

Some properties of $\mathbf{\Phi}(t)$

(a) $\mathbf{\Phi}(t_0 - t_0) = \mathbf{\Phi}(0) = \mathbf{I}$ unit matrix $\tag{5-73}$

This property follows directly from (5-72).   Letting $t = t_0$, (5-72) becomes

$$\mathbf{x}(t_0) = \mathbf{\Phi}(t_0 - t_0)\mathbf{x}(t_0) \tag{5-74}$$

which leads to (5-73).

(b) $\mathbf{\Phi}(t_2 - t_1)\mathbf{\Phi}(t_1 - t_0) = \mathbf{\Phi}(t_2 - t_0)$ any t_0, t_1, t_2 $\tag{5-75}$

Equation (5-72) leads to the following expression:

$$\mathbf{x}(t_2) = \mathbf{\Phi}(t_2 - t_0)\mathbf{x}(t_0) = \mathbf{\Phi}(t_2 - t_1)\mathbf{x}(t_1) \tag{5-76}$$

Since

$$\mathbf{x}(t_1) = \mathbf{\Phi}(t_1 - t_0)\mathbf{x}(t_0) \tag{5-77}$$

substituting (5-77) in (5-76) yields

$$\begin{aligned}\mathbf{x}(t_2) &= \mathbf{\Phi}(t_2 - t_1)\mathbf{\Phi}(t_1 - t_0)\mathbf{x}(t_0) \\ &= \mathbf{\Phi}(t_2 - t_0)\mathbf{x}(t_0)\end{aligned} \tag{5-78}$$

and (5-75) is obtained.

(c) $\mathbf{\Phi}(t_1 - t_0) = [\mathbf{\Phi}(t_0 - t_1)]^{-1}$ $\tag{5-79}$

or

$$[\boldsymbol{\Phi}(t)]^{-1} = \boldsymbol{\Phi}(-t) \tag{5-80}$$

From (5-72), the following equations are written:

$$\mathbf{x}(t_1) = \boldsymbol{\Phi}(t_1 - t_0)\mathbf{x}(t_0) \tag{5-81}$$

$$\mathbf{x}(t_0) = \boldsymbol{\Phi}(t_0 - t_1)\mathbf{x}(t_1) \tag{5-82}$$

Substituting (5-81) in (5-82) gives

$$\mathbf{x}(t_0) = \boldsymbol{\Phi}(t_0 - t_1)\boldsymbol{\Phi}(t_1 - t_0)\mathbf{x}(t_0) \tag{5-83}$$

Now premultiplying both sides of (5-83) by $[\boldsymbol{\Phi}(t_0 - t_1)]^{-1}$ yields

$$[\boldsymbol{\Phi}(t_0 - t_1)]^{-1}\mathbf{x}(t_0) = \boldsymbol{\Phi}(t_1 - t_0)\mathbf{x}(t_0) \tag{5-84}$$

Thus (5-79) is obtained.

Solution of the nonhomogeneous state equation

When the input vector is nonzero, the nonhomogeneous state equation (5-54) is to be solved when the initial state $\mathbf{x}(t_0)$ and the input vector $\mathbf{r}(t)$ for $t \geq t_0$ are specified. Let us first consider that $t_0 = 0$. One of the methods of carrying out the solution of (5-54) is to premultiply both sides of the equation by the matrix $e^{-\mathbf{A}t}$, yielding

$$e^{-\mathbf{A}t}\frac{d\mathbf{x}(t)}{dt} = e^{-\mathbf{A}t}\mathbf{A}\mathbf{x}(t) + e^{-\mathbf{A}t}\mathbf{B}\mathbf{r}(t) \tag{5-85}$$

Since

$$\begin{aligned}
\frac{d}{dt}[e^{-\mathbf{A}t}\mathbf{x}(t)] &= \frac{d}{dt}e^{-\mathbf{A}t}\mathbf{x}(t) + e^{-\mathbf{A}t}\frac{d\mathbf{x}(t)}{dt} \\
&= \frac{d}{dt}\left[\mathbf{I} - \mathbf{A}t + \frac{\mathbf{A}^2t^2}{2!} - \frac{\mathbf{A}^3t^3}{3!} + \cdots\right]\mathbf{x}(t) + e^{-\mathbf{A}t}\frac{d\mathbf{x}(t)}{dt} \\
&= -\mathbf{A}\left[\mathbf{I} - \mathbf{A}t + \frac{\mathbf{A}^2t^2}{2!} - \cdots\right]\mathbf{x}(t) + e^{-\mathbf{A}t}\frac{d\mathbf{x}(t)}{dt} \\
&= -\mathbf{A}e^{-\mathbf{A}t}\mathbf{x}(t) + e^{-\mathbf{A}t}\frac{d\mathbf{x}(t)}{dt} \tag{5-86}
\end{aligned}$$

(5-85) can be written

$$\frac{d}{dt}[e^{-\mathbf{A}t}\mathbf{x}(t)] = e^{-\mathbf{A}t}\mathbf{Br}(t) \tag{5-87}$$

This equation is integrated to give

$$e^{-\mathbf{A}t}\mathbf{x}(t) = \int_0^t e^{-\mathbf{A}\tau}\mathbf{Br}(\tau)\, d\tau + \mathbf{K} \tag{5-88}$$

where $\mathbf{K}$ is the constant matrix of integration, and τ is a dummy variable. From (5-88) the solution of (5-54) for $t > 0$ is obtained:

$$\mathbf{x}(t) = e^{\mathbf{A}t}\int_0^t e^{-\mathbf{A}\tau}\mathbf{Br}(\tau)\, d\tau + e^{\mathbf{A}t}\mathbf{K} \tag{5-89}$$

Using the property of the state-transition matrix in (5-75), (5-89) is written

$$\mathbf{x}(t) = e^{\mathbf{A}t}\mathbf{K} + \int_0^t e^{\mathbf{A}(t-\tau)}\mathbf{Br}(\tau)\, d\tau \tag{5-90}$$

The matrix $\mathbf{K}$ is determined by substituting $t = 0$ in (5-90). Therefore

$$\mathbf{K} = \mathbf{x}(0) \tag{5-91}$$

The solution of (5-54) for $t > 0$ is given by

$$\mathbf{x}(t) = e^{\mathbf{A}t}\mathbf{x}(0) + \int_0^t e^{\mathbf{A}(t-\tau)}\mathbf{Br}(\tau)\, d\tau \tag{5-92}$$

or

$$\mathbf{x}(t) = \mathbf{\Phi}(t)\mathbf{x}(0) + \int_0^t \mathbf{\Phi}(t-\tau)\mathbf{Br}(\tau)\, d\tau \tag{5-93}$$

To find the solution of (5-54) when $\mathbf{r}(t)$ is specified for $t \geq t_0$, and given the initial state $\mathbf{x}(t_0)$, we set $t = t_0$ in (5-93). Therefore

$$\mathbf{x}(t_0) = \mathbf{\Phi}(t_0)\mathbf{x}(0) + \int_0^{t_0} \mathbf{\Phi}(t_0-\tau)\mathbf{Br}(\tau)\, d\tau \tag{5-94}$$

Solving for $\mathbf{x}(0)$ from the last equation and using the property of $\mathbf{\Phi}(t)$

given in (5-80), we have

$$\mathbf{x}(0) = \boldsymbol{\Phi}(-t_0)\mathbf{x}(t_0) - \boldsymbol{\Phi}(-t_0) \int_0^{t_0} \boldsymbol{\Phi}(t_0 - \tau)\mathbf{Br}(\tau) \, d\tau \qquad (5\text{-}95)$$

Substituting from (5-95) in (5-93) and using (5-75) gives

$$\mathbf{x}(t) = \boldsymbol{\Phi}(t - t_0)\mathbf{x}(t_0) - \boldsymbol{\Phi}(t - t_0) \int_0^{t_0} \boldsymbol{\Phi}(t_0 - \tau)\mathbf{Br}(\tau) \, d\tau$$

$$+ \int_0^t \boldsymbol{\Phi}(t - \tau)\mathbf{Br}(\tau) \, d\tau$$

$$= \boldsymbol{\Phi}(t - t_0)\mathbf{x}(t_0) - \int_0^{t_0} \boldsymbol{\Phi}(t - \tau)\mathbf{Br}(\tau) \, d\tau$$

$$+ \int_0^t \boldsymbol{\Phi}(t - \tau)\mathbf{Br}(\tau) \, d\tau \qquad t \geq t_0 \geq 0 \quad (5\text{-}96)$$

Equation (5-96) is simplified to

$$\mathbf{x}(t) = \boldsymbol{\Phi}(t - t_0)\mathbf{x}(t_0) + \int_{t_0}^t \boldsymbol{\Phi}(t - \tau)\mathbf{Br}(\tau) \, d\tau \qquad t \geq t_0 \geq 0 \quad (5\text{-}97)$$

The first term on the right-hand side of (5-97) may be interpreted as the solution of the homogeneous state equation, and the second term represents the contribution to the solution from the input $r(t)$. Equation (5-97) is also defined as the *state-transition equation* for the time interval $t_0 \leq \tau \leq t$ of the system described by the state equation (5-54).

Notice that an advantage of the state-variable method of characterizing a linear system is that a general solution in the form of the state-transition equation can be obtained in terms of the initial state and the input, whereas, if the system is described by the ordinary differential equation (5-45), a general solution cannot be obtained without knowing n and the coefficients of the equation. However, without using the Laplace transformation, the state-variable method suffers from one disadvantage, in that the evaluation of $\boldsymbol{\Phi}(t)$ can be tedious, since by definition $\boldsymbol{\Phi}(t)$ is an infinite series in t [Eq. (5-69)].

Let us illustrate the evaluation of the state-transition matrix by referring to the network of Fig. 5-2. The vector-matrix state equation of the network is given in (5-19), and for $L = 1h$, $R = 3$ ohms, and $C = 0.5f$, the state equation becomes

$$\begin{bmatrix} \dfrac{di_L(t)}{dt} \\[2mm] \dfrac{dv_c(t)}{dt} \end{bmatrix} = \begin{bmatrix} -3 & -1 \\ 2 & 0 \end{bmatrix} \begin{bmatrix} i_L(t) \\ v_c(t) \end{bmatrix} + \begin{bmatrix} 1 \\ 0 \end{bmatrix} v(t) \qquad (5\text{-}98)$$

Therefore

$$\mathbf{A} = \begin{bmatrix} -3 & -1 \\ 2 & 0 \end{bmatrix} \qquad \mathbf{A}^2 = \begin{bmatrix} 7 & 3 \\ -6 & -2 \end{bmatrix}$$

$$\mathbf{A}^3 = \begin{bmatrix} -15 & -7 \\ 14 & 6 \end{bmatrix} \qquad \cdots$$

The state-transition matrix is now written

$$\boldsymbol{\Phi}(t) = \mathbf{I} + \mathbf{A}t + \frac{1}{2!}\mathbf{A}^2 t^2 + \frac{1}{3!}\mathbf{A}^3 t^3 + \cdots$$

$$= \begin{bmatrix} 1 - 3t + \frac{7}{2}t^2 - \frac{5}{2}t^3 + \cdots & -t + \frac{3}{2}t^2 - \frac{7}{6}t^3 + \cdots \\ 2t - 3t^2 + \frac{7}{3}t^3 + \cdots & 1 - t^2 + t^3 + \cdots \end{bmatrix}$$

$$(5\text{-}99)$$

Normally, it is not easy to find the closed-form expressions for the infinite series in (5-99). However, in this case, the solution can be obtained by other means, and it can be shown that (5-99) is equivalent to

$$\boldsymbol{\Phi}(t) = \begin{bmatrix} -e^{-t} + 2e^{-2t} & -e^{-t} + e^{-2t} \\ 2e^{-t} - 2e^{-2t} & 2e^{-t} - e^{-2t} \end{bmatrix} \qquad (5\text{-}100)$$

If the input voltage $v(t)$ is a unit step function applied at $t = 0$, the complete solution of the state equation for $t > 0$ is

$$\mathbf{x}(t) = \boldsymbol{\Phi}(t)\mathbf{x}(0) + \int_0^t \boldsymbol{\Phi}(t - \tau)\mathbf{B}r(\tau)\, d\tau$$

$$= \boldsymbol{\Phi}(t)\mathbf{x}(0) + \int_0^t \begin{bmatrix} -e^{-(t-\tau)} + 2e^{-2(t-\tau)} \\ 2e^{-(t-\tau)} - 2e^{-2(t-\tau)} \end{bmatrix} d\tau \qquad (5\text{-}101)$$

or

$$\mathbf{x}(t) = \begin{bmatrix} -e^{-t} + 2e^{-2t} & -e^{-t} + e^{-2t} \\ 2e^{-t} - 2e^{-2t} & 2e^{-t} - e^{-2t} \end{bmatrix} \begin{bmatrix} x_1(0) \\ x_2(0) \end{bmatrix}$$

$$+ \begin{bmatrix} e^{-t} - e^{-2t} \\ 1 - 2e^{-t} + e^{-2t} \end{bmatrix} \qquad (5\text{-}102)$$

where the state variables are $x_1 = i_L$ and $x_2 = v_c$. If the initial state of the network is zero, $\mathbf{x}(0) = \mathbf{0}$, (5-102) becomes

$$\mathbf{x}(t) = \begin{bmatrix} e^{-t} - e^{-2t} \\ 1 - 2e^{-t} + e^{-2t} \end{bmatrix} \qquad t > 0 \qquad (5\text{-}103)$$

which agrees with the results obtained earlier in (5-6) and (5-7).

Although the method of evaluating $\boldsymbol{\Phi}(t)$ by the infinite series is impractical, we show later that the Laplace-transform method is preferable to other methods in determining $\boldsymbol{\Phi}(t)$ and the state-transition equation.

5-5 DIFFERENCE EQUATIONS AND DISCRETE STATE EQUATIONS

The networks and systems considered in the preceding sections all have
one common feature, in that the signals found in these systems are functions of the continuous variable t.   In other words, the input signals and
the signals inside these systems are defined at all times.   Therefore these
systems are described as continuous-data systems.   In terms of mathematical descriptions, the dependent variables and state variables of a
continuous-data system are functions of t, which is a continuous variable,
and the state equations are differential equations.   There is a class of
system in which the signals, at part of the system, at least, are functions of
a discrete variable t_n or nT, for $n = 0, 1, 2, \ldots$ Moreover, some systems may have inputs that are discrete in nature.   A radar system, whose
input is usually a pulse train, is a common example of this type of system.
There is also another kind of system which accepts only pulse or numeri-
cally coded signals as inputs and sends out a sequence of numbers as
outputs.   A familiar example of this type is a digital computer.   In general, all such systems having discrete signals or inputs are called *discrete-
data systems*, or *sampled-data systems*.[3-6]

Unlike the continuous-data dynamic systems described by differential
equations, discrete-data systems are partially or totally described by difference equations which describe the behavior of the systems only at
discrete time intervals.   As a simple illustration of the idea of difference
equations, we may refer to the RC-network problem discussed in Sec. 5-1.
The voltage across the capacitor, as a function of time, given by (5-1), is
repeated here:

$$v_c(t) = [V_2 - v_c(t_0)](1 - e^{-(t-t_0)/RC}) + v_c(t_0) \qquad t \geq t_0 \qquad (5\text{-}104)$$

This equation is also known as the continuous-data state-transition equation of the RC network for the time interval $t \geq t_0$, with the input voltage
V_2 defined for the same time period.

More generally, (5-104) can be written

$$v_c(t) = \Phi(t - t_0)v_c(t_0) + \int_{t_0}^{t} \Phi(t - \tau)Bv(\tau) \, d\tau \qquad t \geq t_0 \qquad (5\text{-}105)$$

In this particular case, $v(\tau) = V_2 = $ const for all $\tau \geq t_0$; we have

$$v_c(t) = \Phi(t - t_0)v_c(t_0) + h(t - t_0)V_2 \qquad t \geq t_0 \qquad (5\text{-}106)$$

Comparing (5-106) with (5-104), it is apparent that

$$\Phi(t - t_0) = e^{-(t-t_0)/RC} \qquad (5\text{-}107)$$

and

$$h(t - t_0) = 1 - e^{-(t-t_0)/RC} \qquad (5\text{-}108)$$

Now, if we are interested only in the values of $v_c(t)$ at some discrete intervals of time, say, at $t = 0, T, 2T, 3T, \ldots, kT$, where T is in seconds, we substitute $t = kT$ and $t_0 = 0$ in (5-106); then the state-transition equation becomes

$$
\begin{aligned}
v_c(kT) &= \Phi(kT)v_c(0) + h(kT)V_2 \\
&= e^{-kT/RC}v_c(0) + (1 - e^{-kT/RC})V_2
\end{aligned}
\qquad (5\text{-}109)
$$

As an alternative, we can let $t = (k + 1)T$ and $t_0 = kT$; then (5-104) becomes

$$
\begin{aligned}
v_c(k + 1)T &= \Phi(T)v_c(kT) + h(T)V_2 \\
&= e^{-T/RC}v_c(kT) + (1 - e^{-T/RC})V_2
\end{aligned}
\qquad (5\text{-}110)
$$

which is a typical linear first-order difference equation with constant coefficients.   In this case, it is also a typical discrete state equation.   In fact, it is interesting to show that (5-109) is the solution of (5-110) simply by substitution.

Given the values of $v_c(0)$ and V_2, the values of $v_c(kT)$ at $k = 1, 2, 3, \ldots$ can be calculated directly from (5-109).   However, without the closed-form solution of (5-109), the values of $v_c(t)$ at $t = T, 2T, \ldots$ can also be computed from (5-110) by iteration.   The difference equation (5-110) also gives a clear description of how the state transition takes place in the discrete sense.   Since the value of the state variable $v_c(t)$ at $t = (k + 1)T$ is determined from the knowledge of its previous value at $t = kT$, the state transition may be regarded as taking place from $t = 0$ to T, from T to $2T$, $2T$ to $3T$, and so on.   Therefore the state transition takes place only at instants of kT.   No information is given on $v_c(t)$ in between the instants of $t = kT$.

A linear constant-coefficient difference equation of the nth order may be expressed as

$$
\begin{aligned}
y(k + n)T &+ a_1 y(k + n - 1)T + a_2 y(k + n - 2)T + \cdots \\
&+ a_{n-1}y(k + 1)T + a_n y(kT) = b_0 r(k + n)T + b_1 r(k + n - 1)T \\
&\qquad + \cdots + b_{n-1}r(k + 1)T + b_n r(kT) \qquad (5\text{-}111)
\end{aligned}
$$

where $y(kT)$ denotes the discrete dependent variable, and $r(kT)$ is the input specified at kT† $(k = 0, 1, 2, \ldots)$.   Notice that this difference equation is analogous to the nth-order differential equation (5-45).

† Although a great majority of our problems deal with time as the independent variable, in general, kT may represent any other discrete variable, such as distance or temperature.

The discrete form of the state equation is also analogous to the continuous state equations.   Therefore we should be able to represent (5-111) by a set of first-order vector-matrix difference equations, or simply, discrete dynamic equations,

$$\mathbf{x}(k+1)T = \mathbf{A}\mathbf{x}(kT) + \mathbf{B}r(kT) \tag{5-112}$$

and

$$\mathbf{y}(kT) = \mathbf{C}\mathbf{x}(kT) + \mathbf{D}r(kT) \tag{5-113}$$

where $\mathbf{x}(kT)$ is the state vector, and $\mathbf{y}(kT)$ denotes the output vector.

First, let us consider a simple case where the nth-order difference equation

$$y(k+n)T + a_1 y(k+n-1)T + a_2 y(k+n-2)T + \cdots$$
$$+ a_{n-1} y(k+1)T + a_n y(kT) = b_n r(kT) \tag{5-114}$$

is to be written in the state-equation form.   A convenient way of defining the state variables is to let

$$
\begin{aligned}
x_1(kT) &= y(kT) \\
x_2(kT) &= x_1(k+1)T = y(k+1)T \\
x_3(kT) &= x_2(k+1)T = y(k+2)T \\
&\cdots\cdots\cdots\cdots\cdots\cdots\cdots\cdots\cdots \\
x_n(kT) &= x_{n-1}(k+1)T = y(k+n-1)T
\end{aligned} \tag{5-115}
$$

Using the relationships of these state variables and (5-114), the discrete state equations are written

$$
\begin{bmatrix}
x_1(k+1)T \\
x_2(k+1)T \\
\cdot \\
\cdot \\
\cdot \\
x_n(k+1)T
\end{bmatrix}
=
\begin{bmatrix}
0 & 1 & 0 & \cdots & 0 \\
0 & 0 & 1 & \cdots & 0 \\
\cdot & \cdot & \cdot & \cdots & \cdot \\
-a_n & -a_{n-1} & -a_{n-2} & \cdots & -a_1
\end{bmatrix}
\begin{bmatrix}
x_1(kT) \\
x_2(kT) \\
\cdot \\
\cdot \\
\cdot \\
x_n(kT)
\end{bmatrix}
$$

$$
+
\begin{bmatrix}
0 \\
0 \\
\cdot \\
\cdot \\
\cdot \\
b_n
\end{bmatrix}
r(kT) \tag{5-116}
$$

and the output equation is

$$y(kT) = [1 \quad 0 \quad 0 \quad \cdots \quad 0]\mathbf{x}(kT) \tag{5-117}$$

Since difference equations deal with sequences of numbers, rather than continuous functions of time, they are generally easier to solve than differential equations. In fact, the state equations of (5-116) can be solved simply by means of a recursion procedure. In other words, given the initial state $\mathbf{x}(0)$ and the input vector $\mathbf{r}(kT)$ for $k = 0, 1, 2, \ldots$, the state vector $\mathbf{x}(kT)$ can be solved from (5-112) by setting $k = 0, 1, 2, \ldots$, consecutively. Therefore, when $k = 0$, (5-112) becomes

$$\mathbf{x}(T) = \mathbf{A}\mathbf{x}(0) + \mathbf{B}\mathbf{r}(0) \tag{5-118}$$

Letting $k = 1$ in (5-112) and using (5-118), we get

$$\begin{aligned}
\mathbf{x}(2T) &= \mathbf{A}\mathbf{x}(T) + \mathbf{B}\mathbf{r}(T) \\
&= \mathbf{A}^2\mathbf{x}(0) + \mathbf{A}\mathbf{B}\mathbf{r}(0) + \mathbf{B}\mathbf{r}(T)
\end{aligned} \tag{5-119}$$

Next, setting $k = 2$ in (5-112) and using (5-119), the following expression results:

$$\begin{aligned}
\mathbf{x}(3T) &= \mathbf{A}\mathbf{x}(2T) + \mathbf{B}\mathbf{r}(2T) \\
&= \mathbf{A}^3\mathbf{x}(0) + \mathbf{A}^2\mathbf{B}\mathbf{r}(0) + \mathbf{A}\mathbf{B}\mathbf{r}(T) + \mathbf{B}\mathbf{r}(2T)
\end{aligned} \tag{5-120}$$

By repeating this recursive procedure, a general solution is obtained as

$$\begin{aligned}
\mathbf{x}(kT) &= \mathbf{A}^k\mathbf{x}(0) + \sum_{i=1}^{k} \mathbf{A}^{k-i}\mathbf{B}\mathbf{r}(i-1)T \\
&= \mathbf{A}^k\mathbf{x}(0) + \sum_{i=0}^{k-1} \mathbf{A}^{k-i-1}\mathbf{B}\mathbf{r}(iT)
\end{aligned} \tag{5-121}$$

which is the *state-transition equation* of the discrete-data system described by (5-112).

Substituting (5-121) in (5-113), the output vector is given by

$$\mathbf{y}(kT) = \mathbf{C}\mathbf{A}^k\mathbf{x}(0) + \mathbf{C}\sum_{i=0}^{k-1} \mathbf{A}^{k-i-1}\mathbf{B}\mathbf{r}(iT) + \mathbf{D}\mathbf{r}(kT) \tag{5-122}$$

Note that the discrete state-transition equation in (5-121) is analogous to its counterpart for continuous-data systems, which is given by (5-93) or

(5-97).   In the present case, it is convenient to define *a discrete state-transition matrix* $\mathbf{\Phi}(kT)$ for the matrix $\mathbf{A}$:

$$\mathbf{\Phi}(kT) = A^k \tag{5-123}$$

It is of interest to compare the significance of the state equation in (5-112) and its solution, the state-transition equation (5-121). The expression (5-112) states that, if the state and the input signal at $t = kT$ are specified, the state at the next transition point, $(k + 1)T$, is uniquely defined by this state equation. The state-transition equation contains essentially the same information, except that the state at kT is given in terms of only the initial state $\mathbf{x}(0)$, and the inputs at all points from $t = 0$ to $t = (k - 1)T$.

Example 5-1   Find the dynamic equations and the solutions of the second-order difference equation

$$y[(k + 2)T] - 0.503y[(k + 1)T] + 0.0497y(kT) = kT \tag{5-124}$$

with the initial conditions given as $y(0) = 1$ and $y(T) = 0$; and $T = 1$. Let the state variables be defined as

$$x_1(kT) = y(kT) \tag{5-125}$$
$$x_2(kT) = x_1(k + 1)T = y(k + 1)T \tag{5-126}$$

and substituting these in (5-124), the state equations are obtained as

$$x_1(k + 1)T = x_2(kT) \tag{5-127}$$
$$x_2(k + 1)T = -0.0497x_1(kT) + 0.503x_2(kT) + kT \tag{5-128}$$

In matrix form, the state equations become

$$\begin{bmatrix} x_1(k + 1)T \\ x_2(k + 1)T \end{bmatrix} = \begin{bmatrix} 0 & 1 \\ -0.0497 & 0.503 \end{bmatrix} \begin{bmatrix} x_1(kT) \\ x_2(kT) \end{bmatrix} + \begin{bmatrix} 0 \\ 1 \end{bmatrix} kT \tag{5-129}$$

Thus

$$\mathbf{A} = \begin{bmatrix} 0 & 1 \\ -0.0497 & 0.503 \end{bmatrix} \qquad \mathbf{B} = \begin{bmatrix} 0 \\ 1 \end{bmatrix} \tag{5-130}$$

The output equation is

$$y(kT) = x_1(kT) \tag{5-131}$$

and thus

$$C = [1 \quad 0] \qquad D = [0]$$

The solution of this second-order difference equation can be carried out using one of the two methods described above. Since $x_1(0) = y(0) = 1$ and $x_2(0) = y(T) = 0$, the values of $y(kT)$ for $k = 2, 3, 4, \ldots$ can be found from (5-124) by recursion. Therefore the following results are easily computed:

$$
\begin{array}{lll}
y(2T) = -0.0497y(0) + 0.503y(T) = -0.0497 & \quad k = 0 \\
y(3T) = T - 0.0497y(T) + 0.503y(2T) = 0.975 & \quad k = 1 \\
y(4T) = 2T - 0.0497y(2T) + 0.503y(3T) = 2.49 & \quad k = 2 \\
\cdots\cdots\cdots\cdots\cdots\cdots\cdots\cdots\cdots\cdots\cdots & \quad \cdots\cdots
\end{array}
$$

$$(5\text{-}132)$$

After $y(2T)$ is found from the first step, it is used to determine $y(3T)$, and then $y(3T)$ is used to find $y(4T)$, and so on. The advantage of this recursion procedure is its simplicity; but the difficulty lies in that $y(kT)$ for any k can be determined only if the preceding $y(kT)$'s have been found. However, the method is very convenient for digital-computer computations.

A closed-form solution of (5-124) can be obtained by use of (5-122). Therefore

$$y(kT) = CA^k x(0) + C \sum_{i=0}^{k-1} A^{k-i-1} BiT + DkT \qquad (5\text{-}133)$$

where A, B, C, and D are given in (5-130). For instance, when $k = 2$,

$$
y(2T) = [1 \quad 0] \begin{bmatrix} 0 & 1 \\ -0.497 & 0.503 \end{bmatrix}^2 \begin{bmatrix} x_1(0) \\ x_2(0) \end{bmatrix}
$$

$$
\qquad + [1 \quad 0] \begin{bmatrix} 0 & 1 \\ -0.497 & 0.503 \end{bmatrix} [0] + [1 \quad 0] \begin{bmatrix} 0 \\ 1 \end{bmatrix}
$$

$$
= [1 \quad 0] \begin{bmatrix} -0.497 & 0.503 \\ -0.25 & -0.244 \end{bmatrix} \begin{bmatrix} 1 \\ 0 \end{bmatrix}
$$

$$
= [-0.497 \quad 0.503] \begin{bmatrix} 1 \\ 0 \end{bmatrix} = -0.497 \quad (5\text{-}134)
$$

At this point, it would seem that the closed-form solution given by (5-133) involves tedious matrix multiplications, especially when the value of k is large.   We show later, however, that the matrix $\mathbf{A}^k$ can be carried out using the z-transform method, so that $y(kT)$ is found in much the same way as the Laplace-transform solution of $y(t)$ in the continuous-data case.

PROBLEMS

5-1 Set up the state equations for the system characterized by the differential equation

$$\frac{d^2y}{dt^2} + 5\frac{dy}{dt} + 2y = r$$

5-2 Set up the dynamic equations for the system characterized by the differential equation

$$2\frac{d^2y}{dt^2} + 3\frac{dy}{dt} + y = \frac{dr}{dt} + 2r$$

5-3 Set up the state equations for the system characterized by the differential equation

$$\frac{d^3y}{dt^3} + 3\frac{d^2y}{dt^2} + 2y = r$$

5-4 Given a second-order differential equation with constant coefficients,

$$\frac{d^2y}{dt^2} + 3\frac{dy}{dt} + 2y = 3\frac{d^2r}{dt^2} + 5\frac{dr}{dt} + r$$

Represent the equation by the vector-matrix state equation

$$\dot{\mathbf{x}} = \mathbf{Ax} + \mathbf{Br}$$

and the output equation

$$y = \mathbf{Cx} + \mathbf{Dr}$$

Find $\mathbf{A}, \mathbf{B}, \mathbf{C}, \mathbf{D}$.

5-5 The state equations of a linear dynamic system are given as

$$\begin{bmatrix} \dot{x}_1 \\ \dot{x}_2 \end{bmatrix} = \begin{bmatrix} 3 & -2 \\ 1 & -1 \end{bmatrix} \begin{bmatrix} x_1 \\ x_2 \end{bmatrix}$$

Find the new state equations of the system if the state variables are redefined as

$$q_1 = x_1 + x_2 \qquad q_2 = x_1 - x_2$$

5-6 Solve the following difference equation,

$$y(k+2) + 2y(k+1) - 3y(k) = k+1$$

by means of recursion.   The initial conditions are $y(1) = 1$ and $y(0) = 0$.

5-7 For the difference equation given in Prob. 5-6:

    (a)   Write the state equations for the system.

    (b)   Find the discrete state-transition matrix $\Phi(kT)$.

    (c)   Find the state-transition equation of the system in terms of the initial state.

5-8 A discrete-data system is described by the following difference equation:

$$y[(k+2)T] + 3y[(k+1)T] + 2y(kT) = kT$$

    (a)   Write the state equations for the system.

    (b)   Find the discrete state-transition matrix $\Phi(kT)$.

    (c)   Find the state-transition equation of the system in terms of the initial state. Assume that $T = 1$.

5-9 Prove the following properties of the discrete state-transition matrix $\Phi(k)$:

    (a) $\Phi(k)\Phi(j) = \Phi(k+j)$

    (b) $\Phi^{-1}(k) = \Phi(-k)$

BIBLIOGRAPHY

1 Andronow, A. A., and E. E. Chaikin: "Theory of Oscillations," Princeton University Press, Princeton, N.J., 1949.

2 Zadeh, L. A., and C. A. Desoer: "Linear System Theory," McGraw-Hill Book company, New York, 1963.

3 Kuo, B. C.: "Analysis and Synthesis of Sampled-data Control Systems," Prentice-Hall, Inc., Englewood Cliffs, N.J., 1963.

4 Ragazzini, J. R., and G. F. Franklin: "Sampled-data Control Systems," McGraw-Hill Book Company, New York, 1958.

5 Tou, J. T.: "Digital and Sampled-data Control Systems," McGraw-Hill Book Company, New York, 1959.

6 Lindorff, D. P.: "Theory of Sampled-data Control Systems," John Wiley & Sons, Inc., New York, 1965.

ADDITIONAL REFERENCES

Freeman, H.: "Discrete-time Systems," John Wiley & Sons, Inc., New York, 1965.

Jury, E. I.: "Sampled-data Control Systems," John Wiley & Sons, Inc., New York, 1958.

SIX

STATE EQUATIONS OF ELECTRIC NETWORKS

6-1 INTRODUCTION

From the introductory examples and discussion presented in Sec. 5-1, we realize that the state-variable approach to network analysis is totally different from the more familiar loop-and-node analysis. In the loop-and-node analysis, the complete solution of the dependent variables i (loop current) and v (node voltage) relies upon the knowledge of the initial conditions of i and v. However, since the initial values of the loop currents and the node voltages must all be derived from the initial values of the inductor currents and the capacitor voltages, and the process may be difficult as well as tedious, it is for many purposes more convenient to write network equations directly in terms of the inductor currents and the capacitor voltages as unknown variables. In this way, the initial conditions can be applied directly in solving the network equations. The direct use of the initial condition in the state-variable method is merely one of the many advantages which this method has over the conventional methods.   Since the state equations are first-order differential equations, they are in the direct form to be programmed on an analog computer. We show later that state equations can be portrayed by state-transition signal flow graphs.   Analog-computer simulation, as well as the analytical solution of the system or network, can then be obtained directly from the flow graph in a straightforward manner.

The crux of the state-variable analysis of network problems is that, by definition, the state variables are usually chosen to be the currents in the inductors and the voltages across the capacitors, or linear functions of these.   Where the inductor currents and the capacitor voltages are used as state variables, the formulation of the state equations depends on expressing the voltages across the inductors, $L\, di_L/dt$, and the currents through the capacitors, $C\, dv_c/dt$, as functions of the state variables and the inputs.   For a network with m inductors (without mutual induct-ances), n capacitor,† and q inputs (current and voltage sources), the state equations of the network can be written

$$L_i \frac{di_i}{dt} = \sum_{k=1}^{m} R_{ik}i_k + \sum_{k=m+1}^{m+n} G_{ik}v_k + \sum_{k=1}^{q} S_{ik}r_k \qquad \begin{matrix} \text{voltage across} \\ \text{inductors} \end{matrix}$$

$$\text{(6-1)}$$

$$C_j \frac{dv_j}{dt} = \sum_{k=1}^{m} \mathcal{R}_{jk}i_k + \sum_{k=m+1}^{m+n} \mathcal{G}_{jk}v_k + \sum_{k=1}^{q} \mathcal{S}_{jk}r_k \qquad \begin{matrix} \text{current in} \\ \text{capacitors} \end{matrix} \quad \text{(6-2)}$$

where $i = 1, 2, \ldots, m, j = m + 1, m + 2, \ldots, m + n$

v_j = voltage across jth capacitor

i_i = current in ith inductor

r_k = kth source (voltage or current source)

and R_{jk} is dimensionally a resistance, G_{jk} is a conductance, and S_{jk} and $\mathcal{S}_{jk}$ may have the dimension of a resistance or a conductance, according to whether the source r_k is a current or a voltage source, respectively.

In general, the state equations of an electric network can be written, using one of the three following methods:

Inspection method

This method relies on the use of Kirchhoff's current and voltage laws in forming Eqs. (6-1) and (6-2).   However, the method is recommended only for simple network configurations.

† We shall assume that none of the inductances and capacitances is superfluous or redundant.   In other words, the network under consideration does not contain any loop which has only capacitors and ideal voltage sources or a node which is connected to only inductors and ideal current sources.

Method of equivalent sources[1]

This method relies on the use of equivalent sources in place of the capacitors and inductors in the network.   Equations (6-1) and (6-2) are then written, using the principle of superposition.   The procedure breaks down when the network has a loop containing only capacitors and ideal voltage sources (an all-capacitor loop) or a node which is connected to only inductors and ideal current sources (an all-inductor node).

Method of network graph theory[2,3]

The state equations of an electric network can be written by means of network graph theory.   This method utilizes the concepts of trees, branches, and links, and is far more flexible and reliable than the two previous methods.

In this section we demonstrate how the state equations of some simple networks are written by inspection.

We write the state equations for the network shown in Fig. 6-1 by the inspection method.   The voltage across C is designated as the output

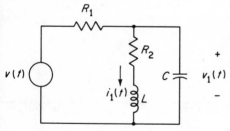

Fig. 6-1   An electric network.

voltage.   Since C and L represent two energy-storage devices in this network, it is convenient in this case to assign the voltage across the capacitor, v_1, and the current in the inductor, i_1, as the state variables.   The state equations are then written by inspection in accordance with the general form given by (6-1) and (6-2).   The state equations are

$$C \frac{dv_1}{dt} = \frac{v - v_1}{R_1} - i_1 \qquad \text{current through } C \qquad (6\text{-}3)$$

$$L \frac{di_1}{dt} = v_1 - R_2 i_1 \qquad \text{voltage across } L \qquad (6\text{-}4)$$

Rearranging, these equations become

$$\frac{dv_1}{dt} = -\frac{1}{R_1 C} v_1 - \frac{1}{C} i_1 + \frac{1}{CR_1} v \tag{6-5}$$

$$\frac{di_1}{dt} = \frac{1}{L} v_1 - \frac{1}{R_2 L} i_1 \tag{6-6}$$

Or in normal form, the state equations are

$$\begin{bmatrix} \dfrac{dv_1}{dt} \\ \dfrac{di_1}{dt} \end{bmatrix} = \begin{bmatrix} -\dfrac{1}{R_1 C} & -\dfrac{1}{C} \\ \dfrac{1}{L} & -\dfrac{1}{R_2 L} \end{bmatrix} \begin{bmatrix} v_1 \\ i_1 \end{bmatrix} + \begin{bmatrix} \dfrac{1}{CR_1} \\ 0 \end{bmatrix} v \tag{6-7}$$

Therefore

$$\mathbf{A} = \begin{bmatrix} -\dfrac{1}{R_1 C} & -\dfrac{1}{C} \\ \dfrac{1}{L} & -\dfrac{1}{R_2 L} \end{bmatrix}$$

and

$$\mathbf{B} = \begin{bmatrix} \dfrac{1}{CR_1} \\ 0 \end{bmatrix}$$

Since the output variable is also the state variable v_1, the output equation is simply

$$\mathbf{y} = v_1 = \begin{bmatrix} 1 & 0 \end{bmatrix} \begin{bmatrix} v_1 \\ i_1 \end{bmatrix} + [0]v \tag{6-8}$$

and

$$\mathbf{C} = \begin{bmatrix} 1 & 0 \end{bmatrix} \qquad \mathbf{D} = [0]$$

Now consider that a resistor R_3 is placed in series with C; the result is the network shown in Fig. 6-2. In this case the total number of state variables is still three, since only a resistor is added to the network. However, we encounter some difficulty in obtaining the normal-form state equations by inspection, since the voltage v_1 is no longer across the branch containing R_2 and L. The following equations are first written by inspection:

$$C \frac{dv_1}{dt} = \frac{v}{R_1} - \frac{1}{R_1}\left(v_1 - R_3 C \frac{dv_1}{dt}\right) - i_1 \qquad \text{current through } C \quad (6\text{-}9)$$

$$L \frac{di_1}{dt} = v_1 + R_3 C \frac{dv_1}{dt} - R_2 i_1 \qquad \text{voltage across } L \quad (6\text{-}10)$$

These equations could be referred to as the state equations of the network, since only the first derivatives of the state variables appear.

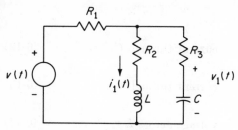

Fig. 6-2 *An electric network.*

However, they are not in the proper form, since there are also derivative terms on the right-hand side of the equations. Rearranging (6-9) and (6-10), the normal-form state equations are obtained as

$$\begin{bmatrix} \dfrac{dv_1}{dt} \\ \dfrac{di_1}{dt} \end{bmatrix} = \begin{bmatrix} -\dfrac{1}{C(R_1 + R_3)} & -\dfrac{R_1}{C(R_1 + R_3)} \\ \dfrac{R_1}{L(R_1 + R_3)} & -\dfrac{R_1 R_2 + R_2 R_3 + R_3 R_1}{L(R_1 + R_3)} \end{bmatrix} \begin{bmatrix} v_1 \\ i_1 \end{bmatrix}$$

$$+ \begin{bmatrix} \dfrac{1}{C(R_1 + R_3)} \\ \dfrac{R_3}{L(R_1 + R_3)} \end{bmatrix} v \quad (6\text{-}11)$$

Example 6-1   Write the state equations for the network shown in Fig. 6-3 by the inspection method. The voltage across C_2 is designated as the output voltage. Find the matrices **A**, **B**, **C**, and **D**.

Since C_1, C_2, and L represent the three energy-storage devices in the network, it is convenient to assign the voltages across the capacitors,

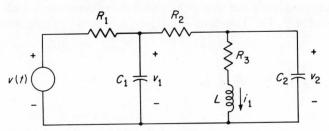

Fig. 6-3   Network in Example 6-1.

v_1, v_2, and the current in the inductor, i_1, as the state variables. The state equations are then written by inspection, in accordance with the general form of (6-1) and (6-2):

$$C_1 \frac{dv_1}{dt} = \frac{v - v_1}{R_1} + \frac{v_2 - v_1}{R_2} \qquad \text{current through } C_1 \qquad (6\text{-}12)$$

$$C_2 \frac{dv_2}{dt} = \frac{v_1 - v_2}{R_2} - i_1 \qquad \text{current through } C_2 \qquad (6\text{-}13)$$

$$L \frac{di_1}{dt} = v_2 - R_3 i_1 \qquad \text{voltage across } L \qquad (6\text{-}14)$$

Rearranging, these equations are written

$$\frac{dv_1}{dt} = -\frac{1}{C_1}\left(\frac{1}{R_1} + \frac{1}{R_2}\right)v_1 + \frac{1}{C_1 R_2}v_2 + \frac{1}{C_1 R_1}v \qquad (6\text{-}15)$$

$$\frac{dv_2}{dt} = \frac{1}{C_2 R_2}v_1 - \frac{1}{C_2 R_2}v_2 - \frac{1}{C_2}i_1 \qquad (6\text{-}16)$$

$$\frac{di_1}{dt} = \frac{1}{L}v_2 - \frac{R_3}{L}i_1 \qquad (6\text{-}17)$$

The $\mathbf{A}$ matrix is now obtained from the coefficients associated with v_1, v_2, and i_1 in the state equations.

$$\mathbf{A} = \begin{bmatrix} -\dfrac{1}{C_1}\left(\dfrac{1}{R_1} + \dfrac{1}{R_2}\right) & \dfrac{1}{C_1 R_2} & 0 \\[2ex] \dfrac{1}{C_2 R_2} & -\dfrac{1}{C_2 R_2} & -\dfrac{1}{C_2} \\[2ex] 0 & \dfrac{1}{L} & -\dfrac{R_3}{L} \end{bmatrix} \qquad (6\text{-}18)$$

The **B** matrix is determined from the coefficients of v; that is,

$$\mathbf{B} = \begin{bmatrix} \dfrac{1}{C_1 R_1} \\ 0 \\ 0 \end{bmatrix} \tag{6-19}$$

Since the output variable is also the state variable v_2, we have

$$\mathbf{C} = [0 \quad 1 \quad 0] \qquad \mathbf{D} = [0]$$

Therefore the output equation is

$$\mathbf{y} = [v_2] = [0 \quad 1 \quad 0] \begin{bmatrix} v_1 \\ v_2 \\ i_1 \end{bmatrix} + [0]v \tag{6-20}$$

Example 6-2   State equations of a network with mutual coupling   It is of interest to investigate how the state equations of networks with magnetic coupling are written.   Let us consider the network shown in Fig. 6-4.   In this case, the state variables of the network are the

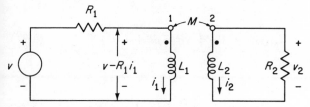

Fig. 6-4   A transformer network.

two currents i_1 and i_2 in the two coils of the transformer.   At first glance, we are not quite sure how the state equations can be written directly from the network.   However, since the two loop currents are also i_1 and i_2, let us first formulate the two loop equations of the network:

$$v(t) = R_1 i_1 + L_1 \frac{di_1}{dt} + M \frac{di_2}{dt} \tag{6-21}$$

$$0 = M \frac{di_1}{dt} + R_2 i_2 + L_2 \frac{di_2}{dt} \tag{6-22}$$

Since these two equations involve only i_1, i_2 and their time derivatives, we can solve for di_1/dt and di_2/dt from these equations to give

$$\frac{di_1}{dt} = -\frac{R_1 L_2}{L_1 L_2 - M^2} i_1 + \frac{M R_2}{L_1 L_2 - M^2} i_2 + \frac{L_2}{L_1 L_2 - M^2} v \qquad (6\text{-}23)$$

$$\frac{di_2}{dt} = \frac{R_1 M}{L_1 L_2 - M^2} i_1 - \frac{L_1 R_2}{L_1 L_2 - M^2} i_2 - \frac{M}{L_1 L_2 - M^2} v \qquad (6\text{-}24)$$

It is clear that these are the state equations in normal form. It is also recognized that the coefficients of (6-23) and (6-24) can be expressed in the inverse inductances. Thus these two equations become

$$\frac{di_1}{dt} = -\Gamma_1 R_1 i_1 + \Gamma_M R_2 i_2 + \Gamma_1 v \qquad (6\text{-}25)$$

$$\frac{di_2}{dt} = \Gamma_M R_1 i_1 - \Gamma_2 R_2 i_2 - \Gamma_M v \qquad (6\text{-}26)$$

The use of the inverse inductances suggests that, in general, perhaps the node method may lead us to the state equations more directly in networks with mutual couplings. Applying Kirchhoff's current law to nodes 1 and 2 in the circuit of Fig. 6-4, we get

$$i_1(t) = \Gamma_1 \int_{t_0^+}^{t} (v - R_1 i_1)\, dt + \Gamma_M \int_{t_0^+}^{t} R_2 i_2\, dt + i_1(t_0^+) \qquad (6\text{-}27)$$

and

$$i_2(t) = -\Gamma_M \int_{t_0^+}^{t} (v - R_1 i_1)\, dt - \Gamma_2 \int_{t_0^+}^{t} R_2 i_2\, dt + i_2(t_0^+) \qquad (6\text{-}28)$$

Taking the derivative with respect to time on both sides of these last two equations yields the same results as in (6-25) and (6-26). Normally, we can combine the steps of writing the node equations and the taking of the time derivatives.

Example 6-3   As another illustrative example of writing state equations of magnetically coupled circuits, let us refer to the network in Fig. 6-5. The currents in L_1 and L_2 and the voltage across C are assigned as the state variables in this case. Applying Kirchhoff's current law at

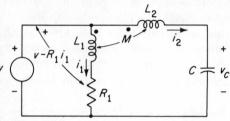

Fig. 6-5   A network with magnetic coupling.

the three nodes indicated on the network, we have

$$i_1 = \Gamma_1 \int_{t_0^+}^{t} (v - R_1 i_1)\, dt - \Gamma_M \int_{t_0^+}^{t} (v - v_c)\, dt + i_1(t_0^+) \qquad (6\text{-}29)$$

$$i_2 = -\Gamma_M \int_{t_0^+}^{t} (v - R_1 i_1)\, dt + \Gamma_2 \int_{t_0^+}^{t} (v - v_c)\, dt + i_2(t_0^+) \qquad (6\text{-}30)$$

$$C \frac{dv_c}{dt} = i_2 \qquad (6\text{-}31)$$

Taking the derivative with respect to time on both sides of (6-29) and (6-30) and rearranging the terms, we get

$$\frac{di_1}{dt} = (\Gamma_1 - \Gamma_M)v + \Gamma_M v_c - \Gamma_1 R_1 i_1 \qquad (6\text{-}32)$$

$$\frac{di_2}{dt} = (\Gamma_2 - \Gamma_M)v - \Gamma_2 v_c + \Gamma_M R_1 i_1 \qquad (6\text{-}33)$$

and from (6-31), we get

$$\frac{dv_c}{dt} = \frac{1}{C} i_2 \qquad (6\text{-}34)$$

6-2   STATE EQUATIONS OF ELECTRIC NETWORKS OBTAINED THROUGH NETWORK GRAPHS

In order to illustrate the fundamentals of the state-variable approach, we have intentionally selected the examples in the last section to be of such a nature that the state equations are all written by inspection.   We should realize that the inspection method may not always be successful.

The original work by Bashkow[2] allows the writing of the state equations of an electric network by means of the network graph. Bryant[3] later also made contributions to the method. The method utilizes the concepts of trees and links, whose definitions have been given in the preceding chapter. However, since the state equations essentially include the voltages across capacitances and currents through inductances as independent variables, it is necessary to define a new term, the *proper tree*.

A proper tree of a network is defined as one whose branches contain every capacitive element of the network or every capacitive element plus resistive elements.

Of course, it is not guaranteed that a proper tree may be constructed for any given network. For instance, a proper tree cannot be obtained for a network which has a loop containing only capacitances or only capacitances and voltage sources. Similar difficulty will arise in a network with a node which has only inductive elements or inductive elements and current sources connected to it. In general, any capacitances and inductances which prevent the formation of a proper tree will be called *excess*. When a network has excess elements, a proper tree cannot be formed in the usual sense. However, a *modified proper tree* can be constructed by *designating the capacitive excess elements as links and the inductive excess elements as tree branches.*

It is important to point out that, since the definition of the proper tree relies on the isolation of the L and C elements, this requires that no parallel combinations of RC, LR, or RLC elements can be regarded as a single branch. We recall that this restriction is not placed on the graphs used for node-and-loop analysis. Figure 6-6 gives some illustrative examples of how the proper tree is formed for a given network. Notice that, as in the usual manner, all voltage sources have been short-circuited and all current sources open-circuited in forming the proper tree.

In Fig. 6-7 modified proper trees are illustrated for two networks having excess elements. In Fig. 6-7a, the capacitances C_1, C_2, and C_3 form a closed loop; thus a proper tree cannot be formed. We can call any one of the capacitive elements an excess, and the modified proper tree is obtained by designating the excess capacitive element as a link (instead of as a tree branch as called for by the original definition). The modified proper tree with C_3 (excess) as a link is shown in Fig. 6-7a. In Fig. 6-7b, node 1 is a junction with only inductive elements and a current source. Therefore a proper tree cannot be drawn if all the inductances are to be regarded as link branches. A modified proper tree is formed in the figure by considering L_1 a tree branch.

Consider that a network has k external current sources, p external voltage sources, N nodes, B branches, n capacitances, and m inductances

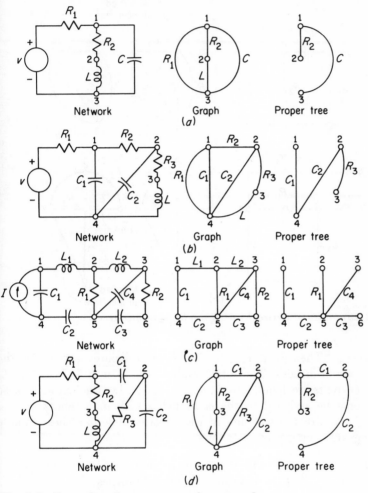

Fig. 6-6   *Examples of proper trees of a network.*

(the numbers n and m do not include the excess elements) and assume that a proper tree, or a modified proper tree if necessary, of the network is formed.   The state equations of the network may be written using the following procedure:

1. Assign a current and current direction in each branch of the network.   There are a total of $N - 1$ tree branches in the proper tree, and the tree-branch currents are denoted by $I_1, I_2, \ldots, I_{N-1}$.   Let the first n of these tree-branch currents be assigned to the n branches with

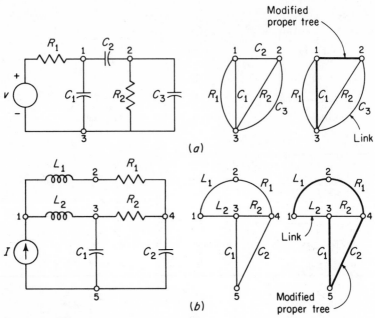

Fig. 6-7 *Examples of networks with modified proper trees.*

capacitances. Then I_{n+1}, I_{n+2}, . . . , I_{N-1} designate currents in the resistive tree branches. The total number of links is $B - N + 1 = L$. The link currents are denoted by $i_1, i_2, . . . , i_L$. Let the first m of these link currents be assigned to the m branches with inductances. Then $i_{m+1}, . . . , i_L$ are the currents in the resistive link branches. These definitions are summarized as follows:

$$I_j(j = 1, . . . , N - 1) = \text{currents in all proper tree branches}$$
$$i_j(j = 1, . . . , L) = \text{currents in all link branches}$$
$$I_k(k = 1, . . . , n) = \text{currents in capacitive proper tree branches}$$
$$i_k(k = 1, . . . , m) = \text{currents in inductive link branches}$$

2. Assign a branch voltage in each branch of the network. As established in Chap. 4, the positive side of the branch voltage is assumed to be located at the tail end of the arrow on the branch.

Let $V_j(j = 1, . . . , L) = \text{link-branch voltages}$
$\quad v_j(j = 1, . . . , N - 1) = \text{tree-branch voltages}$
$\quad V_k(k = 1, . . . , m) = \text{voltages across inductive link branches}$
$\quad v_k(k = 1, . . . , n) = \text{voltages across capacitive proper tree branches}$

3. Express the capacitive tree-branch currents and the resistive tree-branch currents in terms of all the link currents and current sources. The following sets of matrix equations can be written:

$$
\begin{bmatrix} I_1 \\ I_2 \\ \cdot \\ \cdot \\ \cdot \\ I_n \end{bmatrix} = \begin{bmatrix} C_1 \dfrac{dv_1}{dt} \\ C_2 \dfrac{dv_2}{dt} \\ \cdot \\ \cdot \\ \cdot \\ C_n \dfrac{dv_n}{dt} \end{bmatrix} = \mathbf{A}_T \begin{bmatrix} i_1 \\ i_2 \\ \cdot \\ \cdot \\ \cdot \\ i_m \end{bmatrix} + \mathbf{B}_T \begin{bmatrix} i_{m+1} \\ i_{m+2} \\ \cdot \\ \cdot \\ \cdot \\ i_L \end{bmatrix} + \mathbf{F}_T \begin{bmatrix} I_{g1} \\ I_{g2} \\ \cdot \\ \cdot \\ \cdot \\ I_{gk} \end{bmatrix} \qquad (6\text{-}35)
$$

↑	↑	↑	↑
Capacitive tree-branch currents	Inductive link currents	Resistive and excess link currents	Current sources

$\mathbf{A}_T$ is an $n \times m$ matrix, and $\mathbf{B}_T$ is an $n \times (L - m)$ matrix.

$$
\begin{bmatrix} I_{n+1} \\ I_{n+2} \\ \cdot \\ \cdot \\ \cdot \\ I_{N-1} \end{bmatrix} = \mathbf{D}_T \begin{bmatrix} i_1 \\ i_2 \\ \cdot \\ \cdot \\ \cdot \\ i_m \end{bmatrix} + \mathbf{E}_T \begin{bmatrix} i_{m+1} \\ i_{m+2} \\ \cdot \\ \cdot \\ \cdot \\ i_L \end{bmatrix} + \mathbf{H}_T \begin{bmatrix} I_{g1} \\ I_{g2} \\ \cdot \\ \cdot \\ \cdot \\ I_{gk} \end{bmatrix} \qquad (6\text{-}36)
$$

↑
Resistive and excess tree currents

$\mathbf{D}_T$ is an $(N - n - 1) \times m$ matrix, and $\mathbf{E}_T$ is an $(N - n - 1) \times (L - m)$ matrix. $I_{g1}, \ldots, I_{gk}$ are the k external current sources in the network.

The entries of the matrices $\mathbf{A}_T$, $\mathbf{B}_T$, $\mathbf{D}_T$, $\mathbf{E}_T$, $\mathbf{F}_T$, and $\mathbf{H}_T$ are $+1$, -1, and 0, and can be determined from the tie-sets of the network graph. If each of the tie-sets is assigned to a unique link branch and has the same direction as the link current, the link currents $i_1, i_2, \ldots, i_L$ are also the tie-set (loop) currents. Therefore the (i,j) element of the $\mathbf{A}_T$, $\mathbf{B}_T$, $\mathbf{D}_T$, or $\mathbf{E}_T$ matrices is determined as follows:

If I_i is in tie-set j, enter a $+1$ if I_i and i_j are in the same direction; enter a -1 if the two currents are in opposite directions. If I_i is not in tie-set j, enter a 0. As an alternative, the current equations (6-35) and (6-36) can also be written, using the cut-sets of the proper tree, i.e., by writing the current relationship at the cut-sets.

A current source I_g connecting two nodes of the network can be treated as an additional link current. In other words, an additional tie-set can be formed using the I_g branch as link branch. Therefore the elements of the matrices $\mathbf{F}_T$ and $\mathbf{H}_T$ can be determined from these additional tie-sets due to the current sources, using the same rules as for the elements of $\mathbf{A}_T$, $\mathbf{B}_T$, $\mathbf{D}_T$, and $\mathbf{E}_T$. The voltage sources will not affect (6-35) and (6-36) since these are current equations.

4. Express the inductive link-branch voltages and the resistive link-branch voltages in terms of all the tree-branch voltages and the source voltages. The following sets of matrix equations may be written:

$$
\begin{bmatrix} V_1 \\ V_2 \\ \cdot \\ \cdot \\ \cdot \\ V_m \end{bmatrix} = \begin{bmatrix} L_1 \dfrac{di_1}{dt} \\ L_2 \dfrac{di_2}{dt} \\ \cdot \\ \cdot \\ \cdot \\ L_m \dfrac{di_m}{dt} \end{bmatrix} = \mathbf{A}_L \begin{bmatrix} v_1 \\ v_2 \\ \cdot \\ \cdot \\ \cdot \\ v_n \end{bmatrix} + \mathbf{B}_L \begin{bmatrix} v_{n+1} \\ v_{n+2} \\ \cdot \\ \cdot \\ \cdot \\ v_{N-1} \end{bmatrix} + \mathbf{F}_L \begin{bmatrix} V_{g1} \\ V_{g2} \\ \cdot \\ \cdot \\ \cdot \\ V_{gp} \end{bmatrix} \qquad (6\text{-}37)
$$

↑	↑	↑	↑
Inductive link-branch voltages	Capacitive tree voltages	Resistive tree voltages	Voltage sources

$$
\begin{bmatrix} V_{m+1} \\ V_{m+2} \\ \cdot \\ \cdot \\ \cdot \\ V_L \end{bmatrix} = \mathbf{D}_L \begin{bmatrix} v_1 \\ v_2 \\ \cdot \\ \cdot \\ \cdot \\ v_n \end{bmatrix} + \mathbf{E}_L \begin{bmatrix} v_{n+1} \\ v_{n+2} \\ \cdot \\ \cdot \\ \cdot \\ v_{N-1} \end{bmatrix} + \mathbf{H}_L \begin{bmatrix} V_{g1} \\ V_{g2} \\ \cdot \\ \cdot \\ \cdot \\ V_{gp} \end{bmatrix} \qquad (6\text{-}38)
$$

↑
Resistive link-branch voltages

The elements of the matrices $\mathbf{A}_L$, $\mathbf{B}_L$, $\mathbf{D}_L$, $\mathbf{E}_L$, $\mathbf{F}_L$, and $\mathbf{H}_L$ are also $+1$, -1, and 0, and can be determined easily from the network graph by following through the tie-sets. The voltage sources are usually connected in series with the branches. If the voltage source V_{gi} $(i = 1, \ldots , p)$ is found in the tie-set that has a link branch with branch voltage V_j $(j = 1, \ldots , L)$, then the (i,j) position of $\mathbf{F}_L$ (or of $\mathbf{H}_L$) is $+1$ if V_{gi} and V_j are opposing; -1 if they are aiding; enter a 0 if V_{gi} is not in the tie-set j.

5. Equations (6-35) and (6-37) are combined in one equation, which reads

$$
\begin{bmatrix} I_1 \\ I_2 \\ \cdot \\ \cdot \\ \cdot \\ I_n \\ \hline V_1 \\ V_2 \\ \cdot \\ \cdot \\ \cdot \\ V_m \end{bmatrix}
=
\begin{bmatrix} C_1 \dfrac{dv_1}{dt} \\ C_2 \dfrac{dv_2}{dt} \\ \cdot \\ \cdot \\ C_n \dfrac{dv_n}{dt} \\ \hline L_1 \dfrac{di_1}{dt} \\ L_2 \dfrac{di_2}{dt} \\ \cdot \\ \cdot \\ L_m \dfrac{di_m}{dt} \end{bmatrix}
=
\begin{bmatrix} \mathbf{0} & \vdots & \mathbf{A}_T \\ \cdots & & \cdots \\ \mathbf{A}_L & \vdots & \mathbf{0} \end{bmatrix}
\begin{bmatrix} v_1 \\ v_2 \\ \cdot \\ \cdot \\ v_n \\ \hline i_1 \\ i_2 \\ \cdot \\ \cdot \\ i_m \end{bmatrix}
$$

$$
+
\begin{bmatrix} \mathbf{0} & \vdots & \mathbf{B}_T \\ \cdots & & \cdots \\ \mathbf{B}_L & \vdots & \mathbf{0} \end{bmatrix}
\begin{bmatrix} v_{n+1} \\ v_{n+2} \\ \cdot \\ \cdot \\ \cdot \\ v_{N-1} \\ \hline i_{m+1} \\ i_{m+2} \\ \cdot \\ \cdot \\ \cdot \\ i_L \end{bmatrix}
+
\begin{bmatrix} \mathbf{0} & \vdots & \mathbf{F}_T \\ \cdots & & \cdots \\ \mathbf{F}_L & \vdots & \mathbf{0} \end{bmatrix}
\begin{bmatrix} V_{g1} \\ \cdot \\ \cdot \\ V_{gp} \\ \hline I_{g1} \\ \cdot \\ \cdot \\ \cdot \\ I_{gk} \end{bmatrix}
\tag{6-39}
$$

In (6-39), $v_1, v_2, \ldots, v_n$ are the capacitor voltages and $i_1, i_2, \ldots, i_m$ are the inductor currents. These $n + m$ independent variables are defined as the state variables. However, the equation also contains $v_{n+1}, \ldots, v_{N-1}, i_{m+1}, \ldots, i_L$, which are not state variables. These voltages and currents, which are associated with the resistive tree and link branches, must be expressed in terms of the state variables and the input sources so that (6-39) is finally converted to the proper state-equation form.

6. Now combining (6-36) and (6-38) into one equation, we have

$$
\begin{bmatrix} I_{n+1} \\ I_{n+2} \\ \cdot \\ \cdot \\ \cdot \\ I_{N-1} \\ \hline V_{m+1} \\ V_{m+2} \\ \cdot \\ \cdot \\ \cdot \\ V_L \end{bmatrix}
=
\begin{bmatrix} \mathbf{0} & \mathbf{D}_T \\ \hline \mathbf{D}_L & \mathbf{0} \end{bmatrix}
\begin{bmatrix} v_1 \\ v_2 \\ \cdot \\ \cdot \\ \cdot \\ v_n \\ \hline i_1 \\ i_2 \\ \cdot \\ \cdot \\ \cdot \\ i_m \end{bmatrix}
+
\begin{bmatrix} \mathbf{0} & \mathbf{E}_T \\ \hline \mathbf{E}_L & \mathbf{0} \end{bmatrix}
\begin{bmatrix} v_{n+1} \\ v_{n+2} \\ \cdot \\ \cdot \\ \cdot \\ v_{N-1} \\ \hline i_{m+1} \\ i_{m+2} \\ \cdot \\ \cdot \\ \cdot \\ i_L \end{bmatrix}
$$

$$
+
\begin{bmatrix} \mathbf{0} & \mathbf{H}_T \\ \hline \mathbf{H}_L & \mathbf{0} \end{bmatrix}
\begin{bmatrix} V_{g1} \\ \cdot \\ \cdot \\ \cdot \\ V_{gp} \\ \hline I_{g1} \\ \cdot \\ \cdot \\ \cdot \\ I_{gk} \end{bmatrix}
\tag{6-40}
$$

The resistive tree-branch voltages $v_{n+1}, \ldots , v_{N-1}$ can be expressed as functions of their corresponding tree-branch currents, and the resistive link currents, $i_{m+1}, i_{m+2}, \ldots , i_L$, can be expressed in terms of their corresponding link voltages. Therefore the following partitioned matrix equation is written

$$
\begin{bmatrix} v_{n+1} \\ v_{n+2} \\ \cdot \\ \cdot \\ \cdot \\ v_{N-1} \\ \hline i_{m+1} \\ \cdot \\ \cdot \\ \cdot \\ i_L \end{bmatrix}
=
\begin{bmatrix} \mathbf{R}_b & \mathbf{0} \\ \hline \mathbf{0} & \mathbf{G}_b \end{bmatrix}
\begin{bmatrix} I_{n+1} \\ I_{n+2} \\ \cdot \\ \cdot \\ \cdot \\ I_{N-1} \\ \hline V_{m+1} \\ \cdot \\ \cdot \\ \cdot \\ V_L \end{bmatrix}
\tag{6-41}
$$

where $\mathbf{R}_b$ is an $(N - n - 1) \times (N - n - 1)$ diagonal matrix, which contains the resistances in the resistance tree branches, and $\mathbf{G}_b$ is an $(L - m) \times (L - m)$ diagonal matrix containing the branch transconductances of the resistive link branches. Sometimes in networks with excess elements, the elements of $\mathbf{R}_b$ and $\mathbf{G}_b$ may contain the operator d/dt.

Now substituting from (6-40) in (6-41) and solving for the left-hand side of (6-41) gives

$$
\begin{bmatrix}
v_{n+1} \\
v_{n+2} \\
\cdot \\
\cdot \\
\cdot \\
v_{N-1} \\
i_{m+1} \\
\cdot \\
\cdot \\
\cdot \\
i_L
\end{bmatrix}
=
\begin{bmatrix}
\mathbf{I} & -\mathbf{R}_b\mathbf{E}_T \\
-\mathbf{G}_b\mathbf{E}_L & \mathbf{I}
\end{bmatrix}^{-1}
\begin{bmatrix}
\mathbf{0} & \mathbf{R}_b\mathbf{D}_T \\
\mathbf{G}_b\mathbf{D}_L & \mathbf{0}
\end{bmatrix}
\begin{bmatrix}
v_1 \\
v_2 \\
\cdot \\
\cdot \\
\cdot \\
v_n \\
i_1 \\
i_2 \\
\cdot \\
\cdot \\
\cdot \\
i_m
\end{bmatrix}
$$

$$
+
\begin{bmatrix}
\mathbf{I} & -\mathbf{R}_b\mathbf{E}_T \\
-\mathbf{G}_b\mathbf{E}_L & \mathbf{I}
\end{bmatrix}^{-1}
\begin{bmatrix}
\mathbf{0} & \mathbf{R}_b\mathbf{H}_T \\
\mathbf{G}_b\mathbf{H}_L & \mathbf{0}
\end{bmatrix}
\begin{bmatrix}
V_{g1} \\
V_{g2} \\
\cdot \\
\cdot \\
\cdot \\
V_{gp} \\
I_{g1} \\
I_{g2} \\
\cdot \\
\cdot \\
\cdot \\
I_{gk}
\end{bmatrix}
\quad (6\text{-}42)
$$

Substituting from (6-42) in (6-39) gives

$$
\begin{bmatrix} C_1 \dfrac{dv_1}{dt} \\ \cdot \\ \cdot \\ \cdot \\ C_n \dfrac{dv_n}{dt} \\ L_1 \dfrac{di_1}{dt} \\ \cdot \\ \cdot \\ \cdot \\ L_m \dfrac{di_m}{dt} \end{bmatrix}
= \left\{ \begin{bmatrix} \mathbf{0} & \mathbf{A}_T \\ \mathbf{A}_L & \mathbf{0} \end{bmatrix} + \begin{bmatrix} \mathbf{0} & \mathbf{B}_T \\ \mathbf{B}_L & \mathbf{0} \end{bmatrix} \begin{bmatrix} \mathbf{I} & -\mathbf{R}_b\mathbf{E}_T \\ -\mathbf{G}_b\mathbf{E}_L & \mathbf{I} \end{bmatrix}^{-1} \begin{bmatrix} \mathbf{0} & \mathbf{R}_b\mathbf{D}_T \\ \mathbf{G}_b\mathbf{D}_L & \mathbf{0} \end{bmatrix} \right\}
$$

$$
\begin{bmatrix} v_1 \\ v_2 \\ \cdot \\ \cdot \\ \cdot \\ v_n \\ i_1 \\ i_2 \\ \cdot \\ \cdot \\ \cdot \\ i_m \end{bmatrix}
$$

$$
+ \left\{ \begin{bmatrix} \mathbf{0} & \mathbf{F}_T \\ \mathbf{F}_L & \mathbf{0} \end{bmatrix} + \begin{bmatrix} \mathbf{0} & \mathbf{B}_T \\ \mathbf{B}_L & \mathbf{0} \end{bmatrix} \begin{bmatrix} \mathbf{I} & -\mathbf{R}_b\mathbf{E}_T \\ -\mathbf{G}_b\mathbf{E}_L & \mathbf{I} \end{bmatrix}^{-1} \begin{bmatrix} \mathbf{0} & \mathbf{R}_b\mathbf{H}_T \\ \mathbf{G}_b\mathbf{H}_L & \mathbf{0} \end{bmatrix} \right\}
\begin{bmatrix} V_{g1} \\ \cdot \\ \cdot \\ \cdot \\ V_{gp} \\ I_{g1} \\ \cdot \\ \cdot \\ \cdot \\ I_{gk} \end{bmatrix} \quad (6\text{-}43)
$$

which is the desired matrix state equation.

It should be pointed out that if the network has excess elements, the right-hand side of (6-43) may contain the first derivatives of the independent state variables. These terms must be transferred to the left-hand side of the equation so that the equation may eventually be put into the normal form.

Equation (6-43) may seem formidable to use. However, the equation is not intended to be used as a formula. If we follow the steps outlined above, the procedure of writing the state equations from the network graph is quite straightforward. The following illustrative examples may be helpful in gaining an understanding of the use of the method described in this section.

Example 6-4   Consider the network shown in Fig. 6-8a. The proper tree of the network is shown in Fig. 6-8b. The branch voltages

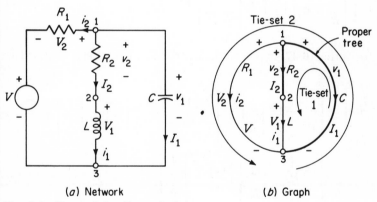

(a) Network   (b) Graph

Fig. 6-8   Network for Example 6-4.

and branch currents are assigned according to the procedure outlined in steps 1 and 2 above and are shown in Fig. 6-8b. In this case, the left-hand side of (6-39) should contain the capacitor branch current I_1 and the inductor branch voltage V_1. Therefore, following through the currents and voltages in the two tie-sets, we get

$$\begin{bmatrix} I_1 \\ V_1 \end{bmatrix} = \begin{bmatrix} C_1 \dfrac{dv_1}{dt} \\ L_1 \dfrac{di_1}{dt} \end{bmatrix} = \begin{bmatrix} 0 & -1 \\ 1 & 0 \end{bmatrix} \begin{bmatrix} v_1 \\ i_1 \end{bmatrix} + \begin{bmatrix} 0 & -1 \\ -1 & 0 \end{bmatrix} \begin{bmatrix} v_2 \\ i_2 \end{bmatrix} \qquad (6\text{-}44)$$

Similarly, (6-40) gives

$$\begin{bmatrix} I_2 \\ V_2 \end{bmatrix} = \begin{bmatrix} 0 & 1 \\ 1 & 0 \end{bmatrix} \begin{bmatrix} v_1 \\ i_1 \end{bmatrix} + \begin{bmatrix} 0 & 0 \\ 0 & 0 \end{bmatrix} \begin{bmatrix} v_2 \\ i_2 \end{bmatrix} + \begin{bmatrix} 0 \\ -1 \end{bmatrix} V \qquad (6\text{-}45)$$

Notice that the voltage V_2 is defined as the branch voltage of R_1 only. Thus $V_2 = v_1 - V$. Now using (6-41), we get

$$\begin{bmatrix} v_2 \\ i_2 \end{bmatrix} = \begin{bmatrix} R_2 & 0 \\ 0 & \dfrac{1}{R_1} \end{bmatrix} \begin{bmatrix} I_2 \\ V_2 \end{bmatrix} \qquad (6\text{-}46)$$

Substituting (6-45) in (6-46), we have

$$\begin{bmatrix} v_2 \\ i_2 \end{bmatrix} = \begin{bmatrix} 0 & R_2 \\ \dfrac{1}{R_1} & 0 \end{bmatrix} \begin{bmatrix} v_1 \\ i_1 \end{bmatrix} + \begin{bmatrix} 0 \\ -\dfrac{1}{R_1} \end{bmatrix} V \qquad (6\text{-}47)$$

Upon substituting (6-47) in (6-44), the matrix state equation is obtained as

$$\begin{bmatrix} C_1 \dfrac{dv_1}{dt} \\ L_1 \dfrac{di_1}{dt} \end{bmatrix} = \begin{bmatrix} 0 & -1 \\ 1 & 0 \end{bmatrix} \begin{bmatrix} v_1 \\ i_1 \end{bmatrix} + \begin{bmatrix} -\dfrac{1}{R_1} & 0 \\ 0 & -R_2 \end{bmatrix} \begin{bmatrix} v_1 \\ i_1 \end{bmatrix} + \begin{bmatrix} \dfrac{1}{R_1} \\ 0 \end{bmatrix} V$$

$$= \begin{bmatrix} -\dfrac{1}{R_1} & -1 \\ 1 & -R_2 \end{bmatrix} \begin{bmatrix} v_1 \\ i_1 \end{bmatrix} + \begin{bmatrix} \dfrac{1}{R_1} \\ 0 \end{bmatrix} V \qquad (6\text{-}48)$$

Actually, the state equations of this simple network can be written out by the inspection method described in Sec. 6-1. Therefore the validity of (6-48) may be checked quite easily.

Example 6-5   When the state equations of a given network can be written simply by inspection, there is no need to carry out the matrix manipulations using the network graph. The same statement can be applied to writing loop and node equations. However, the use of the proper tree always assures us a solution when all inspection methods fail. For instance, if a resistance R_3 is now connected in series with C in the network of Fig. 6-8, the network in Fig. 6-9a results. We have shown

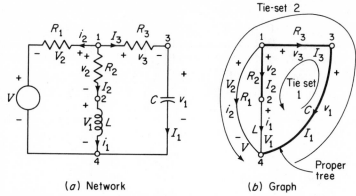

(a) Network   (b) Graph

Fig. 6-9   Network for Example 6-5.

that the state equations of this network can no longer be written by mere inspection, even though the number of independent state variables is still two.   The proper tree of the network is shown in Fig. 6-9b.   The equation corresponding to (6-39) is written

$$\begin{bmatrix} I_1 \\ V_1 \end{bmatrix} = \begin{bmatrix} C_1 \dfrac{dv_1}{dt} \\ L_1 \dfrac{di_1}{dt} \end{bmatrix} = \begin{bmatrix} 0 & -1 \\ 1 & 0 \end{bmatrix} \begin{bmatrix} v_1 \\ i_1 \end{bmatrix} + \begin{bmatrix} 0 & 0 & -1 \\ -1 & 1 & 0 \end{bmatrix} \begin{bmatrix} v_2 \\ v_3 \\ i_2 \end{bmatrix}$$

$$(6\text{-}49)$$

and (6-40) gives

$$\begin{bmatrix} I_2 \\ I_3 \\ V_2 \end{bmatrix} = \begin{bmatrix} 0 & 1 \\ 0 & -1 \\ 1 & 0 \end{bmatrix} \begin{bmatrix} v_1 \\ i_1 \end{bmatrix} + \begin{bmatrix} 0 & 0 & 0 \\ 0 & 0 & -1 \\ 0 & 1 & 0 \end{bmatrix} \begin{bmatrix} v_2 \\ v_3 \\ i_2 \end{bmatrix} + \begin{bmatrix} 0 \\ 0 \\ -1 \end{bmatrix} V \quad (6\text{-}50)$$

From (6-41), the following matrix equation is written:

$$\begin{bmatrix} v_2 \\ v_3 \\ i_2 \end{bmatrix} = \begin{bmatrix} R_2 & 0 & 0 \\ 0 & R_3 & 0 \\ 0 & 0 & \dfrac{1}{R_1} \end{bmatrix} \begin{bmatrix} I_2 \\ I_3 \\ V_2 \end{bmatrix}$$

$$(6\text{-}51)$$

Now substituting (6-50) in (6-51) and solving for the vector matrix of

v_2, v_3, and i_2, we have

$$
\begin{bmatrix} v_2 \\ v_3 \\ i_2 \end{bmatrix} = \begin{bmatrix} 1 & 0 & 0 \\ 0 & 1 & R_3 \\ 0 & -\dfrac{1}{R_1} & 1 \end{bmatrix}^{-1} \begin{bmatrix} 0 & R_2 \\ 0 & -R_3 \\ \dfrac{1}{R_1} & 0 \end{bmatrix} \begin{bmatrix} v_1 \\ i_1 \end{bmatrix}
$$

$$
+ \begin{bmatrix} 1 & 0 & 0 \\ 0 & 1 & R_3 \\ 0 & -\dfrac{1}{R_1} & 1 \end{bmatrix}^{-1} \begin{bmatrix} 0 \\ 0 \\ -\dfrac{1}{R_1} \end{bmatrix} V
$$

$$
= \begin{bmatrix} 0 & R_2 \\ \dfrac{-R_3}{R_1 + R_3} & \dfrac{-R_1 R_3}{R_1 + R_3} \\ \dfrac{1}{R_1 + R_3} & \dfrac{-R_3}{R_1 + R_3} \end{bmatrix} \begin{bmatrix} v_1 \\ i_1 \end{bmatrix} + \begin{bmatrix} 0 \\ \dfrac{R_3}{R_1 + R_3} \\ \dfrac{-1}{R_1 + R_3} \end{bmatrix} V \qquad (6\text{-}52)
$$

Substituting (6-52) in (6-49) yields

$$
\begin{bmatrix} C_1 \dfrac{dv_1}{dt} \\ L_1 \dfrac{di_1}{dt} \end{bmatrix} = \begin{bmatrix} \dfrac{-1}{R_1 + R_3} & \dfrac{-R_1}{R_1 + R_3} \\ \dfrac{R_1}{R_1 + R_3} & -\dfrac{R_1 R_2 + R_2 R_3 + R_3 R_1}{R_1 + R_3} \end{bmatrix} \begin{bmatrix} v_1 \\ i_1 \end{bmatrix}
$$

$$
+ \begin{bmatrix} \dfrac{1}{R_1 + R_3} \\ \dfrac{R_3}{R_1 + R_3} \end{bmatrix} V \qquad (6\text{-}53)
$$

which represents the state equations of the network in Fig. 6-9a.

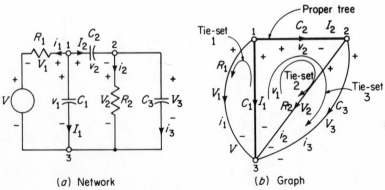

(a) Network   (b) Graph

Fig. 6-10   Network for Example 6-6.

Example 6-6   A network with a capacitive excess branch   A
network with a capacitive excess branch is shown in Fig. 6-10a.   Let us
designate C_3 as the excess element.   Then, according to the procedure
described earlier in regard to this situation, the branch containing C_3 is
regarded as a link branch.   The modified proper tree is shown in Fig.
6-10b.   The matrix equations which correspond to (6-39), (6-40), and
(6-41) are written

$$
\begin{bmatrix} I_1 \\ I_2 \end{bmatrix} = \begin{bmatrix} C_1 \dfrac{dv_1}{dt} \\ C_2 \dfrac{dv_2}{dt} \end{bmatrix} = \begin{bmatrix} 0 & 0 \\ 0 & 0 \end{bmatrix} \begin{bmatrix} v_1 \\ v_2 \end{bmatrix} + \begin{bmatrix} -1 & -1 & -1 \\ 0 & 1 & 1 \end{bmatrix} \begin{bmatrix} i_1 \\ i_2 \\ i_3 \end{bmatrix} \qquad (6\text{-}54)
$$

$$
\begin{bmatrix} V_1 \\ V_2 \\ V_3 \end{bmatrix} = \begin{bmatrix} 1 & 0 \\ 1 & -1 \\ 1 & -1 \end{bmatrix} \begin{bmatrix} v_1 \\ v_2 \end{bmatrix} + \begin{bmatrix} 0 & 0 & 0 \\ 0 & 0 & 0 \\ 0 & 0 & 0 \end{bmatrix} \begin{bmatrix} i_1 \\ i_2 \\ i_3 \end{bmatrix} + \begin{bmatrix} -1 \\ 0 \\ 0 \end{bmatrix} V \qquad (6\text{-}55)
$$

$$
\begin{bmatrix} i_1 \\ i_2 \\ i_3 \end{bmatrix} = \begin{bmatrix} \dfrac{1}{R_1} & 0 & 0 \\ 0 & \dfrac{1}{R_2} & 0 \\ 0 & 0 & C_3 \dfrac{d}{dt} \end{bmatrix} \begin{bmatrix} V_1 \\ V_2 \\ V_3 \end{bmatrix} \qquad (6\text{-}56)
$$

Substituting (6-55) in (6-56) yields

$$
\begin{bmatrix} i_1 \\ i_2 \\ i_3 \end{bmatrix} = \begin{bmatrix} \dfrac{1}{R_1} & 0 \\ \dfrac{1}{R_2} & -\dfrac{1}{R_2} \\ C_3 \dfrac{d}{dt} & -C_3 \dfrac{d}{dt} \end{bmatrix} \begin{bmatrix} v_1 \\ v_2 \end{bmatrix} + \begin{bmatrix} -\dfrac{1}{R_1} \\ 0 \\ 0 \end{bmatrix} V \qquad (6\text{-}57)
$$

Now substituting (6-57) in (6-54), we get

$$
\begin{bmatrix} C_1 \dfrac{dv_1}{dt} \\ C_2 \dfrac{dv_2}{dt} \end{bmatrix} = \begin{bmatrix} -\left(\dfrac{R_1 + R_2}{R_1 R_2}\right) & \dfrac{1}{R_2} \\ \dfrac{1}{R_2} & -\dfrac{1}{R_2} \end{bmatrix} \begin{bmatrix} v_1 \\ v_2 \end{bmatrix}
$$

$$
+ \begin{bmatrix} -1 & 1 \\ 1 & -1 \end{bmatrix} \begin{bmatrix} C_3 \dfrac{dv_1}{dt} \\ C_3 \dfrac{dv_2}{dt} \end{bmatrix} + \begin{bmatrix} \dfrac{1}{R_1} \\ 0 \end{bmatrix} V \quad (6\text{-}58)
$$

When the derivative terms on the right-hand side of (6-58) are shifted to the left-hand side of the equation, and after simplification, we have

$$
\begin{bmatrix} \dfrac{dv_1}{dt} \\[2ex] \dfrac{dv_2}{dt} \end{bmatrix} = \dfrac{1}{C_T} \begin{bmatrix} -\left(\dfrac{C_2+C_3}{R_1}\right)+\dfrac{C_2}{R_2} & \dfrac{C_2}{R_2} \\[2ex] \dfrac{C_1}{R_2}-\dfrac{C_3}{R_1} & -\dfrac{C_1}{R_2} \end{bmatrix} \begin{bmatrix} v_1 \\[2ex] v_2 \end{bmatrix} + \dfrac{1}{C_T} \begin{bmatrix} \dfrac{C_2+C_3}{R_1} \\[2ex] \dfrac{C_3}{R_1} \end{bmatrix} V
$$

(6-59)

where $C_T = C_1C_2 + C_2C_3 + C_3C_1$.

Example 6-7   A network with an inductive excess branch
It was stated earlier that when a network has an inductive excess element, the branch should be treated as a tree branch of the modified proper tree. Shown in Fig. 6-11a is a network which has an inductive excess.   Notice

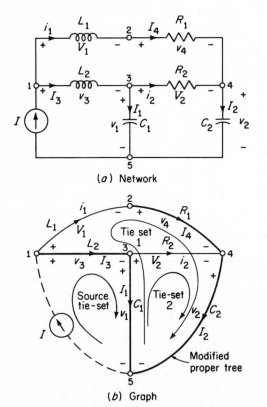

(a) Network

(b) Graph

Fig. 6-11   Network for Example 6-7.

that, since node 1 has only inductances and a current source connected to it, a proper tree cannot be formed in the usual manner. Let us designate L_2 as the excess element and treat it as a tree branch. Then the modified proper tree is shown in Fig. 6-11b.

The first step is to write the currents in C_1 and C_2 and the voltage in L_1 as functions of the tree-branch voltages and link currents. Using (6-39), we get

$$
\begin{bmatrix} I_1 \\ I_2 \\ V_1 \end{bmatrix} = \begin{bmatrix} C_1 \dfrac{dv_1}{dt} \\ C_2 \dfrac{dv_2}{dt} \\ L_1 \dfrac{di_1}{dt} \end{bmatrix} = \begin{bmatrix} 0 & 0 & -1 \\ 0 & 0 & 1 \\ 1 & -1 & 0 \end{bmatrix} \begin{bmatrix} v_1 \\ v_2 \\ i_1 \end{bmatrix}
$$

$$
+ \begin{bmatrix} 0 & 0 & -1 \\ 0 & 0 & 1 \\ 1 & -1 & 0 \end{bmatrix} \begin{bmatrix} v_3 \\ v_4 \\ i_2 \end{bmatrix} + \begin{bmatrix} 1 \\ 0 \\ 0 \end{bmatrix} I \quad (6\text{-}60)
$$

Writing I_3, I_4, and V_2 in terms of the tree-branch voltages and link currents, we have

$$
\begin{bmatrix} I_3 \\ I_4 \\ V_2 \end{bmatrix} = \begin{bmatrix} 0 & 0 & -1 \\ 0 & 0 & 1 \\ 1 & -1 & 0 \end{bmatrix} \begin{bmatrix} v_1 \\ v_2 \\ i_1 \end{bmatrix} + \begin{bmatrix} 0 & 0 & 0 \\ 0 & 0 & 0 \\ 0 & 0 & 0 \end{bmatrix} \begin{bmatrix} v_3 \\ v_4 \\ i_2 \end{bmatrix} + \begin{bmatrix} 1 \\ 0 \\ 0 \end{bmatrix} I \quad (6\text{-}61)
$$

Now v_3, v_4, and i_2 are expressed in terms of their corresponding branch currents and voltage. From (6-41), we get

$$
\begin{bmatrix} v_3 \\ v_4 \\ i_2 \end{bmatrix} = \begin{bmatrix} L_2 \dfrac{d}{dt} & 0 & 0 \\ 0 & R_1 & 0 \\ 0 & 0 & \dfrac{1}{R_2} \end{bmatrix} \begin{bmatrix} I_3 \\ I_4 \\ V_2 \end{bmatrix} \quad (6\text{-}62)
$$

Substituting (6-61) in (6-62) yields

$$
\begin{bmatrix} v_3 \\ v_4 \\ i_2 \end{bmatrix} = \begin{bmatrix} 0 & 0 & -L_2 \dfrac{d}{dt} \\ 0 & 0 & R_1 \\ \dfrac{1}{R_2} & -\dfrac{1}{R_2} & 0 \end{bmatrix} \begin{bmatrix} v_1 \\ v_2 \\ i_1 \end{bmatrix} + \begin{bmatrix} L_2 \dfrac{d}{dt} \\ 0 \\ 0 \end{bmatrix} I \quad (6\text{-}63)
$$

When (6-63) is substituted in (6-60), we have

$$
\begin{bmatrix} C_1 \dfrac{dv_1}{dt} \\[2ex] C_2 \dfrac{dv_2}{dt} \\[2ex] L_1 \dfrac{di_1}{dt} \end{bmatrix} = \begin{bmatrix} -\dfrac{1}{R_2} & \dfrac{1}{R_2} & -1 \\[2ex] \dfrac{1}{R_2} & -\dfrac{1}{R_2} & 1 \\[2ex] 1 & -1 & -R_1 \end{bmatrix} \begin{bmatrix} v_1 \\[1ex] v_2 \\[1ex] i_1 \end{bmatrix}
$$

$$
+ \begin{bmatrix} 0 & 0 & 0 \\ 0 & 0 & 0 \\ 0 & 0 & -1 \end{bmatrix} \begin{bmatrix} C_1 \dfrac{dv_1}{dt} \\[2ex] C_2 \dfrac{dv_2}{dt} \\[2ex] L_2 \dfrac{di_1}{dt} \end{bmatrix} + \begin{bmatrix} 1 \\[1ex] 0 \\[1ex] L_2 \dfrac{d}{dt} \end{bmatrix} I \quad (6\text{-}64)
$$

which is simplified to

$$
\begin{bmatrix} \dfrac{dv_1}{dt} \\[2ex] \dfrac{dv_2}{dt} \\[2ex] \dfrac{di_1}{dt} \end{bmatrix} = \begin{bmatrix} -\dfrac{1}{C_1 R_2} & \dfrac{1}{C_1 R_2} & -\dfrac{1}{C_1} \\[2ex] \dfrac{1}{C_2 R_2} & -\dfrac{1}{C_2 R_2} & \dfrac{1}{C_2} \\[2ex] \dfrac{1}{L_1+L_2} & -\dfrac{1}{L_1+L_2} & -\dfrac{R_1}{L_1+L_2} \end{bmatrix} \begin{bmatrix} v_1 \\[1ex] v_2 \\[1ex] i_1 \end{bmatrix}
$$

$$
+ \begin{bmatrix} \dfrac{1}{C_1} \\[2ex] 0 \\[2ex] \dfrac{L_2}{L_1+L_2} \dfrac{d}{dt} \end{bmatrix} I \quad (6\text{-}65)
$$

Ordinarily, (6-65) would be regarded as the normal-form state equations of the network in Fig. 6-11a. There is still one minor difficulty, however, in that the current source appears as dI/dt in the equation. In general, when I is given as a function of time, dI/dt may or may not be defined. Therefore the dI/dt term should be eliminated before the equation can be considered a state equation. This calls for a new definition of the state variables. In other words, this problem is an example showing that sometimes the state variables cannot be defined merely as the currents in the inductors and the voltages across the capacitors. In this case, it is necessary to define the state variables x_1, x_2, x_3 as

$$x_1 = v_1$$
$$x_2 = v_2$$
$$x_3 = i_1 - \frac{L_2}{L_1 + L_2} I$$

In matrix form, these definitions are written

$$\begin{bmatrix} v_1 \\ v_2 \\ i_1 \end{bmatrix} = \begin{bmatrix} 1 & 0 & 0 \\ 0 & 1 & 0 \\ 0 & 0 & 1 \end{bmatrix} \begin{bmatrix} x_1 \\ x_2 \\ x_3 \end{bmatrix} + \begin{bmatrix} 0 \\ 0 \\ \dfrac{L_2}{L_1 + L_2} \end{bmatrix} I \tag{6-66}$$

Substituting (6-66) in (6-65) and simplifying, we have the final result,

$$\begin{bmatrix} \dfrac{dx_1}{dt} \\ \dfrac{dx_2}{dt} \\ \dfrac{dx_3}{dt} \end{bmatrix} = \begin{bmatrix} \dfrac{-1}{C_1 R_2} & \dfrac{1}{C_1 R_2} & -\dfrac{1}{C_1} \\ \dfrac{1}{C_2 R_2} & -\dfrac{1}{C_2 R_2} & \dfrac{1}{C_2} \\ \dfrac{1}{L_1 + L_2} & -\dfrac{1}{L_1 + L_2} & \dfrac{-R_1}{L_1 + L_2} \end{bmatrix} \begin{bmatrix} x_1 \\ x_2 \\ x_3 \end{bmatrix}$$

$$+ \begin{bmatrix} \dfrac{L_1}{C_1(L_1 + L_2)} \\ \dfrac{L_2}{C_2(L_1 + L_2)} \\ \dfrac{-R_1 L_2}{(L_1 + L_2)^2} \end{bmatrix} I \tag{6-67}$$

Example 6-8 In this example we demonstrate that the state equations of a network with magnetic coupling can be written using the network-graph method. Consider the network with a transformer as shown in Fig. 6-12a. Assuming that the currents in L_1 and L_2 are as shown in the figure, an equivalent circuit including the mutual inductance effect is shown in Fig. 6-12b. Since M is an inductive branch, it becomes an excess in this case. In Fig. 6-12c, the network graph is drawn, showing the modified proper tree, with M considered as a tree branch. Then the problem is reduced to one similar to that of Example 6-7. The procedure

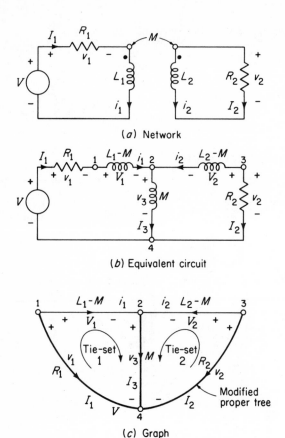

(a) Network

(b) Equivalent circuit

(c) Graph

Fig. 6-12   *A network with a transformer.*

of arriving at the state equations is carried out as follows:

$$
\begin{bmatrix} V_1 \\ V_2 \end{bmatrix} = \begin{bmatrix} (L_1 - M)\dfrac{di_1}{dt} \\ (L_2 - M)\dfrac{di_2}{dt} \end{bmatrix} = \begin{bmatrix} 0 & 0 \\ 0 & 0 \end{bmatrix} \begin{bmatrix} i_1 \\ i_2 \end{bmatrix}
$$

$$
+ \begin{bmatrix} 1 & 0 & -1 \\ 0 & 1 & -1 \end{bmatrix} \begin{bmatrix} v_1 \\ v_2 \\ v_3 \end{bmatrix} + \begin{bmatrix} 1 \\ 0 \end{bmatrix} V \quad (6\text{-}68)
$$

$$
\begin{bmatrix} I_1 \\ I_2 \\ I_3 \end{bmatrix} = \begin{bmatrix} -1 & 0 \\ 0 & -1 \\ 1 & 1 \end{bmatrix} \begin{bmatrix} i_1 \\ i_2 \end{bmatrix} + \begin{bmatrix} 0 & 0 \\ 0 & 0 \\ 0 & 0 \end{bmatrix} \begin{bmatrix} v_1 \\ v_2 \\ v_3 \end{bmatrix} \quad (6\text{-}69)
$$

$$
\begin{bmatrix} v_1 \\ v_2 \\ v_3 \end{bmatrix} = \begin{bmatrix} R_1 & 0 & 0 \\ 0 & R_2 & 0 \\ 0 & 0 & M\dfrac{d}{dt} \end{bmatrix} \begin{bmatrix} I_1 \\ I_2 \\ I_3 \end{bmatrix} = \begin{bmatrix} -R_1 & 0 \\ 0 & -R_2 \\ M\dfrac{d}{dt} & M\dfrac{d}{dt} \end{bmatrix} \begin{bmatrix} i_1 \\ i_2 \end{bmatrix} \qquad (6\text{-}70)
$$

Thus

$$
\begin{bmatrix} V_1 \\ V_2 \end{bmatrix} = \begin{bmatrix} (L_1 - M)\dfrac{di_1}{dt} \\ (L_2 - M)\dfrac{di_2}{dt} \end{bmatrix} = \begin{bmatrix} -R_1 - M\dfrac{d}{dt} & -M\dfrac{d}{dt} \\ -M\dfrac{d}{dt} & -R_2 - M\dfrac{d}{dt} \end{bmatrix} \begin{bmatrix} i_1 \\ i_2 \end{bmatrix}
$$

$$
+ \begin{bmatrix} 1 \\ 0 \end{bmatrix} V \qquad (6\text{-}71)
$$

which is simplified to

$$
\begin{bmatrix} \dfrac{di_1}{dt} \\ \dfrac{di_2}{dt} \end{bmatrix} = \frac{1}{L_1 L_2 - M^2} \begin{bmatrix} -R_1 L_2 & R_2 M \\ M R_1 & -R_2 L_1 \end{bmatrix} \begin{bmatrix} i_1 \\ i_2 \end{bmatrix}
$$

$$
+ \frac{1}{L_1 L_2 - M^2} \begin{bmatrix} L_2 \\ -M \end{bmatrix} V \qquad (6\text{-}72)
$$

When expressed in terms of the inverse inductances, (6-72) is written

$$
\begin{bmatrix} \dfrac{di_1}{dt} \\ \dfrac{di_2}{dt} \end{bmatrix} = \begin{bmatrix} -\Gamma_1 R_1 & R_2 \Gamma_M \\ R_1 \Gamma_M & -\Gamma_2 R_2 \end{bmatrix} \begin{bmatrix} i_1 \\ i_2 \end{bmatrix} + \begin{bmatrix} \Gamma_1 \\ -\Gamma_M \end{bmatrix} V \qquad (6\text{-}73)
$$

which agrees with the results obtained earlier, in (6-25) and (6-26).

Example 6-9   In this problem we direct our attention toward networks with dependent sources, such as those encountered in equivalent circuits of networks with transistors or vacuum tubes. This example shows that, in the case of a network with dependent sources, the application of the network-graph method is quite straightforward.

The voltage source μv_2 shown in the network of Fig. 6-13a is considered to be dependent on the voltage drop across the resistor R_1. The network graph and its proper tree are shown in Fig. 6-13b.

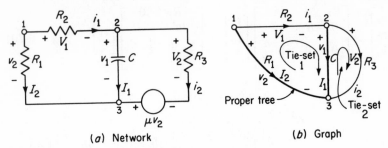

(a) Network   (b) Graph

Fig. 6-13 *A network with a dependent source.*

The equations corresponding to (6-39), (6-40), (6-41), and (6-42) are written

$$I_1 = C \frac{dv_1}{dt} = [0][v_1] + [0 \quad 1 \quad -1] \begin{bmatrix} v_2 \\ i_1 \\ i_2 \end{bmatrix} \tag{6-74}$$

$$\begin{bmatrix} I_2 \\ V_1 \\ V_2 \end{bmatrix} = \begin{bmatrix} 0 \\ -1 \\ 1 \end{bmatrix} [v_1] + \begin{bmatrix} 0 & -1 & 0 \\ 1 & 0 & 0 \\ \mu & 0 & 0 \end{bmatrix} \begin{bmatrix} v_2 \\ i_1 \\ i_2 \end{bmatrix} \tag{6-75}$$

$$\begin{bmatrix} v_2 \\ i_1 \\ i_2 \end{bmatrix} = \begin{bmatrix} R_1 & 0 & 0 \\ 0 & \dfrac{1}{R_2} & 0 \\ 0 & 0 & \dfrac{1}{R_3} \end{bmatrix} \begin{bmatrix} I_2 \\ V_1 \\ V_2 \end{bmatrix} = \begin{bmatrix} 0 \\ -\dfrac{1}{R_2} \\ \dfrac{1}{R_3} \end{bmatrix} [v_1]$$

$$+ \begin{bmatrix} 0 & -R_1 & 0 \\ \dfrac{1}{R_2} & 0 & 0 \\ \dfrac{\mu}{R_3} & 0 & 0 \end{bmatrix} \begin{bmatrix} v_2 \\ i_1 \\ i_2 \end{bmatrix} \tag{6-76}$$

Solving for the v_2, i_1, and i_2 vector matrix from (6-76), we have

$$\begin{bmatrix} v_2 \\ i_1 \\ i_2 \end{bmatrix} = \frac{R_2}{R_1 + R_2} \begin{bmatrix} 1 & -R_1 & 0 \\ \dfrac{1}{R_2} & 1 & 0 \\ \dfrac{\mu}{R_3} & -\dfrac{\mu R_1}{R_3} & \dfrac{R_1 + R_2}{R_2} \end{bmatrix} \begin{bmatrix} 0 \\ -\dfrac{1}{R_2} \\ \dfrac{1}{R_3} \end{bmatrix} v_1$$

$$= \frac{R_2}{R_1 + R_2} \begin{bmatrix} \dfrac{R_1}{R_2} \\ \dfrac{-1}{R_2} \\ \dfrac{\mu R_1}{R_2 R_3} + \dfrac{R_1 + R_2}{R_2 R_3} \end{bmatrix} v_1 \tag{6-77}$$

Thus

$$C \frac{dv_1}{dt} = \frac{R_2}{R_1 + R_2} \left[-\frac{1}{R_2} - \frac{\mu R_1}{R_2 R_3} - \frac{R_1 + R_2}{R_2 R_3} \right] v_1$$

$$= - \left[\frac{R_1 + R_2 + R_3 + \mu R_1}{R_3 (R_1 + R_2)} \right] v_1 \tag{6-78}$$

6-3 WRITING THE STATE EQUATIONS BY MEANS OF EQUIVALENT SOURCES

Another method of writing state equations of electric networks which is worth mentioning is the use of equivalent generators in place of the capacitors and inductors in the networks. Referring to the state equations (6-1) and (6-2), we can regard these as a set of cause-and-effect relationships between the state variables and the input signals. In other words, we may regard the state variables i_k and v_k and the sources v_k as inputs (causes) and $L_i \, di_i/dt$ and $C_j \, dv_j/dt$ as outputs (effects). Then (6-1) simply describes the dependence of $L_i \, di_i/dt$ upon the combined effects of i_k, v_k, and r_k. A similar statement can be made for $C_j \, dv_j/dt$ in (6-2). Using this idea, we may replace all the capacitors in a circuit by equivalent voltage generators with voltage strengths v_k, and all inductances by equivalent current generators whose current magnitudes are i_k. The circuit then becomes an all-resistor circuit, and the currents in the capacitor, $C_j \, dv_j/dt$, and the voltage across the inductor, $L_i \, di_i/dt$, can be found, using the principle of superposition. A word of caution is in order here: The method will be successful only for networks without any excess elements.

Example 6-10 As an illustration of the method described above, let us refer to the circuit shown in Fig. 6-14. Figure 6-15a shows the circuit after the inductor and the capacitor are replaced by their corresponding current and voltage sources. The direction of i_L and the polarity of v_c are arbitrarily assumed in the usual manner. The problem

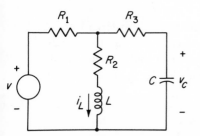

Fig. 6-14   An electric network for Example 6-10.

of writing the state equations for the circuit is now reduced to solving for the current $C \, dv_c/dt$ and the voltage $L \, di_L/dt$ from this circuit, consisting of only resistors and current and voltage sources.

A simple method of analyzing the circuit of Fig. 6-15a is to use the principle of superposition. That is, we consider only one of the sources

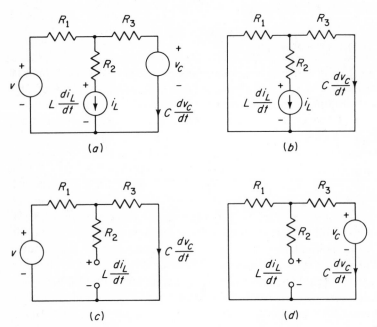

Fig. 6-15   Circuit diagrams used to write the state equations by means of superposition.

at a time, while setting the others equal to zero. Setting the sources to zero implies that a voltage source is replaced by a short circuit, and a current source by an open-circuit. Ordinarily, the method of super-position can be carried out by simple inspection of the circuit of Fig. 6-15a. However, as an illustration, we present the details of the steps in the following discussion.

In the circuit of Fig. 6-15a, let us first short-circuit the voltage source v and the capacitor voltage source v_c; we obtain the circuit shown in Fig. 6-15b. Using the concepts of voltage and current dividers, the voltage $L \, di_L/dt$ due to i_L acting alone is clearly equal to

$$\frac{-(R_1R_2 + R_2R_3 + R_3R_1)}{R_1 + R_3} i_L$$

and the current $C\, dv_c/dt$ is

$$\frac{-R_1}{R_1 + R_3}\, i_L$$

We notice that these quantities correspond to the elements in the second column of the matrix on the right-hand side of (6-53). Next, we restore the voltage source v and open the current source i_L, keeping v_c short-circuited (Fig. 6-15c). The current $C\, dv_c/dt$ due to v is $v/(R_1 + R_3)$, and the voltage $L\, di_L/dt$ is equal to $R_3 v/(R_1 + R_3)$. It is apparent that these quantities agree with the column matrix associated with v in (6-53). In the final step we restore v_c while short-circuiting v and keeping i_L open (Fig. 6-15d), resulting in

$$L\frac{di_L}{dt} = \frac{R_1}{R_1 + R_3}\, v_c \tag{6-79}$$

$$C\frac{dv_c}{dt} = \frac{-1}{R_1 + R_3}\, v_c \tag{6-80}$$

When the effects of all the three equivalent sources are added together, the same result as in (6-53) is obtained.

Example 6-11   As our second example illustrating the method of superposition, let us consider the circuit shown in Fig. 6-16. Since the

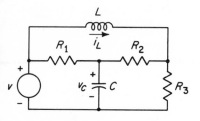

Fig. 6-16   Electric circuit for Example 6-11.

network has two reactive elements in L and C, we assign i_L and v_c as the state variables. We proceed in the same manner as described in Example 6-10 by replacing L by a current source i_L, and C by a voltage source v_c. An all-resistor network results in Fig. 6-17a. Short-circuiting the voltage source v and v_c first, we have the circuit shown in Fig. 6-17b. The voltage $L\, di_L/dt$ due to the source i_L alone is

$$L\frac{di_L}{dt} = -\frac{R_2 R_3}{R_2 + R_3}\, i_L \tag{6-81}$$

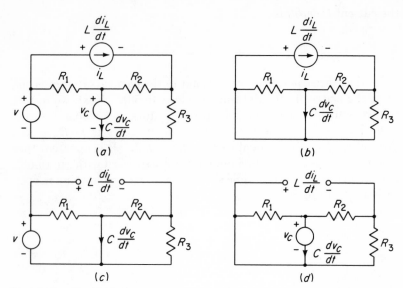

Fig. 6-17   Method of superposition applied to the circuit of Fig. 6-16.

The current $C\,dv_c/dt$ due to i_L is

$$C\frac{dv_c}{dt} = \frac{R_3}{R_2 + R_3}\,i_L \tag{6-82}$$

Next, we consider only the voltage source v, but shorting the voltage source v_c and opening the current source i_L. We have, from Fig. 6-17c,

$$L\frac{di_L}{dt} = v \tag{6-83}$$

and

$$C\frac{dv_c}{dt} = \frac{v}{R_1} \tag{6-84}$$

Finally, we consider only the voltage source v_c as shown in Fig. 6-17d:

$$L\frac{di_L}{dt} = -\frac{R_3}{R_2 + R_3}\,v_c \tag{6-85}$$

$$C\frac{dv_c}{dt} = -\frac{R_1 + R_2 + R_3}{R_1(R_2 + R_3)}\,v_c \tag{6-86}$$

Adding up all the current and voltage components found above, the state equations of the circuit are

$$\frac{di_L}{dt} = -\frac{R_2 R_3}{(R_2 + R_3)L} i_L - \frac{R_3}{(R_2 + R_3)L} v_c + \frac{1}{L} v \qquad (6\text{-}87)$$

$$\frac{dv_c}{dt} = \frac{R_3}{(R_2 + R_3)C} i_L - \frac{R_1 + R_2 + R_3}{R_1(R_2 + R_3)C} v_c + \frac{1}{R_1 C} v \qquad (6\text{-}88)$$

PROBLEMS

6-1 Write the state equations in normal form for the networks in Fig. P6-1 by inspection.

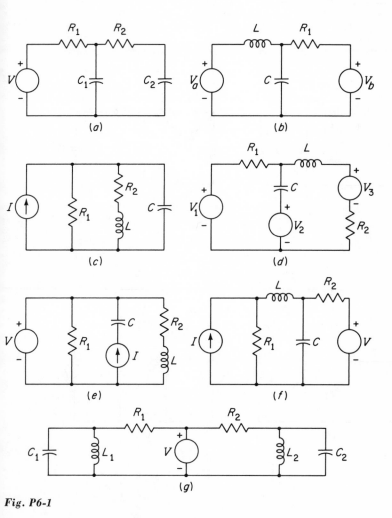

Fig. P6-1

6-2   Draw proper trees or modified proper trees for the networks shown in Fig. P6-2.

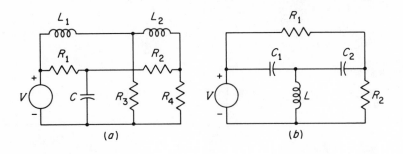

(a)

(b)

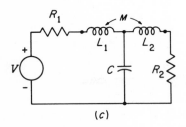
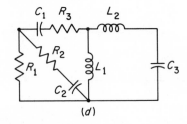

(c)

(d)

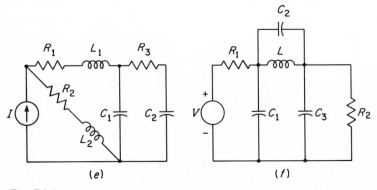

(e)

(f)

Fig. P6-2

6-3   Write the state equations in normal form for the networks shown in Fig. P6-3, using the network graphs.

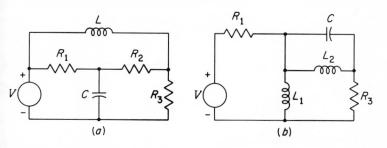

(a)   (b)

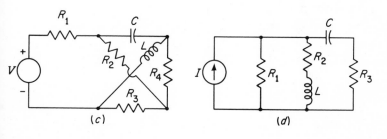

(c)   (d)

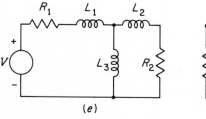

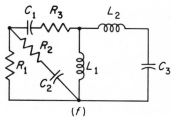

(e)   (f)

Fig. P6-3

6-4 Write the state equations in normal form for the networks shown in Fig. P6-4. Use any method.

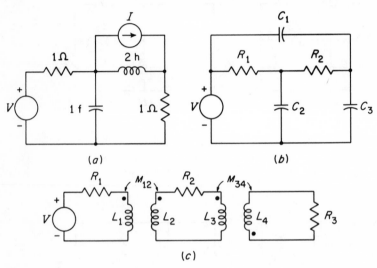

Fig. P6-4

6-5 Write the state equations in normal form for the network shown in Fig. P6-5.

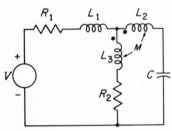

Fig. P6-5

6-6 Write the state equations in normal form for the network shown in Fig. P6-6.

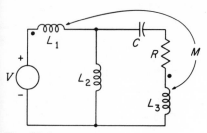

Fig. P6-6

6-7 Write the state equations for the networks shown in Fig. P6-7, using the method of equivalent sources of Sec. 6.3.

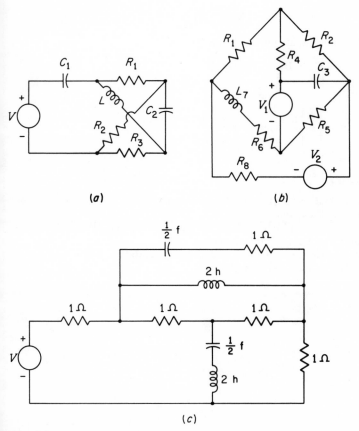

(a)

(b)

(c)

Fig. P6-7

6-8　(*a*)　Explain why, in the network of Fig. P6-8, it is improper to assign v_c, i_3, and i_4 as state variables.　Define a set of state variables **x** and write a set of independent state equations in normal form.

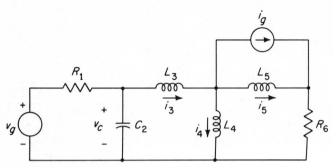

Fig. P6-8

(*b*)　Write the output equation in the form of

$$\mathbf{y} = \mathbf{Cx} + \mathbf{Dr}$$

where

$$\mathbf{y} = \begin{bmatrix} v_c \\ i_3 \\ i_4 \end{bmatrix} \quad \text{and} \quad \mathbf{r} = \begin{bmatrix} v_g \\ i_g \end{bmatrix}$$

BIBLIOGRAPHY

1　Zadeh, L. A., and C. A. Desoer: "Linear System Theory," McGraw-Hill Book Company, New York, 1963.
2　Bashkow, T.: The A Matrix: A New Network Description, *IRE Trans. Circuit Theory*, vol. CT-4, pp. 117–119, September, 1957.
3　Bryant, P. R.: The Explicit Form of Bashkow's A Matrix, *IRE Trans. Circuit Theory*, vol. CT-9, no. 3, pp. 303–306, 1962.

SEVEN

SIGNAL FLOW GRAPHS

7-1 INTRODUCTION

One of the most important methods used in the modern analysis of linear networks and systems is the signal-flow-graph technique first introduced by Mason[1] in 1953. In essence, the signal-flow-graph technique is a graphical method of solving linear algebraic equations; it can be regarded as a counterpart of the matrix representation and solution.   For instance, the following set of linear simultaneous equations,

$$v_j = \sum_{k=1}^{N} z_{kj} i_k \qquad j = 1, 2, \ldots, N \tag{7-1}$$

can be represented by a matrix equation of the form

$$\mathbf{V} = \mathbf{ZI} \tag{7-2}$$

where $\mathbf{V} = [v_{ij}]_{N,1}$

   $\mathbf{Z} = [z_{ij}]_{N,N}$

   $\mathbf{I} = [i_{ij}]_{N,1}$

Usually, whether (7-1) is in the algebraic form or in its matrix form, it can be conveniently solved by means of a digital computer. It is difficult, however, to visualize from a matrix equation the relationships and interactions between signals and variables inside a system. Since a matrix is but an array of numbers arranged in some specific manner, it is often difficult to visualize the interactions among signals inside a system from its matrix representation. A signal flow graph, however, as the name implies, is used to portray the physical layout of a system. It is devised to describe the flow of signals from one point of a system to another, as well as to provide cause-and-effect relationships between signals. We have often heard the saying that a picture is better than a thousand words. In this case, in portraying a physical system, it is reasonable to state that sometimes a signal flow graph is better than a score of equations.

The applications of the signal-flow-graph concept are extremely broad. The technique can be applied to the analysis of numerous kinds of linear systems and networks with continuous or discrete signals. Extensions[2] have also been attempted to apply the flow-graph representations to nonlinear systems. In 1959, Coates[3] introduced a modified version of the signal flow graph, which he called the "flow graph." Although the formulation and the interpretation of the flow graph are basically different from those of Mason's signal flow graph, we can show that the two kinds of graphs are closely related to each other. In fact, the graphs can be converted to each other with relative ease.

The flow graph is essentially an alternative topological representation of a set of linear algebraic equations. It does not portray any "flow of signal" in a system in the way the signal flow graph does. This is perhaps an unfortunate disadvantage of the flow-graph technique. However, the flow graph does have the advantage of simplicity, and is often less involved than Mason's signal flow graph, especially for the analysis of complex systems.

7-2   WHAT IS A SIGNAL FLOW GRAPH?

In this section we discuss the construction and the properties of Mason's signal flow graph. In accordance with the terminology used in current literature, we refer to Mason's flow graph as the *signal flow graph* and to Coates' graph as the *flow graph*.

Definition of the signal flow graph

A signal flow graph of a linear system may be defined as a graph with junction points called *nodes*, and the nodes are connected by directional paths known as *branches*.†

Nodes   The nodes are used to represent the signals or variables of a system.   To each node is associated a node variable which denotes the strength of the signal.

Branches   A branch connecting two nodes is used to indicate the functional dependence of one variable (or signal) upon the other, thus forming the basic cause-and-effect relationship between the two signals. An arrow is assigned to each branch to denote the direction of the flow of signal in the branch.   The arrow is always oriented in such a direction that the signal flows from a source (cause) to a sink (effect).   A branch must also have a *branch gain*, or *transmittance*, to represent thè algebraic relation between the source variable and the sink variable.

As a simple illustration of the construction of a basic signal flow graph, let us consider the equation

$$y_2 = t_{12}y_1 \qquad\qquad\qquad (7\text{-}3)$$

where y_1 and y_2 are system variables, and t_{12} denotes the transmittance between the variables.   In general, y_1 and y_2 may be functions of an independent variable, say, time; t_{12} may be a constant.   In the complex domain, y_1, y_2, and t_{12} may also be functions of the Laplace-transform variable s, or in general, functions of any other independent variables so long as (7-3) represents a linear algebraic cause-and-effect relationship. We explore these possibilities as the signal-flow-graph concept is being developed.

The signal-flow-graph representation of (7-3) is now shown in Fig. 7-1. This is done by first drawing the nodes denoting y_1 and y_2, then the

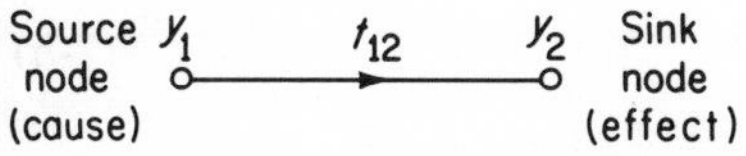

Source y_1 t_{12} y_2 Sink
node   node
(cause)   (effect)

Fig. 7-1 Signal-flow-graph representation of $y_2 = t_{12}y_1$.

branch with transmittance t_{12} from y_1 to y_2.   Notice that the arrow on the branch must be drawn from y_1 to y_2 since the equation is interpreted only as a dependence of y_2 upon y_1, but not the reverse.

† Although it seems that the definitions given here for *network*, *node*, and *branch* are similar to those for the linear graph in linear network theory, it should be pointed out that they have completely different meanings.

Another realistic way of looking at the basic signal flow graph of Fig. 7-1 is that it represents a unilateral amplifier. The amplifier has an input y_1 and output y_2, and the gain between the input and the output is t_{12}. The signal flow graph implies that, when a signal is applied at y_1, it is multiplied by the transmittance t_{12}, and the signal y_2 appearing at the output of the amplifier is equal to $t_{12}y_1$. Notice that this signal flow graph tells absolutely nothing about the dependence of y_1 upon y_2. In other words, although algebraically we can obtain from (7-3)

$$y_1 = \frac{1}{t_{12}} y_2 \tag{7-4}$$

this relationship is not defined by the signal flow graph of Fig. 7-1. From a physical point of view, if a signal is applied at the output of an electronic amplifier with unilateral transmission, no signal should be transmitted to the input terminals unless there is a feedback path.

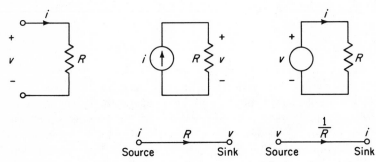

Fig. 7-2   *Signal flow graphs of voltage-current relations in a resistor.*

In the case of a bilateral element, such as the resistor shown in Fig. 7-2, the voltage-current relationship can be written either as

$$v = Ri \tag{7-5}$$

or

$$i = \frac{1}{R} v \tag{7-6}$$

However, the signal-flow-graph representation of (7-5) is necessarily different from that of (7-6). From the cause-and-effect viewpoint, (7-5) implies that a current source of strength i is applied to R, and the resultant

voltage measured across R is v.   On the other hand, (7-6) must be interpreted as the application of a voltage source of strength v across R, and
the resulting current is i.   So we see that the situations under which
these two equations are written are not entirely the same.   The signal
flow graphs of (7-5) and (7-6) are shown in Fig. 7-2.

Based on the development presented above, we are now ready to
discuss the signal-flow-graph representation of a linear system.   Let us
consider that a linear system is described by the following set of algebraic
equations:†

$$y_j = \sum_{k=1}^{N} t_{kj} y_k \qquad j = 1, 2, \ldots, N \qquad (7\text{-}7)$$

where t_{kj} is the transmittance denoting the contribution of the variable
y_k to the value of y_j.   If the variables y_j and y_k are portrayed by nodes,
and the transmission t_{kj} by directed branches, (7-7) implies that the
system equations may be portrayed by a signal flow graph.   *The construction of the signal flow graph is basically a matter of following the cause-
and-effect relationships through the system relating each variable to itself and
to the others, using the basic building block of Fig.* 7-1.   As an illustrative
example, let us consider the following set of algebraic equations:

$$y_2 = t_{12}y_1 + t_{22}y_2 + t_{32}y_3 + t_{42}y_4$$
$$y_3 = t_{23}y_2 + t_{33}y_3 + t_{43}y_4 \qquad\qquad (7\text{-}8)$$
$$y_4 = t_{34}y_3$$

The step-by-step construction of the signal flow graph for the system is
directed in Fig. 7-3.   The nodes y_1, y_2, y_3, and y_4 are located in order from
left to right.   It is customary to have the cause node placed to the left
of the effect node (except in the case of feedback) and proceed from left
to right.   The first equation of (7-8) states that y_2 is equal to the sum of
four signals, $t_{12}y_1$, $t_{22}y_2$, $t_{32}y_3$, and $t_{42}y_4$.   The signal flow graph portraying

† It should be noted that, in the present case, the system equations are written in the
form of

Effect at node j = Σ(transmission from k to j)(cause at k)

These equations are unlike the conventional loop and node equations for network
analysis whose form is basically

Excitation (cause) at k = Σ(transmission from k to j)(response at j)

This also means that loop and node equations for networks must first be converted
into the form of (7-7) before the signal flow graphs can be drawn for them.

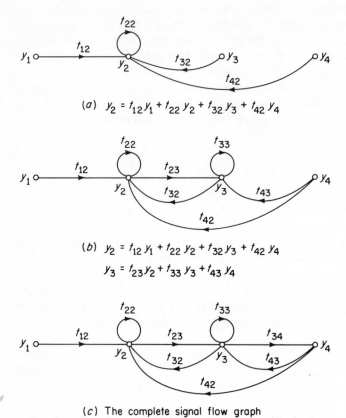

(a) $y_2 = t_{12} y_1 + t_{22} y_2 + t_{32} y_3 + t_{42} y_4$

(b) $y_2 = t_{12} y_1 + t_{22} y_2 + t_{32} y_3 + t_{42} y_4$

$y_3 = t_{23} y_2 + t_{33} y_3 + t_{43} y_4$

(c) The complete signal flow graph

Fig. 7-3   Step-by-step construction of the signal flow graph for (7-8).

this equation is shown in Fig. 7-3a.   The second equation states that y_3 depends upon $t_{23} y_2$, $t_{33} y_3$, and $t_{43} y_4$.   On the signal flow graph of Fig. 7-3a, we draw a branch of gain t_{23} from node y_2 to node y_3, a branch with gain t_{33} from t_3 to itself, and finally a branch with gain t_{43} from y_4 to y_3.   The signal flow graph of the first two equations of (7-8) is shown in Fig. 7-3b. In a similar manner, the third equation in (7-8) is represented, and the complete signal flow graph for the system is shown in Fig. 7-3c.

7-3   IMPORTANT PROPERTIES OF SIGNAL FLOW GRAPHS

Following the introductory remarks and the simple illustrations of signal flow graphs given in the last section, we can now summarize the basic properties of the signal flow graphs:

1. The nodes on the signal flow graphs represent the variables of a system.   Normally, the nodes are arranged from left to right following a succession of causes and effects throughout the system.

2. The directed branch from node y_k to y_j represents the dependence of the variable y_j upon y_k, but not the reverse.

3. A signal may travel along a branch only in the direction described by the arrow of the branch.

4. A signal y_k traveling along a branch between node y_k and node y_j is multiplied by the gain t_{kj} of the branch, so that a signal of strength $t_{kj}y_k$ is delivered at node y_j.

5. The value of the variable represented by any node is transmitted to all branches leaving the node.   Therefore we may regard a node as a

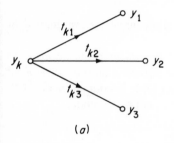

(a)

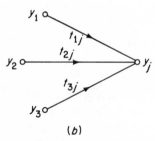

(b)

Fig. 7-4   (a) *Node as a transmitting point.* (b) *Node as a summing point.*

transmitting point.   The signal flow graph of Fig. 7-4a shows that the signal y_k is transmitted to all three branches that leave the node.   Thus

$$y_1 = t_{k1}y_k$$

$$y_2 = t_{k2}y_k$$

$$y_3 = t_{k3}y_k$$

6. The value of the variable represented by a node is equal to the sum of all the signals entering the node.   Thus we may regard a node also

as a *summing point*. In Fig. 7-4b we see that the signal at y_j is equal to the sum of all signals transmitted through the three incoming branches. Therefore

$$y_j = t_{1j}y_1 + t_{2j}y_2 + t_{3j}y_3$$

7. The total transmittance of several branches connected in cascade is equal to the product of all the branch transmittances. In Fig. 7-5 we can write

$$y_5 = t_{45}y_4 = t_{45}t_{34}y_3 = t_{45}t_{34}t_{23}y_2$$

$$= t_{45}t_{34}t_{23}t_{12}y_1$$

For the purpose of identification, the following terms are defined in connection with the signal flow graph:

Input node (source)   *A node which has only outgoing branches is called an input node.* An input node may be regarded as the cause of all the eventual effects. An example of an input node is node y_1 in Fig. 7-3. Note that y_1 does not have any branches that enter the node.

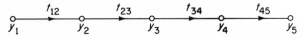

Fig. 7-5 Signal flow graph with branches connected in cascade.

Output node (sink)   *A node which has only incoming branches is called an output node.* Following this definition of the output node, it would seem that none of the four nodes in the signal flow graph of Fig. 7-3c satisfies the requirement of an output node. However, it is easy to show that any noninput node y_j can be made an output node simply by introducing a branch with unity gain directed from y_j to another node also marked y_j. Thus a superficial equation is written in the form of $y_j = y_j$ which does not affect the system's behavior in any way. With the added superficial branches and nodes, y_2, y_3, and y_4 in the signal flow graph of Fig. 7-3c now satisfy the requirement of output nodes (Fig. 7-6). However, we should keep in mind that *an input node cannot be formed using this method.* As long as a node has one or more incoming branches, it is not, and cannot be, made an input node. For instance, if we reverse the arrow of the branch with unity gain connected between y_4 and y_4, in an attempt to convert y_4 into an input node, the signal at y_4 becomes

$$y_4 = t_{34}y_3 + y_4$$

which apparently is incorrect since it contradicts the original equation given in (7-8).   Therefore there is no way that we can convert y_2, y_3, or y_4 into input nodes except by rewriting the original system equations in a different form.

   Path   Any connected, unidirectional succession of branches traversed in the indicated branch directions is called a path.   For example, in Fig. 7-6,

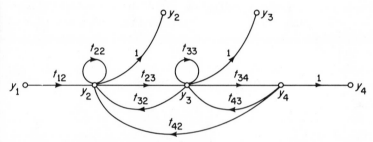

Fig. 7-6   Modification of the signal flow graph in Fig. 7-3c so that y_2, y_3, and y_4 become output nodes.

the branches connected from y_1 to y_2 to y_3 to y_4 form a path; $y_1 \rightarrow y_2 \rightarrow y_3 \rightarrow y_4$ through t_{42} and back to y_2 is also a path.   The definition of a path is entirely general.   A path can include a node virtually an unlimited number of times.

   Forward path   A path which starts from an input node and ends at an output node, along which no node is encountered more than once, is called a forward path.   An example of the forward path is $y_1 \rightarrow y_2 \rightarrow y_3 \rightarrow y_4$ in Fig. 7-6.   In fact, this is the only forward path of this signal flow graph, between y_1 and y_4.

   Loop   A path which originates at and terminates on the same node and along which no node is encountered more than once is called a loop.   The two apparent loops in the signal flow graph of Fig. 7-6 are $y_2 \rightarrow y_2$ and $y_3 \rightarrow y_3$; the other loops in the graph are $y_2 \rightarrow y_3 \rightarrow y_2$, $y_3 \rightarrow y_4 \rightarrow y_3$, and $y_2 \rightarrow y_3 \rightarrow y_4 \rightarrow y_2$.   However, the path $y_2 \rightarrow y_3 \rightarrow y_4 \rightarrow y_3 \rightarrow y_2$ through $t_{23}t_{34}t_{43}t_{32}$ is not a loop, since y_3 is encountered twice in the process.   If a loop involves only one node, it is called a *self-loop*.   (Example: $y_2 \rightarrow y_2$ and $y_3 \rightarrow y_3$ in Fig. 7-6.)

   Path gain   The product of the branch gains encountered in traversing a path of any kind is called the path gain.   The path gain associated with a forward path is the *forward-path gain*, and that associated with a loop is the loop gain.   For instance, the forward-path gain between y_1 and y_4 for the signal flow graph in Fig. 7-6 is $t_{12}t_{23}t_{34}$.   The loop gain of the loop $y_2 \rightarrow y_3 \rightarrow y_4 \rightarrow y_2$ is $t_{23}t_{34}t_{42}$.

7-4   CONSTRUCTION OF SIGNAL FLOW GRAPHS— SOME ILLUSTRATIVE EXAMPLES

The construction of signal flow graphs of linear networks and systems is best illustrated by means of several examples.

Example 7-1   Draw a signal flow graph for the ladder network shown in Fig. 7-7.   Since the signal flow graph of a network is constructed

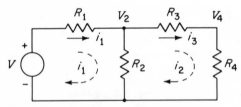

Fig. 7-7   A ladder network.

from the cause-and-effect concept, when we write the network equations, we should use neither the loop nor the node method.   (Not that these methods will not give correct signal flow graphs.)   We may reason that the immediate effect due to the applied voltage V is the current that flows through R_1; therefore we assign the branch current i_1 in R_1.   The current i_1 will in turn act as a cause, since a portion of this i_1 will flow through R_2, producing a voltage drop.   Thus we assign the branch voltage V_2 as another dependent variable of the network.   Repeating the process, we arrive at i_3 and V_4 as indicated in Fig. 7-7.   Now applying the successive cause-and-effect relationship, we have the following set of network equations:

$$i_1 = \frac{1}{R_1}(V - V_2)$$

$$V_2 = R_2(i_1 - i_3)$$

$$i_3 = \frac{1}{R_3}(V_2 - V_4)$$

$$V_4 = R_4 i_3$$

$$(7\text{-}9)$$

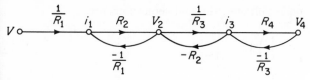

Fig. 7-8   *A signal flow graph of the ladder network in Fig. 7-7.*

The signal flow graph portraying these equations is now shown in Fig. 7-8. We see that writing the network equations in the forms of branch currents and node voltages allows us to arrive at a signal flow graph in a straight-forward manner.   Furthermore, the signal flow graph gives a clear indication of the cause-and-effect relationship among the signals of the network.

If we designate the two loops as shown in Fig. 7-7 and write the loop equations of the network, we have

$$V = (R_1 + R_2)i_1 - R_2i_2 \qquad\qquad (7\text{-}10)$$

$$0 = -R_2i_1 + (R_2 + R_3 + R_4)i_2 \qquad\qquad (7\text{-}11)$$

Since these equations are not in the proper order of cause and effect, we must rearrange them so that V appears only on the right-hand side of the equal sign.   Solving for i_1 in (7-10) and i_2 in (7-11), we get

$$i_1 = \frac{V}{R_1 + R_2} + \frac{R_2}{R_1 + R_2}\, i_2$$

$$i_2 = \frac{R_2}{R_2 + R_3 + R_4}\, i_1$$

The signal flow graph for these two equations is drawn in Fig. 7-9.

Still another signal flow graph for the ladder network in Fig. 7-7 may be obtained from the node equations.   Using V_2 and V_4 in Fig. 7-7

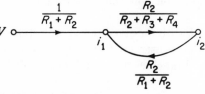

Fig. 7-9   *A signal flow graph of the ladder network in Fig. 7-7.*

as the independent node voltages, the node equations are

$$\frac{V}{R_1} = \left(\frac{1}{R_1} + \frac{1}{R_2} + \frac{1}{R_3}\right) V_2 - \frac{1}{R_3} V_4 \tag{7-12}$$

$$0 = -\frac{1}{R_3} V_2 + \left(\frac{1}{R_3} + \frac{1}{R_4}\right) V_4 \tag{7-13}$$

Again, these node equations are not in the natural form for signal flow graphs; so we rearrange them into the following cause-and-effect relationships:

$$V_2 = \frac{R_2 R_3}{R_1 R_3 + R_2 R_3 + R_1 R_2} V + \frac{R_1 R_2}{R_1 R_3 + R_2 R_3 + R_1 R_2} V_4$$

$$V_4 = \frac{R_4}{R_3 + R_4} V_2$$

The signal flow graph portraying these equations is shown in Fig. 7-10.

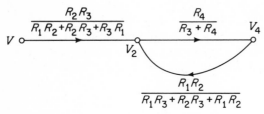

Fig. 7-10 *A signal flow graph of the ladder network in Fig. 7-7.*

From this simple illustrative example we can draw the following conclusions regarding the construction of the signal flow graphs of a network:

1 The signal flow graph of a given network (or system) is not unique. We can virtually draw many different signal flow graphs for the same network, all equally valid, depending on how the network equations are written.
2 The loop and node equations are awkward for signal-flow-graph studies.
3 A signal flow graph may usually be constructed directly from a set of network equations which are branch-current and node-voltage relationships.
4 A ladder network is one of the most convenient forms for study of signal flow graphs.

Example 7-2   Consider the feedback amplifier circuit shown in
Fig. 7-11.   The linear incremental equivalent circuit† of the amplifier is

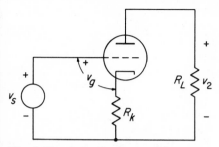

**Fig. 7-11   A feedback amplifier
circuit.**

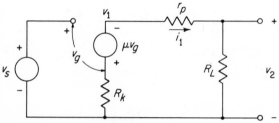

**Fig. 7-12   Linear incremental equivalent circuit
for the feedback amplifier in Fig. 7-11.**

shown in Fig. 7-12.   We arbitrarily assign the dependent variables of the
circuit as v_1, v_g, v_2, and i_1.   Using these variables, the cause-and-effect
equations are obtained as follows:

$$v_g = v_s + R_k i_1$$
$$v_1 = -\mu v_g - R_k i_1$$
$$i_1 = \frac{1}{r_p}(v_1 - v_2)$$
$$v_2 = R_L i_1$$

The signal flow graph for these equations is depicted in Fig. 7-13.

† From the circuit-analysis viewpoint, we need only to identify that the equivalent
circuit of the amplifier in Fig. 7-11 has an independent voltage source v_s and a dependent voltage source μv_g.

Referring to the equivalent circuit in Fig. 7-12, we notice that the number of independent network equations may be reduced to three if we eliminate the voltage v_1. The network equations are

$$v_g = v_s + R_k i_1$$

$$i_1 = -\frac{\mu}{r_p} v_g - \frac{R_k}{r_p} i_1 - \frac{v_2}{r_p}$$

$$v_2 = R_L i_1$$

whose signal flow graph is now drawn as shown in Fig. 7-14.

The relationships between the signals in the feedback amplifier are clearly portrayed by the two signal flow graphs of Figs. 7-13 and 7-14.

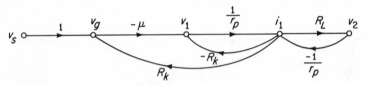

Fig. 7-13   *A signal flow graph for the amplifier circuit in Fig. 7-11.*

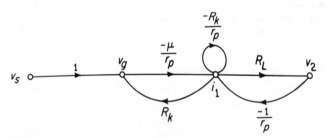

Fig. 7-14   *A signal flow graph for the amplifier circuit in Fig. 7-11.*

The feedback signal, which is due to i_1 flowing through R_k, is illustrated by the feedback path directed from i_1 to v_g. The minus sign in front of μ in the forward-path gain denotes the 180° phase shift which normally exists between the input and the output voltages of a single-stage electronic amplifier. However, the feedback path directed from v_2 to i_1, with a path gain of $-1/r_p$, represents a reaction which is ordinarily not recognized as "feedback." It simply denotes the dependence of the signal i_1 upon v_2. In other words, if the loading condition of the amplifier fluctuates to the extent that v_2 changes, i_1 will also vary in proportion to $(-1/r_p)v_2$.

As alternatives, the interested student may write down the loop and node equations for the network and construct the corresponding signal flow graph for each case.

Thus far, the networks encountered in the last two illustrative examples have all been of the instantaneous (all-resistor) type. When a network contains reactive elements as well as resistors, the natural question is: How does the signal flow graph entail the derivative and integral operations in the integral-differential equations which will now be needed to describe the dynamic network? Intuitively, since the signal flow graph is originally defined to represent graphically linear algebraic equations, we expect that, without some modifications, it will have no mathematical meaning for integral-differential equations. In other words, the properties and the algebra defined for signal flow graphs are merely adequate to solve linear algebraic equations. Without special mathematical tools for solving differential equations, such as the Laplace transformation, or computing devices such as analog or digital computers, signal flow graphs alone cannot bring solutions to integral-differential equations. Nevertheless, we shall show later that signal flow graphs can be used to represent computer diagrams of dynamic systems or networks. The Laplace transformation enables a set of linear integral-differential equations in the time domain to be "transformed" into a set of linear algebraic equations in the Laplace domain. This implies that signal flow graphs can be used to solve these equations once they have been transformed into algebraic form in the Laplace domain.

It is also possible to analyze a dynamic network by a signal flow graph when only the sinusoidal steady-state performance of the network is of interest. Under the assumed condition, inductances and capacitances may be denoted by reactance functions $j\omega L$ and $1/j\omega C$, respectively. The network is then described by algebraic equations of $I(j\omega)$ and $V(j\omega)$. Let us use the following example to illustrate this case.

Example 7-3   Consider the dynamic network shown in Fig. 7-15a. The current in the dependent source is a function of i_1. Assuming that the network is in the sinusoidal steady-state condition, the impedance-circuit diagram is drawn in Fig. 7-15b, with the dependent variables assigned as $I_1(j\omega)$, $I_2(j\omega)$, $V_1(j\omega)$, and $V_2(j\omega)$. The following cause-and-

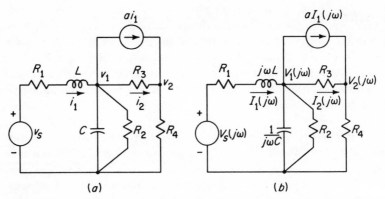

Fig. 7-15 (a) *A dynamic network.* (b) *Impedance circuit diagram under steady-state condition.*

effect network equations are written by inspection from the circuit diagram:

$$I_1 = \frac{1}{R_1 + j\omega L} (V_s - V_1)$$

$$V_1 = (I_1 - aI_1 - I_2) \frac{R_2}{1 + j\omega R_2 C}$$

$$I_2 = \frac{1}{R_3} (V_1 - V_2)$$

$$V_2 = R_4(I_2 + aI_1)$$

where it is understood that all the variables are functions of $j\omega$. The signal flow graph for these equations is drawn as shown in Fig. 7-16.

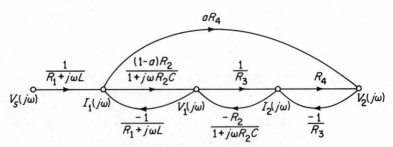

Fig. 7-16 *A signal flow graph for the network in Fig. 7-15.*

7-5 A GENERAL GAIN FORMULA FOR SIGNAL FLOW GRAPHS

The last step in the signal-flow graph analysis of physical systems is usually the determination of the relationships between the input and the output variables of the signal flow graph.   For instance, one of the main purposes of constructing a signal flow graph for the feedback amplifier in Fig. 7-11 may be to determine the voltage gain v_2/v_s.   Just like the branch gain, which is defined as a transmittance between two nodes on a signal flow graph, the overall gain or transmission between an *input node* and an *output node* is regarded as the gain of the signal flow graph between the two nodes.

During the period immediately following the publication of Mason's first paper[1] in 1953, the evaluation of the gain of a complex signal flow graph relied essentially on the reduction of the original graph to a simple configuration whose gain was already known.   Although rules of reduction are available for simplifying signal flow graphs, in general, there are not clear-cut and precise step-by-step instructions showing how a reduction problem should be carried out.   It is possible that even an experienced analyst may find himself tangled in a confusion of tedious algebraic and graphical manipulations.   At the time, this difficulty was certainly an important disadvantage of the signal-flow-graph technique.   Then, in 1956, Mason developed a *general gain formula*[4] (often called Mason's formula) which permits one to write down the input-output relationship of a signal flow graph simply by inspection.

Mason's gain formula is given as

$$G = \sum_n \frac{G_n \Delta_n}{\Delta} = \frac{\text{output-node variable}}{\text{input-node variable}} \tag{7-14}$$

where

G_n = gain of nth forward path

$$\Delta = 1 - \sum_m P_{m1} + \sum_m P_{m2} - \sum_m P_{m3} + \cdots \tag{7-15}$$

P_{mj} = product of gain of mth possible combination of j nontouching loops†

The expression of Δ can also be written

$\Delta = 1 -$ (sum of all individual loop gains) $+$ (sum of gain products of all possible combinations of two nontouching loops) $-$ (sum

---

† Two loops, or two parts, of a signal flow graph are said to be nontouching if they do not share any common nodes.

of gain products of all possible combinations of three nontouching loops) + · · ·

Δ_n = value of Δ for that part of signal flow graph not touching nth forward path

At this point we must emphasize that *the gain formula can be applied only to an input node and an output node.* For instance, the gain formula cannot be used to find the gain between I_2 and V_2, in Fig. 7-16 because I_2 is not an input node.

At first glance it may seem that the gain formula given by (7-14) is difficult to use since it involves many complicated terms. However, we shall see that, if the meaning of each of the terms in (7-14) and (7-15) is fully understood, the actual application of the formula is quite straightforward. Let us use the following examples to illustrate the applications of Mason's formula.

Example 7-4 Evaluate the voltage gain v_2/v_s for the feedback amplifier circuit shown in Fig. 7-11 by means of Mason's gain formula. The signal flow graphs of the network are given in Figs. 7-13 and 7-14. These are redrawn in Figs. 7-17a and 7-18a, respectively. Notice that in each of these graphs we have added an outgoing branch with unity gain to v_2 so that v_2 will now satisfy as an output node.

Let us consider the signal flow graph in Fig. 7-17a first. The following results are obtained from this graph by inspection:

1. As shown in Fig. 7-17b, there is only one forward path between v_s and v_2. The forward-path gain is

$$G_1 = \frac{-\mu R_L}{r_p}$$

2. There are three individual loops as shown in Fig. 7-17c. The loop gains of these loops are

$$P_{11} = \frac{-\mu R_k}{r_p}$$

$$P_{21} = -\frac{R_k}{r_p}$$

$$P_{31} = -\frac{R_L}{r_p}$$

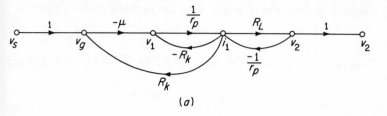

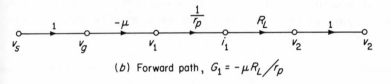

(b) Forward path, $G_1 = -\mu R_L / r_p$

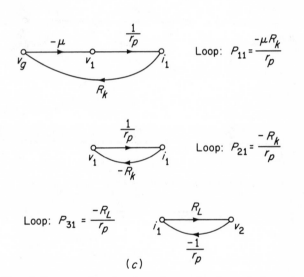

Fig. 7-17 *Signal flow graphs showing the evaluation of the gain*
v_2/v_s *for the amplifier circuit in Fig. 7-11.*

3. Since all three loops share the node for i_1, there are no nontouching loops other than "nontouching loops taken one at a time," which are just the individual loops.   Therefore, using (7-15),

$$\Delta = 1 - P_{11} - P_{21} - P_{31} = 1 + \frac{R_k + \mu R_k + R_L}{r_p}$$

4. There is no loop not in touch with the forward path.   Thus

$$\Delta_1 = 1$$

Substituting these quantities for Δ, Δ_1, and G_1 into (7-14) and simplifying, we get

$$G = \frac{v_2}{v_s} = \frac{G_1 \Delta_1}{\Delta} = \frac{-\mu R_L}{r_p + R_L + (1 + \mu)R_k} \tag{7-16}$$

Let us now turn our attention to the signal flow graph of Fig. 7-18a, which is known to be valid also for the same amplifier circuit.   The

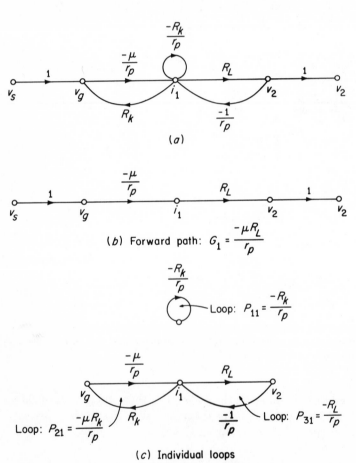

(a)

(b) Forward path: $G_1 = \dfrac{-\mu R_L}{r_p}$

Loop: $P_{11} = \dfrac{-R_k}{r_p}$

Loop: $P_{21} = \dfrac{-\mu R_k}{r_p}$ Loop: $P_{31} = \dfrac{-R_L}{r_p}$

(c) Individual loops

Fig. 7-18   *Signal flow graphs showing the evaluation of the gain v_2/v_s for the amplifier circuit in Fig. 7-11.*

forward path and the loops of the graph are depicted in Fig. 7-18b and c. Applying Mason's gain formula, it is easy to show that the gain between v_s and v_2 is the same as that given by (7-16).

Example 7-5   Let us now evaluate the gain for the amplifier shown in Fig. 7-11 between nodes v_s and v_g, using the signal flow graph in Fig. 7-17a.   The graph with v_g as an output node and v_s as an input node

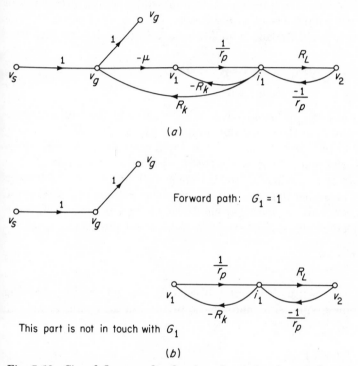

(a)

Forward path: $G_1 = 1$

This part is not in touch with G_1

(b)

Fig. 7-19 Signal flow graphs showing the evaluation of the gain v_o/v_s for the amplifier circuit in Fig. 7-11.

is shown in Fig. 7-19a.   *Since the properties of the loops are not affected by which node is chosen as the output node, as long as no loops are deleted or added, the Δ of the signal flow graph is always the same.*   Therefore, from the previous example, we have

$$\Delta = 1 + \frac{R_k + \mu R_k + R_L}{r_p}$$

The forward path between v_s and v_g, and the part of the signal flow graph that is not in touch with this forward path, are all shown in Fig. 7-19b. The forward-path gain and the associated Δ_1 are

$$G_1 = 1$$

and

$$\Delta_1 = 1 - \left(-\frac{R_k}{r_p} - \frac{R_L}{r_p} \right) = 1 + \frac{R_k + R_L}{r_p}$$

Notice that, in the last expression, Δ_1 is obtained by applying the formula for Δ to the two loops shown in Fig. 7-19b.

Substituting G_1, Δ_1, and Δ in Mason's gain formula, we get, after simplification,

$$\frac{v_g}{v_s} = \frac{G_1 \Delta_1}{\Delta} = \frac{r_p + R_k + R_L}{r_p + R_L + (1 + \mu) R_k} \tag{7-17}$$

Example 7-6   Consider that we wish to find the transmittance between v_g and v_1 in the signal flow graph of Fig. 7-17a. We can easily make v_1 an output node; but v_g is not an input node by definition. Furthermore, it was pointed out earlier that v_g cannot be made an input node by simply adding a node of v_g and a branch with unity gain. The only alternatives are either to go back to the original equations, rewrite them so that v_g appears only on the right-hand side of the equations, and draw the corresponding signal flow graph, or to interpret the gain v_1/v_g as

$$\frac{v_1}{v_g} = \frac{v_1/v_s}{v_g/v_s} \tag{7-18}$$

The second method usually is preferable since it does not require redrawing the signal flow graph. Furthermore, applying Mason's gain formula to the two transmittances of (7-18), we get

$$\frac{v_1}{v_g} = \frac{\left(\sum_n G_n \Delta_n \right)_{v_s - v_1}}{\left(\sum_n G_n \Delta_n \right)_{v_s - v_g}} \tag{7-19}$$

From Fig. 7-17a, we obtain

$$\left(\sum_n G_n \Delta_n \right)_{v_s - v_1} = -\mu \left(1 + \frac{R_L}{r_p} \right)$$

and

$$\left(\sum_n G_n \Delta_n \right)_{v_s - v_g} = 1 + \frac{R_k + R_L}{r_p}$$

Therefore

$$\frac{v_1}{v_g} = \frac{-\mu(r_p + R_L)}{r_p + R_k + R_L}$$

Example 7-7   As an illustration of complex systems, let us consider the signal flow graph shown in Fig. 7-20.   The gain expression of y_8/y_1 is to be determined.

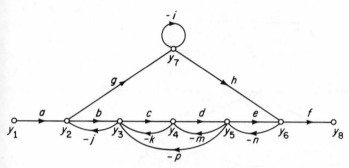

Fig. 7-20   A complex signal flow graph.

The following results are obtained from the signal flow graph leading to the determination of y_8/y_1:
   1. Forward paths   There are two forward paths between y_1 and y_8. These forward paths and their nontouching parts are depicted in Fig. 7-21.

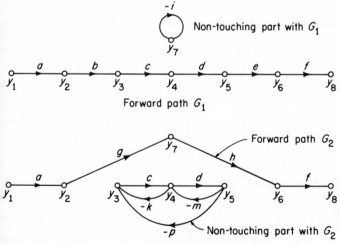

Fig. 7-21   Forward paths and their associated nontouching parts for the signal flow graph in Fig. 7-20.

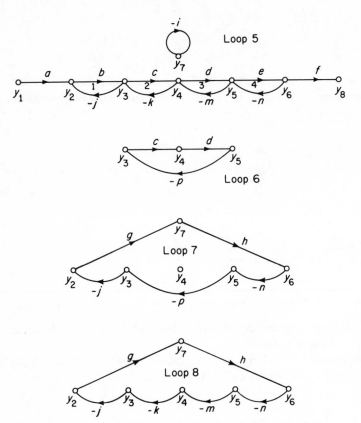

Fig. 7-22 Individual loops of the signal flow graph in Fig. 7-20.

The path gain of the first forward path is

$$G_1 = abcdef$$

and the Δ of the nontouching part associated with G_1 is

$$\Delta_1 = 1 + i$$

The gain of the other forward path is

$$G_2 = aghf$$

and

$$\Delta_2 = 1 + cdp + ck + dm$$

2. There are eight individual loops (Fig. 7-22).   The loop gains are

$$P_{11} = -bj \qquad P_{21} = -ck \qquad P_{31} = -dm \qquad P_{41} = -en$$
$$P_{51} = -cdp \qquad P_{61} = -ghnpj \qquad P_{71} = -i \qquad P_{81} = ghnmkj$$

3. There are eight different combinations of nontouching loops taken *two* at a time (Fig. 7-23).   The products of these nontouching loop gains are

$$P_{12} = bjdm \qquad P_{22} = bjen \qquad P_{32} = cken \qquad P_{42} = bji \qquad P_{52} = cki$$
$$P_{62} = dmi \qquad P_{.72} = eni \qquad P_{82} = cdpi$$

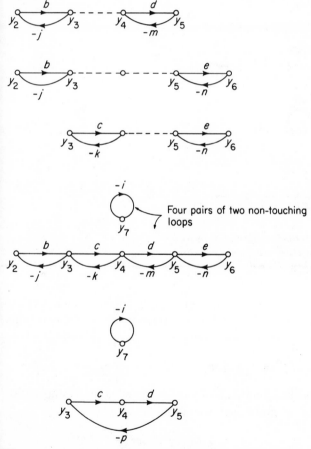

Fig. 7-23   Different combinations of nontouching loops taken two at a time for the signal flow graph in Fig. 7-20.

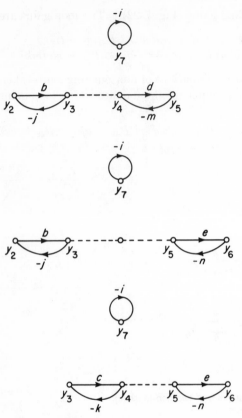

Fig. 7-24 *Different combinations of non-touching loops taken three at a time for the signal flow graph in Fig. 7-20.*

4. There are three different combinations of nontouching loops taken *three* at a time (Fig. 7-24). The products of these nontouching loop gains are

$$P_{13} = -bjdmi \qquad P_{23} = -bjeni \qquad P_{33} = -ckeni$$

5. There are no combinations of *four* or more nontouching loops. The Δ of the signal flow graph is now determined as

$$\Delta = 1 + (bj + ck + dm + en + cdp + ghnpj + i - ghnmkj)$$
$$+ (bjdm + bjen + cken + bji + cki + dmi + eni + cdpi)$$
$$+ (bjdmi + bjeni + ckeni) \qquad (7\text{-}20)$$

Substituting Δ and G_1, G_2, Δ_1, Δ_2 in Mason's gain formula, we get

$$\frac{y_8}{y_1} = \frac{abcdef(1 + i) + aghf(1 + cdp + ck + dm)}{\Delta} \tag{7-21}$$

where Δ is given by (7-20).

Example 7-8   We use this example to demonstrate that signal flow graphs, when used intelligently, can simplify the analysis of certain types of circuit problems.

One of the problems associated with the operation of a d-c amplifier is the drift in the output voltage caused by random changes in cathode emission.   The d-c amplifier shown in Fig. 7-25 has a compensation circuit

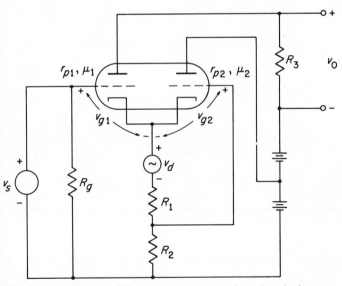

Fig. 7-25   *A d-c amplifier with compensation circuit for suppression of cathode drift.* $\mu_1 = \mu_2 = \mu$, $r_{p1} = r_{p2} = r_p$.

which provides a means of overcoming the cathode drift.   In this case the drift in cathode voltage is simulated by an equivalent generator v_d located in the common cathode lead of the tube sections.   The problem is to find the optimum value of R_2 so that the cathode drift is eliminated and to find the voltage v_0/v_s under the condition of perfect compensation.

The voltage-source equivalent circuit of the d-c amplifier is shown in

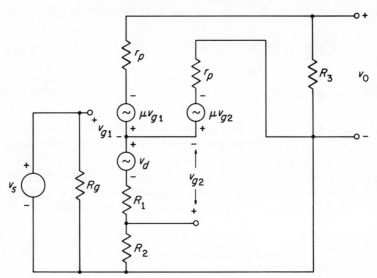

Fig. 7-26 *A voltage-source equivalent circuit of the d-c amplifier shown in Fig. 7-25.*

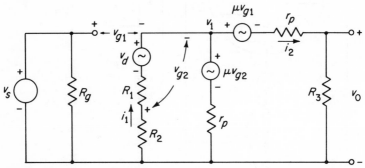

Fig. 7-27 *Rearranged diagram of the equivalent circuit shown in Fig. 7-26.*

Fig. 7-26.   The two sections of the vacuum tube are assumed to be identical, so that $r_{p1} = r_{p2} = r_p$ and $\mu_1 = \mu_2 = \mu$.

The equivalent circuit is redrawn in Fig. 7-27, and the dependent variables are assumed to be v_{g1}, i_1, v_{g2}, v_1, i_2, and v_0.   The six independent cause-and-effect equations are

$$v_{g1} = v_s - v_1$$

$$i_1 = \frac{v_d - v_1}{R_1 + R_2}$$

$$v_{g2} = R_1 i_1 - v_d$$

$$v_1 = \mu v_{g2} + r_p(i_1 - i_2)$$

$$i_2 = \frac{v_1 - \mu v_{g1}}{r_p + R_3}$$

$$v_0 = R_3 i_2$$

The signal flow graph portraying these equations is now drawn as shown in Fig. 7-28.

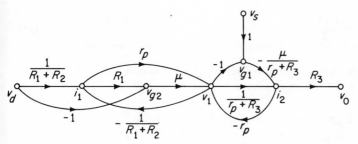

Fig. 7-28 *A signal flow graph of the d-c amplifier circuit shown in Fig. 7-25.*

The proper steps in solving this problem are now clarified by the topological structure of the signal flow graph. We see that if v_0 is not to be affected by v_d, the transmission between v_d and v_0 should be zero; that is, $v_0/v_d = 0$. Since the network elements are assumed to be linear, the principle of superposition holds. The effect of v_d on v_0 is evaluated by setting $v_s = 0$. Thus, under this zero-input condition, we set

$$\left. \frac{v_0}{v_d} \right|_{v_s = 0} = \frac{\sum\limits_{n} G_n \Delta_n}{\Delta} = 0 \tag{7-22}$$

Then

$$\sum_{n} G_n \Delta_n = 0 \tag{7-23}$$

The forward paths between v_d and v_0 are easily identified from the signal flow graph in Fig. 7-28, and (7-23) becomes

$$\left[\left(\frac{\mu R_1}{R_1 + R_2} - \mu \right) + \frac{r_p}{R_1 + R_2} \right] \frac{1 + \mu}{r_p + R_3} R_3 = 0$$

After simplification, the last equation gives

$$R_2 = \frac{r_p}{\mu} \tag{7-24}$$

which is the optimum value for the output voltage v_0 to be insensitive to cathode drift.

If R_2 is set at the optimum value given by (7-24), the output v_0 will not be affected by v_d; v_d can be set to zero as far as v_0 is concerned. The voltage gain of the compensated amplifier is given by

$$\left.\frac{v_0}{v_s}\right|_{v_d=0} = \frac{G_1 \Delta_1}{\Delta} \tag{7-25}$$

since there is only one forward path between v_0 and v_s. From the signal flow graph of Fig. 7-28, we have

$$G_1 = \frac{-\mu R_3}{r_p + R_3}$$

$$\Delta_1 = 1 + \frac{r_p + \mu R_1}{R_1 + R_2}$$

and

$$\Delta = 1 + \frac{r_p + \mu R_1}{R_1 + R_2} + \frac{(1 + \mu)r_p}{r_p + R_3}$$

Substituting these expression for Δ, Δ_1, and G_1 into (7-25) and simplifying, we get

$$\left.\frac{v_0}{v_s}\right|_{v_d=0} = \frac{-\mu R_3(R_1 + R_2 + r_p + \mu R_1)}{(r_p + R_3)(R_1 + R_2 + r_p + \mu R_1) + r_p(1 + \mu)(R_1 + R_2)}$$

7-6 COATES' FLOW GRAPHS—THE FLOW GRAPHS[3]

A generalization of the signal-flow-graph theory was made possible by the work of C. L. Coates. Coates developed a different type of graph called the *flow graph*, which is defined with its topological structure depending only on the structure of the set of algebraic equations. Physically, a flow graph is still a collection of branches and nodes, but the interconnections between nodes no longer follow the principles of cause and effect.

A major difficulty encountered in applying Mason's signal flow graph to the solution of a set of equations of the following form,

$$\sum_{j=1}^{N} a_{ij}y_j = 0 \qquad i = 1, 2, \ldots, N \tag{7-26}$$

(such as a set of loop or node equations in network analysis) is that the equations must first be converted into a set of cause-and-effect relationships. For instance, in (7-26), if $N = 3$, we have

$$a_{11}y_1 + a_{12}y_2 + a_{13}y_3 = 0 \tag{7-27}$$

$$a_{21}y_1 + a_{22}y_2 + a_{23}y_3 = 0 \tag{7-28}$$

$$a_{31}y_1 + a_{32}y_2 + a_{33}y_3 = 0 \tag{7-29}$$

In order to obtain a signal-flow-graph solution, we must rewrite these equations by solving for y_1 in (7-27), y_2 in (7-28), and y_3 in (7-29). The three equations now become

$$y_1 = -\frac{a_{12}}{a_{11}} y_2 - \frac{a_{13}}{a_{11}} y_3$$

$$y_2 = -\frac{a_{21}}{a_{22}} y_1 - \frac{a_{23}}{a_{22}} y_3$$

$$y_3 = -\frac{a_{31}}{a_{33}} y_1 - \frac{a_{32}}{a_{33}} y_2$$

Now the variables on the left-hand side of the equations may be interpreted as effects, and those on the right-hand side are the causes.

A flow graph, however, does not require this rearrangement of variables. We show below that a flow graph can be drawn for equations of the form of (7-26) directly. Although the original definition of the basic elements of a flow graph is altogether different from that of a signal flow graph, for obvious reasons, we attempt to consolidate the definitions and terminology used in both kinds of graphs. Therefore, unless otherwise stated, all the definitions (not the properties) of signal flow graphs given earlier are still applicable to flow graphs.

The association between a flow graph and a set of linear algebraic equations is presented below. Let us consider the set of equations

$$\sum_{j=1}^{M} a_{ij}y_j = 0 \qquad i = 1, 2, \ldots, N \tag{7-30}$$

In these equations, $M \geq N$, indicating that it is possible to have $M - N$ independent sources. If $M = N$, these equations are homogeneous.

By definition, the variables $y_1, y_2, \ldots, y_N, y_{N+1}, \ldots, y_M$ may be represented by nodes, and a_{ij} by the transmittance of a branch. But before attempting to draw the flow graph, we must arbitrarily label each of the N equations with a unique variable chosen from the set of noninput variables, $y_1, y_2, \ldots, y_N$. For instance, if the equations are homogeneous, $N = M$, and letting $N = 3$, we have the three equations in (7-27) to (7-29). We now arbitrarily assign y_1 to be associated with the first equation, y_2 with the second, and y_3 with the third. These equations and their associated variables are written in the following form:

$$y_1 \quad | \quad a_{11}y_1 + a_{12}y_2 + a_{13}y_3 = 0 \qquad (7\text{-}31)$$

$$y_2 \quad | \quad a_{21}y_1 + a_{22}y_2 + a_{23}y_3 = 0 \qquad (7\text{-}32)$$

$$y_3 \quad | \quad a_{31}y_1 + a_{32}y_2 + a_{33}y_3 = 0 \qquad (7\text{-}33)$$

Note that each equation is assigned a unique variable, which is placed on the left for identification purposes. Also remember that it is perfectly permissible to assign y_2 to the first equation, y_1 to the second, and y_3 to the third, or any other combination, so long as one variable is assigned to only one equation.

The construction of the flow graph is effected by first drawing the nodes $y_1, y_2, \ldots, y_N$ in some convenient manner on paper. If the variable y_p is assigned to the ith equation,

$$\sum_{j=1}^{M} a_{ij}y_j = 0$$

the flow-graph representation of this equation is obtained by drawing branches with transmittances a_{ij} from nodes y_j $(j = 1, 2, \ldots, M)$ to the node y_p. As an illustrative example, let us draw the flow graph for (7-31). The three nodes representing y_1, y_2, and y_3 are drawn as shown in Fig. 7-29.

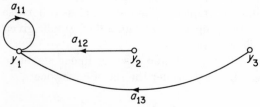

Fig. 7-29 Flow graph of Eq. (7-31) with y_1 assigned as the reference variable.

Since y_1 is assigned to this equation, the node y_1 will act as a summing point.   The first term in (7-31) calls for drawing a branch with gain a_{11} from y_1 to y_1, thus forming a self-loop at the node y_1.   The second term in (7-31) is represented by a branch with gain a_{12} drawn from y_2 to y_1, and finally, a branch with gain a_{13} is directed from y_3 to y_1 for the last term. The flow-graph configuration for (7-31), with y_1 as its reference variable, is depicted in Fig. 7-29.   The complete flow-graph representation of the

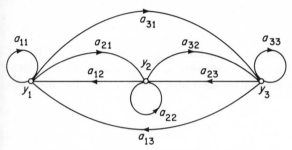

Fig. 7-30   Flow graph of Eqs. (7-31) to (7-33). y_1, y_2, and y_3 are assigned to the three equations in the corresponding order.

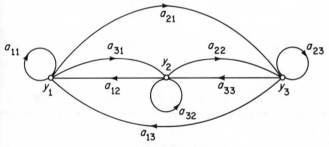

Fig. 7-31   Flow graph of (7-31) to (7-33). y_1, y_3, and y_2 are assigned to the three equations in the corresponding order.

three equations (7-31) to (7-33), with the indicated choice of reference variables, is shown in Fig. 7-30.

It is apparent that the flow-graph representation of a given set of equations is not unique, since a different choice of reference variables for the equations will result in a completely different flow graph.   For instance, if the three equations (7-31) to (7-33) are assigned the variables in the order y_1, y_3, and y_2, we have the flow graph shown in Fig. 7-31. Notice that, although the configuration of this flow graph is identical with the one in Fig. 7-30, the branch gains are different.

Example 7-9   As an example illustrating the construction of the flow graph for a set of linear algebraic equations, let us refer to the feedback amplifier circuit shown in Fig. 7-11. The loop equations of the circuit are written in Example 7-2, and are repeated below in the form of (7-30):

$$v_g \quad\Big|\quad v_g - v_s - R_k i_1 = 0 \tag{7-34}$$

$$i_1 \quad\Big|\quad i_1 + \frac{\mu}{r_p} v_g + \frac{R_k}{r_p} i_1 + \frac{v_2}{r_p} = 0 \tag{7-35}$$

$$v_2 \quad\Big|\quad v_2 - R_L i_1 = 0 \tag{7-36}$$

The three noninput variables v_g, i_1, and v_2 have been assigned to the equations as shown. Using the procedure described above, the complete flow graph for these three equations is drawn in Fig. 7-32. For instance,

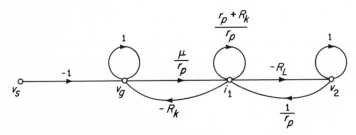

Fig. 7-32   A flow graph for the feedback amplifier shown in Fig. 7-11.

the flow graph for (7-34) is obtained by drawing a branch with unity gain from v_g to v_g, forming a self-loop; a branch with gain -1 from v_s to v_g; and a branch with gain $-R_k$ from i_1 to v_g. The flow-graph representations of (7-35) and (7-36) are done in the same manner.

Example 7-10   As another example of the construction of flow graphs, let us consider the vacuum-tube circuit shown in Fig. 7-33*a*. The current-source equivalent circuit is shown in Fig. 7-33*b*. The node equations of the circuit are written

$$V_1 \quad\Big|\quad Y_1 V_s - (Y_1 + Y_2)V_1 + Y_2 V_0 = 0 \tag{7-37}$$

$$V_0 \quad\Big|\quad -g_m V_1 + Y_2 V_1 - (g_p + Y_L + Y_2)V_0 = 0 \tag{7-38}$$

where the first equation is arbitrarily assigned V_1, and the second equation is assigned V_0. The flow graph of the circuit is now drawn as shown in Fig. 7-34.

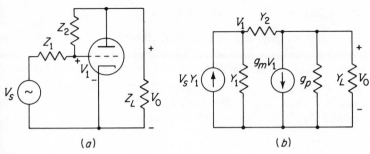

Fig. 7-33   (a) A vacuum-tube feedback amplifier.   (b) Current-source equivalent circuit.

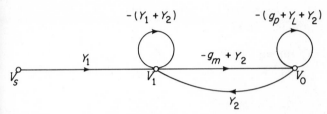

Fig. 7-34   A flow graph for the amplifier circuit in Fig. 7-33.

As a comparison, we may draw a signal flow graph for the same circuit. But in order to use the same dependent variables, V_1 and V_0, we must rewrite the node equations as a set of cause-and-effect relationships. Solving for V_1 in (7-37) and V_0 in (7-38), we get

$$V_1 = \frac{Y_1}{Y_1 + Y_2} V_s + \frac{Y_2}{Y_1 + Y_2} V_0 \tag{7-39}$$

$$V_0 = \frac{Y_2 - g_m}{g_p + Y_L + Y_2} V_1 \tag{7-40}$$

The signal flow graph for the circuit is drawn in Fig. 7-35.

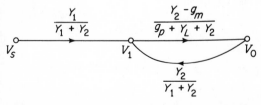

Fig. 7-35   A signal flow graph for the amplifier circuit in Fig. 7-33.

7-7 A GAIN FORMULA FOR FLOW GRAPHS

A comparison of the signal flow graph with the flow graph cannot be made before the general gain formula of the flow graph is presented.   The gain formula devised by Mason allows one to write down the gain between an input node and an output node of a signal flow graph by inspection.   A similar expression is available for flow graphs.   The gain or transmittance between an input node and an output node of a flow graph is given by

$$G = \frac{y_{\text{out}}}{y_{\text{in}}} = \frac{\sum_n G_n \Delta_{cn}}{\Delta_c} \tag{7-41}$$

For uniformity, we have expressed this gain formula in the same form as for the signal flow graphs.   In (7-41),

G_n = gain of nth forward path

$\Delta_c = \sum_m (-1)^j$ product of loop gains found in mth "connection graph";

   if the flow graph does not have any loop, $\Delta_c = 1$ (7-42)

where j = number of loops found in mth connection graph

   m = number of all possible connection graphs in flow graph

A connection graph is that part of the flow graph which includes all the non-input nodes, and each node has one and only one incoming branch and one and only one outgoing branch.   From this description, it is clear that a connection graph contains only loops.

   Δ_{cn} = value of Δ_c of that part of the flow graph which is not in touch with the nth forward path.   If the nth forward path does not have any nontouching part, $\Delta_{cn} = 1$.

   Let us now demonstrate the use of the flow-graph gain formula by means of an illustrative example.

   Example 7-11   The flow graph obtained in Example 7-9 (Fig. 7-32) is shown in Fig. 7-36a.   The forward path between v_s and v_2 is shown in Fig. 7-36b, and its path gain is

$$G_1 = \frac{\mu R_L}{r_p}$$

Since no other part of the flow graph is not in touch with this forward path,

   $\Delta_{c1} = 1$

A connection graph is defined to include all the noninput nodes, v_g, i_1, and v_2.   The three connection graphs of the flow graph are shown in Fig. 7-36c

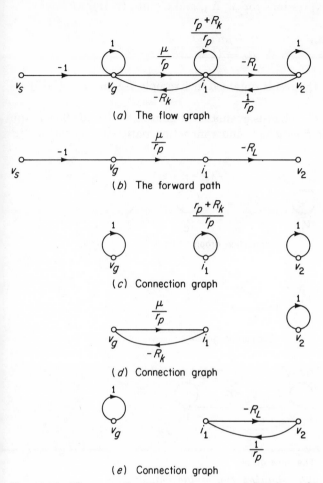

Fig. 7-36 *Flow graphs illustrating the evaluation of the gain for the circuit in Fig. 7-11.*

to e. Notice that each node of the connection graphs has only one incoming branch and one outgoing branch. Furthermore, in Fig. 7-36c, there are three loops, so $j = 3$; in Fig. 7-36d and e, $j = 2$. From (7-42), we have

$$\Delta_c = (-1)^3(1)\left(\frac{r_p + R_k}{r_p}\right)(1) + (-1)^2\left(\frac{-\mu R_k}{r_p}\right)(1)$$
$$+ (-1)^2(1)\left(-\frac{R_L}{r_p}\right)$$

$$= -\frac{r_p + R_L + R_k + \mu R_k}{r_p}$$

Substituting the expressions for Δ_c, Δ_{c1}, and G_1 into (7-41), we have

$$G = \frac{v_2}{v_s} = \frac{G_1\Delta_{c1}}{\Delta_c} = \frac{-\mu R_L}{r_p + R_L + (1 + \mu)R_k}$$

which agrees with the result obtained in Example 7-4 and Eq. (7-16).

Example 7-12   Let us evaluate the gain V_0/V_s for the flow graph of Fig. 7-34. The flow graph and connection paths are shown in Fig.

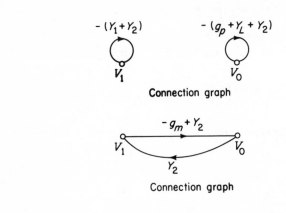

Connection graph

Connection graph

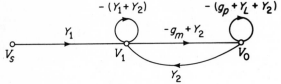

The flow graph

Fig. 7-37 Flow graphs showing the evaluation of the amplifier circuit in Fig. 7-33.

7-37.   We have, by inspection of the flow graph,

$$G_1 = Y_1(-g_m + Y_2)$$

$$\Delta_{c1} = 1$$

and

$$\Delta_c = (-1)^2(Y_1 + Y_2)(g_p + Y_L + Y_2) + (-1)^1 Y_2(-g_m + Y_2)$$

From (7-41), the gain is

$$\frac{V_0}{V_s} = \frac{G_1 \Delta_{c1}}{\Delta_c} = \frac{Y_1(-g_m + Y_2)}{(Y_1 + Y_2)(g_p + Y_L + Y_2) - Y_2(Y_2 - g_m)} \tag{7-43}$$

This result is easily checked by applying Mason's gain formula to the signal flow graph of the same circuit that is given in Fig. 7-35.

7-8 RELATIONSHIPS BETWEEN THE SIGNAL FLOW GRAPH AND THE FLOW GRAPH

Up to this point we have regarded the flow graph and the signal flow graph as two different types of topological structures for portraying linear algebraic equations. However, the two types of graphs are drawn from basically the same equations, although they are necessarily written in different forms. In fact, it is possible to convert a flow graph into a signal flow graph, and vice versa, by simple graphical manipulations.

Let us consider the set of algebraic equations given by (7-30):

$$\sum_{j=1}^{M} a_{ij} y_j = 0 \qquad i = 1, 2, \ldots, N \tag{7-44}$$

The equations are in the proper form for flow-graph formulation. If we add a noninput variable y_i on both sides of the equations in (7-44), we get

$$y_i = y_i + \sum_{j=1}^{M} a_{ij} y_j \qquad i = 1, 2, \ldots, N \tag{7-45}$$

The equations are now in the correct form for signal-flow graphs if we regard y_i as the effect. Having y_i on both sides of the equations adds a self-loop with unity gain at the node y_i on the flow graph. If a self-loop already exists at y_i, its loop gain is simply stepped up by 1. This simply implies that a Coates' flow graph can be converted into a Mason's signal flow graph by adding a self-loop with unity gain at each of the noninput nodes of the flow graph. Or if a self-loop already exists at a node on the flow graph, we simply step up the loop gain by unity.

As an illustrative example, let us refer to the flow graph of Fig. 7-36a, which is again repeated in Fig. 7-38a. An equivalent Mason's signal flow graph may be obtained by adding 1 to the gain of each of the self-loops attached to the noninput nodes i_1, v_g, and v_2. The equivalent signal flow graph obtained this way is shown in Fig. 7-38b. It should not be surpris-

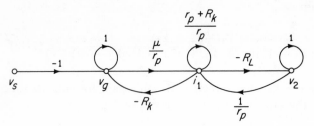

(*a*) The flow graph

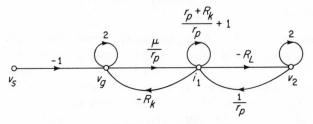

(*b*) The signal flow graph

Fig. 7-38   *A flow graph of the circuit in Fig. 7-11 and its equivalent signal flow graph obtained by adding 1 to the loop gains of all the self-loops.*

ing to find this signal flow graph different from the one shown in Fig. 7-13, since we know that the signal flow graph for a given system is not unique. To show that this signal-flow graph also correctly represents the amplifier circuit of Fig. 7-11, we apply Mason's gain formula as follows:

$$
\frac{v_2}{v_s} = \frac{\mu R_L / r_p}{1 - 2 - 2 - \left(\dfrac{r_p + R_k}{r_p} + 1\right) + \dfrac{\mu R_k}{r_p} + \dfrac{R_L}{r_p} + 2\left(\dfrac{r_p + R_k}{r_p} + 1\right)}
$$
$$
{+ \, 4 + 2\left(\dfrac{r_p + R_k}{r_p} + 1\right) - \dfrac{2\mu R_k}{r_p} - \dfrac{2R_L}{r_p} - 4\left(\dfrac{r_p + R_k}{r_p} + 1\right)}
$$

After simplification, we have

$$
\frac{v_2}{v_s} = \frac{-\mu R_L}{r_p + R_L + (1 + \mu)R_k}
$$

which agrees with (7-16), the correct answer.

We can readily see that, by reversing the process described above, a signal flow graph may be converted into a flow graph.   This is done by adding self-loops with loop gains of -1 to all the noninput nodes of the signal flow graph.   As an illustration of this process, the signal flow graph in Fig. 7-17 is redrawn in Fig. 7-39a.   The equivalent flow graph is

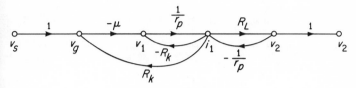

(a) The signal flow graph

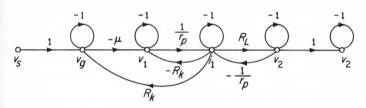

(b) The flow graph

Fig. 7-39   *A signal flow graph of the circuit in Fig. 7-11 and its equivalent flow graph obtained by adding self-loops with gains of -1 to all the noninput nodes of the signal flow graph.*

obtained by adding self-loops with loop gains of -1 to all the noninput nodes, v_g, v_1, i_1, and v_2.   The flow graph thus obtained is shown in Fig. 7-39b.   Now applying the flow-graph gain formula to Fig. 7-39b, we get

$$\frac{v_2}{v_s} = \frac{-\mu R_L/r_p}{\substack{(-1)^5(-1)^5 + (-1)^4(-1)^3(-R_L/r_p) \\ + (-1)^4(-1)^1(-R_k/r_p) + (-1)^3(-1)^2(-\mu R_k/r_p)}}$$

$$= \frac{-\mu R_L}{r_p + R_L + (1 + \mu)R_k}$$

which again agrees with all the earlier results.

Example 7-13   As the last example of this chapter, let us consider the circuit of a transistor amplifier shown in Fig. 7-40a.   The equivalent circuit of the amplifier is shown in Fig. 7-40b.   The network equations using branch currents and node voltages as indicated on the circuit

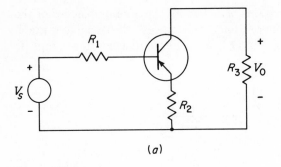

(a)

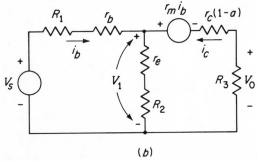

(b)

Fig. 7-40   A transistor amplifier circuit and its equivalent circuit.

diagram are

$$i_b = \frac{1}{R_1 + r_b} (V_s - V_1)$$

$$V_1 = (r_e + R_2)(i_b + i_c)$$

$$i_c = \frac{1}{r_c(1 - a)} (V_0 - V_1 + r_m i_b)$$

$$V_0 = -R_3 i_c$$

The signal flow graph based on these four equations is drawn in Fig. 7-41.   Applying Mason's gain formula to this signal flow graph yields the gain of the amplifier as

$$\frac{V_0}{V_s} = \frac{\dfrac{R_3(r_e + R_2 - r_m)}{r_c(1 - a)(r_b + R_1)}}{\Delta} \tag{7-46}$$

where

$$\Delta = \frac{\begin{aligned}r_c(1-a)(R_1+r_b+r_e+R_2)\\ +\ (R_1+r_b)(R_2+r_e+R_3)+(r_e+R_2)(R_3+r_m)\end{aligned}}{r_c(1-a)(r_b+R_1)}$$

$$(7\text{-}47)$$

An equivalent Coates' flow graph may be obtained by adding a self-loop of gain -1 to each of the noninput nodes of the signal flow graph in Fig. 7-41. The flow graph thus obtained is shown in Fig. 7-42. Applying

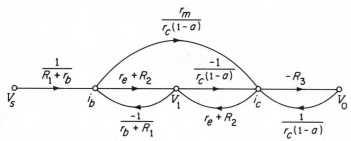

Fig. 7-41   A signal flow graph of the transistor amplifier circuit in Fig. 7-40.

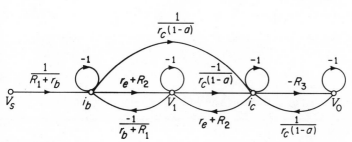

Fig. 7-42   A Coates' flow graph for the transistor amplifier circuit in Fig. 7-40.

the flow-graph gain formula to this flow graph, we should obtain the same result for V_0/V_s as in Eqs. (7-46) and (7-47). The details are left to the student as an exercise.

PROBLEMS

7-1   Draw a signal flow graph for the following set of linear equations:

$$y_1 + 3y_2 - 4y_3 = 1$$
$$2y_1 + 5y_2 \qquad = 0$$
$$\qquad - 9y_2 + 3y_3 = 0$$

7-2   Are the two signal flow graphs shown in Fig. P7-1 equivalent?   Explain.

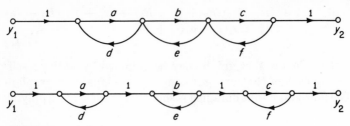

Fig. P7-1

7-3   Draw a signal flow graph for the network shown in Fig. P7-2.   Find the voltage gain $V_0(j\omega)/V_i(j\omega)$.

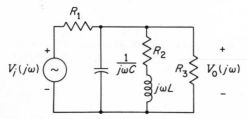

Fig. P7-2

7-4   Find y_7/y_1, y_7/y_2, y_5/y_1 from the signal flow graph shown in Fig. P7-3.

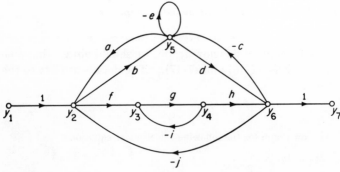

Fig. P7-3

7-5 Find y_8/y_1, y_8/y_2, and y_4/y_1 from the signal flow graph shown in Fig. P7-4.

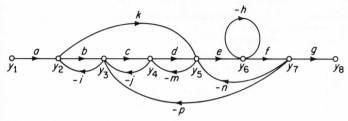

Fig. P7-4

7-6 Write a set of cause-and-effect equations for the transistor amplifier equivalent circuit shown in Fig. P7-5.   Draw a signal flow graph based on these equations.

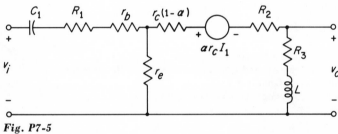

Fig. P7-5

7-7 (a) Draw a signal flow graph for the vacuum-tube circuit shown in Fig. P7-6.
       (b) Find V_3/V_1, V_2/V_1, and the impedance seen looking across R_3.   Assume identical tubes.

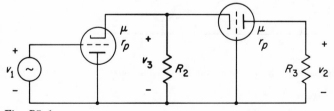

Fig. P7-6

7-8   The circuits shown in Fig. P7-7 are assumed to be operating under sinusoidal steady-state conditions.

     (*a*)   Write a set of cause-and-effect relationships for each network.

     (*b*)   Construct a signal flow graph using the equations in (*a*).

     (*c*)   Find the voltage gain V_0/V_s.

     (*d*)   Find the output impedances of the circuits.

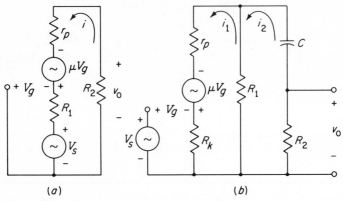

(*a*)   (*b*)

Fig. P7-7

7-9   Repeat Prob. 7-1 using Coates' flow graph.

7-10   (*a*)   Find the currents i_5 and i_7 and the voltage v_5 in the network of Fig. P7-8 by means of a signal flow graph.

        (*b*)   Repeat part *a* using a Coates' flow graph.

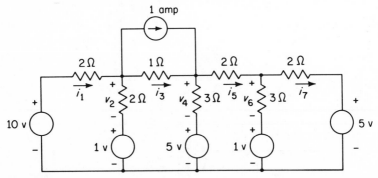

Fig. P7-8

7-11   A system is described by the following set of equations:

$$3y_1 + 4y_2 - y_3 = 10$$

$$-y_1 - 2y_2 + 5y_3 = 0$$

$$4y_1 + 2y_2 + 3y_3 = 0$$

(a)   Draw a Coates' flow graph for the system.

(b)   Draw a different flow graph by assigning a different set of reference variables to the equations.

7-12   Convert the signal flow graph shown in Fig. P7-9 into a flow graph. Apply the corresponding gain formula to the two graphs to find x_4/x_1. Compare the results.

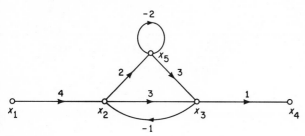

Fig. P7-9

BIBLIOGRAPHY

1   Mason, S. J.: Feedback Theory: Some Properties of Signal-flow Graphs, *Proc. IRE*, vol. 41, pp. 1144–1156, September, 1953.

2   Bickout, T. A.: Flow Graphs for the Representation of Nonlinear Systems, *IRE Trans. Circuit Theory*, vol. CT-8, pp. 49–58, March, 1961.

3   Coates, C. L.: Flow-graph Solutions of Linear Algebraic Equations, *IRE Trans. Circuit Theory*, vol. CT-6, pp. 170–187, June, 1959.

4   Mason, S. J.: Feedback Theory: Further Properties of Signal Flow Graphs, *Proc. IRE*, vol. 44, no. 7, pp. 920–926, July, 1956.

ADDITIONAL REFERENCES

Chow, Y., and E. Cassignol: "Linear Signal Flow Graphs and Applications," John Wiley & Sons, Inc., New York, 1962.

Desoer, C. A.: The Optimum Formula for the Gain of a Flow Graph or a Simple Derivation of Coates Formula, *Proc. IRE*, vol. 48, pp. 883–889, May, 1960.

Mason, S. J., and H. J. Zimmerman: "Electronic Circuits, Signals, and Systems," John Wiley & Sons, Inc., New York, 1960.

Ribichaud, L. P. A., M. Boisvert, and J. Robert: "Signal Flow Graphs and Applications," Prentice-Hall, Inc., Englewood Cliffs, N.J., 1962.

Truxal, J. G.: "Automatic Feedback Control System Synthesis," McGraw-Hill Book Company, New York, 1955.

EIGHT

FOURIER AND LAPLACE TRANSFORMS

8-1 INTRODUCTION

In the preceding chapters the loop-and-node analysis and the state-variable analysis of linear networks were discussed. Thus far, however, we have not mentioned how the network equations can be solved and what is the nature of the probable input signals.

It is assumed that the reader has had adequate background in solving ordinary linear differential equations with constant coefficients by means of the classical methods. We now investigate the transform methods of solving linear systems and equations. We see that the Laplace-transform method, in many situations, is more versatile and more convenient to use than the classical methods of solving linear differential equations. Furthermore, once the linear differential equations are transformed into equivalent algebraic equations, it is possible to represent them by means of a signal flow graph.

224

In order to understand fully and to appreciate the definitions and the properties of the Laplace transformation, it is helpful to examine, first, the properties of the Fourier series and the Fourier transforms.

8-2   FOURIER SERIES

The work done by the French mathematician Fourier in the nineteenth century showed that most periodic functions can be represented by an infinite series of complex exponentials.   If $g(t)$ is a single-valued periodic function of t with period T and, in addition, if $g(t)$ satisfies the following conditions (Dirichlet's conditions),

1   $g(t)$ has at most a finite number of discontinuities in a finite interval,
2   $g(t)$ has at most a finite number of maxima and minima in a finite interval, and
3   $g(t)$ is a bounded function, implying that $\int_{-T/2}^{T/2} |g(t)|\, dt < \infty$,

then it can be expressed by a Fourier series of the form

$$g(t) = \frac{1}{T} \sum_{n=-\infty}^{\infty} C_n e^{j\omega_n t} \qquad \frac{-T}{2} < t < \frac{T}{2} \tag{8-1}$$

where C_n is called the *complex Fourier coefficient* of $g(t)$, and

$$\omega_n = \frac{2\pi n}{T} \tag{8-2}$$

The complex Fourier coefficient C_n is determined by multiplying both sides of (8-1) by $e^{-j\omega_m t}$, where $\omega_m = 2\pi m/T$, and integrating with respect to t from $-T/2$ to $T/2$.   We have

$$\int_{-T/2}^{T/2} g(t) e^{-j\omega_m t}\, dt = \frac{1}{T} \int_{-T/2}^{T/2} \sum_{n=-\infty}^{\infty} C_n e^{j2\pi(n-m)t/T}\, dt \tag{8-3}$$

The integral sign and the summation sign on the right-hand side of (8-3) can be interchanged† to give

$$\int_{-T/2}^{T/2} g(t) e^{-j\omega_m t}\, dt = \frac{1}{T} \sum_{n=-\infty}^{\infty} C_n \int_{-T/2}^{T/2} e^{j2\pi(n-m)t/T}\, dt \tag{8-4}$$

† This step is permissible if the series is uniformly convergent in the interval $-T/2 < t < T/2$.

Using the relationship

$$e^{j\omega t} = \cos \omega t + j \sin \omega t$$

it is clear that the following results may be obtained for the integral on the right-hand side of (8-4):

$$\int_{-T/2}^{T/2} e^{j2\pi(n-m)t/T} \, dt = \begin{cases} T & n = m \\ 0 & n \neq m \end{cases} \qquad (8\text{-}5)$$

From this we conclude that only one term on the right-hand side of (8-4) is nonzero.   Therefore

$$\int_{-T/2}^{T/2} g(t)e^{-j\omega_n t} \, dt = \frac{1}{T} \, C_n T$$

from which we get

$$C_n = \int_{-T/2}^{T/2} g(t)e^{-j\omega_n t} \, dt \qquad (8\text{-}6)$$

Thus, given a function $g(t)$ which satisfies the Dirichlet condition, its Fourier-series representation for the interval $-T/2 < t < T/2$ is given by (8-1), and the complex Fourier coefficient C_n is given by (8-6).

The following examples illustrate the Fourier-series representation of some well-known periodic functions.

Example 8-1   Consider the periodic rectangular signal shown in Fig. 8-1.   The complex Fourier coefficients are given by

$$C_n = \int_{-T/2}^{T/2} g(t)e^{-j\omega_n t} \, dt = 2 \int_{-T/4}^{T/4} e^{-j\omega_n t} \, dt \qquad (8\text{-}7)$$

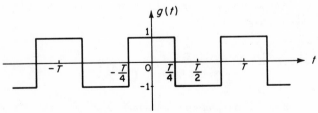

Fig. 8-1   A periodic rectangular signal.

Evaluating C_n from (8-7) gives

$$C_n = 2\frac{e^{j\omega_n T/4} - e^{-j\omega_n T/4}}{j\omega_n} \qquad n \neq 0 \tag{8-8}$$

Since the area under the plot of $g(t)$ over one period is zero, $C_0 = 0$.
Using Euler's equation,

$$\sin \omega T = \frac{e^{j\omega T} - e^{-j\omega T}}{2j}$$

and Eq. (8-8) can be written

$$C_n = T\frac{e^{j\omega_n T/4} - e^{-j\omega_n T/4}}{2j(\omega_n T/4)} = T\frac{\sin (\omega_n T/4)}{\omega_n T/4} \qquad n \neq 0 \tag{8-9}$$

Substituting (8-2) for ω_n in (8-9), we have

$$C_n = T\frac{\sin (n\pi/2)}{n\pi/2}\begin{cases} 0 & n = \text{even integers and } n = 0 \\ \dfrac{2T}{n\pi} & n = 1, 5, 9, 13, \ldots \\ \dfrac{-2T}{n\pi} & n = 3, 7, 11, 15, \ldots \end{cases}$$

We can regard C_n as a complex number, so that

$$C_n = |C_n|e^{j\phi_n}$$

Therefore

$$|C_n| = \begin{cases} 0 & n = \text{even integers and } n = 0 \\ \dfrac{2T}{n\pi} & n = \text{odd integers} \end{cases}$$

$$\phi_n = \begin{cases} 0 & n = \text{even integers and } n = 0, 1, 5, 9, \ldots \\ +\pi \text{ or } -\pi & n = 3, 7, 11, 15, \ldots \end{cases}$$

In Fig. 8-2, $|C_n|$ and ϕ_n are plotted as functions of ω_n. We notice that, since n takes on only integral values, these plots are discrete functions of ω_n. Therefore they are often called the *discrete frequency spectra* of $g(t)$.

Example 8-2   Consider the train of periodic pulses shown in Fig. 8-3. The height of each pulse is unity, and the pulsewidth is ϵ,

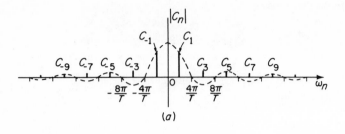

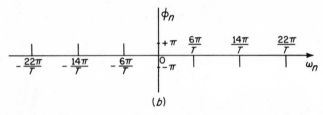

(b)

Fig. 8-2 Discrete amplitude and phase spectra of the rectangular signal shown in Fig. 8-1.

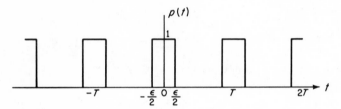

Fig. 8-3 A periodic pulse train.

where $\epsilon < T/2$. Using (8-6), the complex Fourier coefficient of the periodic pulse train is written

$$C_n = \int_{-T/2}^{T/2} p(t) e^{-j\omega_n t}\, dt = \int_{-\epsilon/2}^{\epsilon/2} e^{-j\omega_n t}\, dt$$

$$= -\frac{1}{j\omega_n}\, e^{-j\omega_n t}\, \Big|_{-\epsilon/2}^{\epsilon/2} = \frac{e^{j\omega_n \epsilon/2} - e^{-j\omega_n \epsilon/2}}{j\omega_n} \qquad (8\text{-}10)$$

Using Euler's equation, C_n becomes

$$C_n = \epsilon\, \frac{\sin\,(\omega_n \epsilon/2)}{\omega_n \epsilon/2} = |C_n| e^{j\phi_n} \qquad (8\text{-}11)$$

which again is of the form of $\sin x/x$. Since n takes on only discrete integral values between $-\infty$ and ∞, the magnitude and phase of C_n have values only at discrete intervals of ω_n.   Typical plots of $|C_n|$ and ϕ_n as functions of ω_n are illustrated in Fig. 8-4a and b, respectively.

The number of lines in the interval between $k\pi/\epsilon$ and $(k+1)\pi/\epsilon$ depends upon the magnitude of T; more lines for larger T.   As T approaches infinity, $|C_n|$ approaches the continuous function described by the $|\sin x/x|$ function shown in Fig. 8-4a.

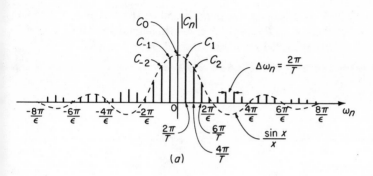

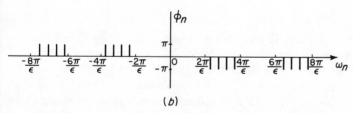

Fig. 8-4 *Discrete amplitude and phase spectra of the rectangular periodic pulse train shown in Fig. 8-3.*

The spacing between successive lines in the $|C_n|$ plots is equal to

$$\Delta\omega_n = \frac{2\pi}{T} \tag{8-12}$$

When $n = 0$, $C_0 = \epsilon$; the constant term of the Fourier series is

$$\frac{C_0}{T} = \frac{\epsilon}{T} \tag{8-13}$$

which apparently is the average value of the pulse train.

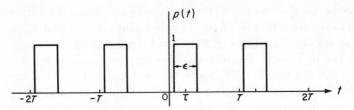

Fig. 8-5   A shifted periodic pulse train.

Example 8-3   Shifting the periodic pulse train of Fig. 8-3 to the right by $t = \tau$, where $\tau < T/2 - \epsilon/2$, gives the signal shown in Fig. 8-5. The complex Fourier coefficient of the shifted pulse train is

$$C_n = \int_{-T/2}^{T/2} p(t)e^{-j\omega_n t}\, dt = \int_{-\frac{\epsilon}{2}+\tau}^{\frac{\epsilon}{2}+\tau} e^{-j\omega_n t}\, dt$$

$$= \frac{e^{j\omega_n \epsilon/2} - e^{-j\omega_n \epsilon/2}}{j\omega_n}\, e^{-j\omega_n \tau}$$

$$= \epsilon \frac{\sin (\omega_n \epsilon/2)}{\omega_n \epsilon/2}\, e^{-j\omega_n \tau} \tag{8-14}$$

Comparing (8-14) with (8-11), we notice that the two C_n's differ by only a factor of $e^{-j\omega_n \tau}$. Since this exponential term affects only the phase shift of the complex coefficient, the magnitude of C_n is not changed by the shift of the time function. The discrete amplitude and phase spectra of the shifted pulse train are shown in Fig. 8-6. We see that the effect of shifting the pulse train to the right by τ is equivalent to adding a linear phase shift of $-\omega_n \tau$ to ϕ_n, or multiplying the C_n by a factor of $e^{-j\omega_n \tau}$. We can prove that this shifting property is also true in general. The proof is given as follows.

Let C_n be the complex Fourier coefficient of a given periodic function $g(t)$, and C_n' be the Fourier coefficient of the function $g(t - \tau)$, which is $g(t)$ shifted by τ (τ can be positive or negative of any magnitude). Then, by definition,

$$C_n' = \int_{-T/2}^{T/2} g(t - \tau)e^{-j\omega_n t}\cdot dt \tag{8-15}$$

Letting $t' = t - \tau$, then $dt' = dt - d\tau = dt$; (8-15) becomes

$$C_n' = \int_{-T/2}^{T/2} g(t')e^{-j\omega_n t'}e^{-j\omega_n \tau}\, dt'$$

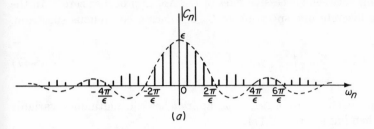

(a)

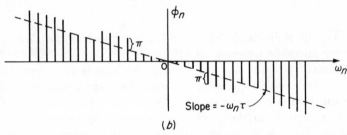

Slope $= -\omega_n \tau$

(b)

Fig. 8-6   Discrete amplitude and phase spectra of the shifted periodic pulse train shown in Fig. 8-5.

Therefore

$$C'_n = e^{-j\omega_n \tau} \int_{-T/2}^{T/2} g(t') e^{-j\omega_n t'} \, dt = e^{-j\omega_n \tau} C_n \tag{8-16}$$

8-3   FOURIER INTEGRAL AND TRANSFORM

Many signals of importance in systems and network analysis are not periodic. These signals cannot be represented by a Fourier series. However, an aperiodic function can be represented by a Fourier integral which may be regarded as a limiting case of the Fourier series. For instance, consider that we are interested in the Fourier representation of a single rectangular pulse with unity height and width ϵ. Such a pulse function cannot be represented by a Fourier series since it is not a periodic function.   However, we can construct a periodic pulse train $p(t)$ using this single pulse as the fundamental component and repeating it every T sec.   Such a periodic pulse train may take the form of Fig. 8-3. When the period T of the periodic function approaches infinity, the function $p(t)$ reverts to the original pulse signal.   Therefore the Fourier representation of the single pulse may be regarded as the limit of the Fourier series of $p(t)$ as T approaches infinity.   As T approaches infinity the spacing between successive lines of C_n, $\Delta\omega_n$ approaches zero. In the limit, the discrete line spectrum of C_n becomes a continuous spectrum. Therefore

$$\lim_{\substack{T\to\infty \\ \Delta\omega_n\to 0}} C_n = \lim_{\substack{T\to\infty \\ \Delta\omega_n\to 0}} \int_{-T/2}^{T/2} p(t)e^{-j\omega_n t}\, dt \tag{8-17}$$

As $\Delta\omega_n$ approaches zero, $n\,\Delta\omega_n = \omega_n$ approaches the continuous variable ω. We then have, from (8-17),

$$\lim_{T\to\infty} C_n = \int_{-\infty}^{\infty} p(t)e^{-j\omega t}\, dt \tag{8-18}$$

The integral on the right-hand side of (8-18) is defined as the *Fourier transform* of the aperiodic pulse signal $p(t)$.

It is important to note that the Fourier coefficients of a periodic function form a discrete line spectrum, whereas the Fourier transform of an aperiodic function is a continuous spectrum of ω. The evolution of the Fourier transform from the Fourier series is clearly shown by the waveforms of Fig. 8-7. As the period T of the periodic function increases, the spacing between the line spectrum of C_n becomes smaller; when T becomes infinite, the function becomes aperiodic, and the line spectrum converges into a continuous spectrum.

In general, given an aperiodic function $g(t)$ which satisfies Dirichlet's conditions,† its Fourier transform is given by

$$G(j\omega) = \mathfrak{F}[g(t)] = \text{Fourier transform of } g(t) = \int_{-\infty}^{\infty} g(t)e^{-j\omega t}\, dt \tag{8-19}$$

From (8-1), the Fourier series of a period function $p(t)$ is given by

$$p(t) = \frac{1}{2\pi} \sum_{n=-\infty}^{\infty} C_n e^{j\omega_n t}\, \Delta\omega_n \tag{8-20}$$

Taking the limit as T approaches infinity on both sides of (8-20), we get

$$\lim_{T\to\infty} p(t) = g(t) = \lim_{T\to\infty} \frac{1}{2\pi} \sum_{n=-\infty}^{\infty} C_n e^{j\omega_n t}\, \Delta\omega_n$$

$$= \frac{1}{2\pi} \int_{-\infty}^{\infty} G(j\omega)e^{j\omega t}\, d\omega \tag{8-21}$$

† As T approaches infinity, one of the conditions becomes $\int_{-\infty}^{\infty} |g(t)|\, dt < \infty$.

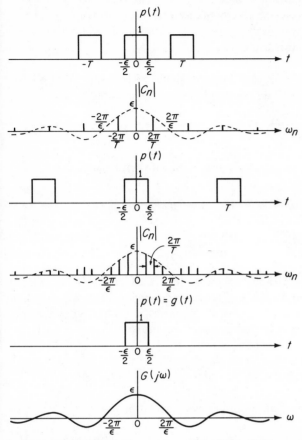

Fig. 8-7 Periodic pulse trains and their frequency spectra, showing the transition from Fourier series to Fourier transform.

which is defined as the *Fourier integral*, or the inverse Fourier transform of $G(j\omega)$.

Equations (8-19) and (8-21) are now rewritten as follows:

$$G(j\omega) = \int_{-\infty}^{\infty} g(t)e^{-j\omega t}\, dt \qquad \text{Fourier transform} \qquad (8\text{-}19)$$

$$g(t) = \frac{1}{2\pi} \int_{-\infty}^{\infty} G(j\omega)e^{j\omega t}\, d\omega \qquad \begin{array}{l}\text{Fourier integral, or in-}\\ \text{verse Fourier transform}\end{array} \qquad (8\text{-}21)$$

These two equations are called the *Fourier-transform pair*. In fact, (8-19) gives the Fourier transform of $g(t)$, which is a real-domain to complex-domain transformation; whereas (8-21) is the *inverse Fourier transform* of $G(j\omega)$, which is a complex-domain to real-domain transformation.

The following examples illustrate the evaluation of the Fourier transforms of some well-known functions.

Example 8-4 Consider the pulse signal with height 1 and width ϵ and centered at $t = 0$. The pulse signal satisfies the condition

$$\int_{-\infty}^{\infty} |g(t)|\, dt < \infty \tag{8-22}$$

and therefore is Fourier-transformable. Using (8-19), we have

$$G(j\omega) = \int_{-\infty}^{\infty} g(t)e^{-j\omega t}\, dt = \int_{-\epsilon/2}^{\epsilon/2} e^{-j\omega t}\, dt$$

$$= \frac{e^{j\omega\epsilon/2} - e^{-j\omega\epsilon/2}}{j\omega} = \epsilon\, \frac{\sin\,(\omega\epsilon/2)}{(\omega\epsilon/2)}$$

Example 8-5 Although the Fourier transform is widely used as a mathematical tool in all fields of science and engineering, many important functions which are of interest in engineering work are not Fourier-transformable. As an example, consider the function

$$g(t) = \begin{cases} e^{at} & t > 0 \\ 0 & t < 0 \end{cases} \tag{8-23}$$

where a is a constant. The Fourier transform of $g(t)$ is

$$G(j\omega) = \int_{0}^{\infty} e^{at}e^{-j\omega t}\, dt = \left[\frac{e^{at}e^{-j\omega t}}{a - j\omega}\right]_{0}^{\infty} \tag{8-24}$$

If a is a negative number, substitution of the upper limit in the last equation will result in zero; therefore (8-24) gives

$$G(j\omega) = \frac{-1}{a - j\omega} \qquad a < 0 \tag{8-25}$$

However, if $a > 0$, $G(j\omega)$ becomes infinite at the upper limit, and the Fourier transform of $g(t)$ does not exist. We could have obtained the same conclusion by using the condition in (8-22), since for $a > 0$, $g(t)$ diverges as t becomes very large.

Another often used function which does not satisfy the absolute convergence condition of (8-22) is the unit step function $u(t)$. Although it may seem that the Fourier transform of $u(t)$ could be obtained by taking the limit as a approaches zero in (8-24) or (8-25), since the step function does not satisfy the absolute convergence condition, strictly, its Fourier transform is not defined. We show later, however, that the Fourier transform of this type of function can still be represented by Fourier transforms if we admit the concept of the impulse function.

Some important properties of the Fourier transform

Several important properties of the Fourier transform are given in the following discussion without proof. Most of these have similar counterparts for the Laplace transforms presented later.

Let $G(j\omega)$ be the Fourier transform of the real-valued $g(t)$. Then

(a) Re $G(j\omega)$ is an even function of ω.
(b) Im $G(j\omega)$ is an odd function of ω.
(c) $|G(j\omega)|$ is an even function of ω.
(d) $\underline{/G(j\omega)}$ is an odd function of ω.
(e) $G(-j\omega) = \mathfrak{F}[g(-t)]$ (8-26)
(f) Linearity:

$$\mathfrak{F}[a_1g_1(t) + a_2g_2(t)] = a_1G_1(j\omega) + a_2G_2(j\omega)$$

where a_1 and $a_2 = $ const (8-27)

(g) Scale change:

$$\mathfrak{F}[g(kt)] = \frac{1}{|k|}\, G\left(\frac{\omega}{k}\right) \qquad \text{where } k = \text{a const} \qquad (8\text{-}28)$$

This property states that compressing $g(t)$ expands its spectrum and reduces it in amplitude by the same factor. The converse is also true.

(h) Real shifting:

$$\mathfrak{F}[g(t - T)] = e^{-j\omega T}G(j\omega) \qquad \text{where } T = \text{a const (positive}$$
$$\text{or negative)} \quad (8\text{-}29)$$

In other words, shifting $g(t)$ by T is equivalent to multiplying its spectrum by $e^{-j\omega T}$.

(i) Complex shifting:

$$\mathfrak{F}[e^{j\omega_0 t}g(t)] = G(j\omega - j\omega_0) \qquad (8\text{-}30)$$

(*j*) Derivatives of a function:

$$\mathfrak{F}\left[\frac{d^n g(t)}{dt^n}\right] = (j\omega)^n G(j\omega) \tag{8-31}$$

(*k*) Integration of a function:

$$\iiint\limits_{-\infty} \cdots \int_{-\infty}^{t} g(\tau)\,d\tau \cdots d\tau = \frac{1}{(j\omega)n}\,G(j\omega) \tag{8-32}$$

The impulse function and its Fourier transform

The properties of the impulse function $\delta(t)$, presented in Chap. 1, are now repeated:

$$\delta(t) = 0 \qquad t \neq 0$$
$$\int_{-\infty}^{\infty} \delta(t)\,dt = 1 \tag{8-33}$$

If $g(t)$ is a function which is continuous at $t = 0$, then

$$\int_{-\infty}^{\infty} \delta(t)g(t)\,dt = g(0) \tag{8-34}$$

Using (8-34), the Fourier transform of $\delta(t)$ is given by

$$\mathfrak{F}[\delta(t)] = \int_{-\infty}^{\infty} \delta(t)e^{-j\omega t}\,dt = [e^{-j\omega t}]_{t=0} = 1$$

Therefore the Fourier transform of the unit impulse function is *unity*. The real and the complex functions for this case are illustrated in Fig. 8-8.

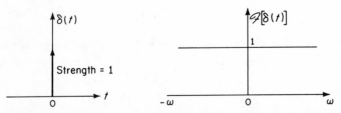

Fig. 8-8   *The Fourier transform of the unit impulse function.*

The inverse Fourier transform of *unity* may be written

$$\delta(t) = \frac{1}{2\pi} \int_{-\infty}^{\infty} e^{j\omega t}\, d\omega \tag{8-35}$$

Interchanging t and ω in the last equation, we have

$$\delta(\omega) = \frac{1}{2\pi} \int_{-\infty}^{\infty} e^{j\omega t}\, dt$$

or

$$\delta(-\omega) = \frac{1}{2\pi} \int_{-\infty}^{\infty} e^{-j\omega t}\, dt \tag{8-36}$$

Multiplying both sides of expression (8-36) by 2π, and the delta function being an even function, we get

$$2\pi\delta(-\omega) = \int_{-\infty}^{\infty} e^{-j\omega t}\, dt = 2\pi\delta(\omega) \tag{8-37}$$

The right-hand side of (8-37) is recognized as the Fourier transform of the function, which is equal to 1 for all t that lie between $-\infty$ and ∞.

Thus we have seen that the Fourier transform of *unity* is an impulse function in the frequency domain with a strength of 2π (Fig. 8-9).

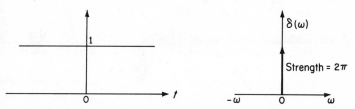

Fig. 8-9   The Fourier transform of a constant, unity.

Using the relationships of the impulse function, it is possible to define the Fourier transforms of functions such as sine and cosine, as well as simplify the work of deriving many other functions.   For instance, the Fourier transform of $\cos \omega_0 t$ is given by

$$\mathcal{F}[\cos \omega_0 t] = \int_{-\infty}^{\infty} \cos \omega_0 t\, e^{-j\omega t}\, dt \tag{8-38}$$

Substituting $\cos \omega_0 t = (e^{j\omega_0 t} + e^{-j\omega_0 t})/2$ in (8-38), we have

$$\mathfrak{F}[\cos \omega_0 t] = \frac{1}{2} \int_{-\infty}^{\infty} e^{-j(\omega-\omega_0)t}\, dt + \frac{1}{2} \int_{-\infty}^{\infty} e^{-j(\omega+\omega_0)t}\, dt$$

It follows directly from (8-37) that

$$\mathfrak{F}[\cos \omega_0 t] = \pi[\delta(\omega - \omega_0) + \delta(\omega + \omega_0)]$$

The following examples illustrate that the impulse function and the properties of the Fourier transforms given earlier can be used for the derivation of Fourier transforms.

Example 8-6   Shown in Fig. 8-10a is a pulse signal $p(t)$ with pulsewidth equal to ϵ.   The Fourier transform of this function is obtained

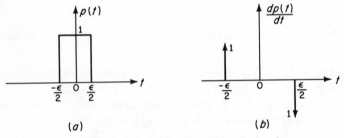

Fig. 8-10   *A pulse signal and its first time derivative.*

in Example 8-4 by means of the defining integral.   We now show that the same result can be obtained by use of the derivative and the shifting properties.

Taking the derivative of $p(t)$ with respect to t, we have the two impulses as shown in Fig. 8-10b. From the derivative property (8-31), the Fourier transform of $dp(t)/dt$ is $j\omega$ times the Fourier transform of $p(t)$. From the shifting property stated in (8-29), the Fourier transform of the two impulses in Fig. 8-10b is simply

$$e^{j\omega\epsilon/2} - e^{-j\omega\epsilon/2}$$

Equating the two transforms, we get

$$j\omega\mathfrak{F}[p(t)] = e^{j\omega\epsilon/2} - e^{-j\omega\epsilon/2} \tag{8-39}$$

A word of caution is due here in regard to the solution of $\mathfrak{F}[p(t)]$ from (8-39). We notice that (8-39) can be looked upon as the result of equating the derivatives of two functions of t.   In other words, if

$$\frac{dg_1(t)}{dt} = \frac{dg_2(t)}{dt} \tag{8-40}$$

taking the Fourier transform on both sides of this equation gives

$$j\omega G_1(j\omega) = j\omega G_2(j\omega) \tag{8-41}$$

It is easy to see that, although (8-41) is an algebraic equation, we cannot cancel the $j\omega$ terms on both sides of the equation, and we conclude that $G_1(j\omega) = G_2(j\omega)$.   In fact, since from the time-domain expression (8-40) we get

$$g_1(t) = g_2(t) + k$$

where k is a constant, taking the Fourier transform on both sides of this last expression gives

$$G_1(j\omega) = G_2(j\omega) + 2\pi k\delta(\omega) \tag{8-42}$$

We show that (8-42) still satisfies (8-41).   Multiplying both sides of (8-42) by $j\omega$, we have

$$j\omega G_1(j\omega) = j\omega G_2(j\omega) + j2\pi k\omega\delta(\omega) \tag{8-43}$$

But by definition, $\delta(\omega) = 0$ for $\omega \neq 0$; therefore $j\omega\delta(\omega)$ is zero for all values of ω.   This proves that (8-43) and (8-41) are identical.

The foregoing development shows that we cannot solve for $\mathfrak{F}[p(t)]$ simply from (8-39); rather, we should write

$$
\begin{aligned}
\mathfrak{F}[p(t)] &= \frac{e^{j\omega\epsilon/2} - e^{-j\omega\epsilon/2}}{j\omega} + 2\pi k\delta(\omega) \\
&= \epsilon\,\frac{\sin(\omega\epsilon/2)}{\omega\epsilon/2} + 2\pi k\delta(\omega)
\end{aligned} \tag{8-44}
$$

To complete the problem, we must find the value of k in (8-42).   The inverse Fourier transform of $\mathfrak{F}[p(t)]$ is given by

$$p(t) = \frac{1}{2\pi} \int_{-\infty}^{\infty} \mathfrak{F}[p(t)]e^{-j\omega t}\,d\omega$$

For the pulse signal in Fig. 7-10a, at $t = 0$,

$$p(0) = 1 = \frac{1}{2\pi} \int_{-\infty}^{\infty} \epsilon \frac{\sin (\omega\epsilon/2)}{\omega\epsilon/2} \, d\omega + \int_{-\infty}^{\infty} k\delta(\omega) \, d\omega \tag{8-45}$$

or

$$p(0) = 1 = \frac{1}{\pi} \int_{-\infty}^{\infty} \frac{\sin (\omega\epsilon/2)}{\omega\epsilon/2} \, d\frac{\omega\epsilon}{2} + k \tag{8-46}$$

Since

$$\int_{-\infty}^{\infty} \frac{\sin x}{x} \, dx = \pi \tag{8-47}$$

the first integral on the right-hand side of (8-46) is unity.   Therefore k is zero.   We have

$$\mathfrak{F}[p(t)] = \epsilon \frac{\sin (\omega\epsilon/2)}{\omega\epsilon/2}$$

which clearly agrees with the result obtained previously, in Example 8-4.

Since the Fourier transform of a constant is a delta function, $\delta(\omega)$, in the complex domain, we can conclude that the Fourier transform of a function $g(t)$ would contain a delta function only if $g(t)$ had a d-c value. The area underneath the pulse signal $p(t)$ shown in Fig. 8-10a is finite, but the d-c value represented by the average from $t = -\infty$ to $+\infty$ is zero.   Therefore we could have arrived at the conclusion that $k = 0$ in (8-44) simply by inspection of the pulse signal $p(t)$.

Example 8-7   Consider the signal shown in Fig. 8-11a.   We first evaluate the Fourier transform of this signal, using the defining integral.   We have

$$G(j\omega) = \int_{-\infty}^{\infty} g(t)e^{-j\omega t} \, dt = \int_{-T/2}^{T/2} \frac{2}{T} te^{-j\omega t} \, dt$$

Therefore

$$\begin{aligned}
G(j\omega) &= \frac{2}{T} \left[-\frac{t}{j\omega} e^{-j\omega t} \right]_{-T/2}^{T/2} - \frac{2}{T} \left(-\frac{1}{j\omega} \right) \int_{-T/2}^{T/2} e^{-j\omega t} \, dt \\
&= -\frac{1}{j\omega} \left(e^{j\omega T/2} + e^{-j\omega T/2} \right) + \frac{2}{j\omega} \frac{\sin (\omega T/2)}{\omega T/2} \\
&= -\frac{2}{j\omega} \cos \left(\frac{\omega T}{2} \right) + \frac{4}{j\omega^2 T} \sin \frac{\omega T}{2} \tag{8-48}
\end{aligned}$$

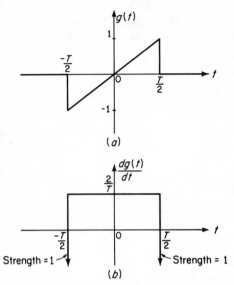

Fig. 8-11   Signals used in Example 8-7.

Let us now verify this result by taking the derivative of $g(t)$ with respect to t. The function $dg(t)/dt$ is shown in Fig. 8-11b. The Fourier transform of $dg(t)/dt$ is readily determined by inspection from Fig. 8-11b. We have

$$j\omega G(j\omega) = -e^{j\omega T/2} - e^{-j\omega T/2} + \frac{2}{T}\, T\, \frac{\sin(\omega T/2)}{\omega T/2}$$

From (8-42), we get

$$G(j\omega) = \frac{-e^{j\omega T/2} - e^{-j\omega T/2}}{j\omega} + \frac{2}{j\omega}\frac{\sin(\omega T/2)}{\omega T/2} + 2\pi k\delta(\omega)$$

$$= -\frac{2}{j\omega}\cos\left(\frac{\omega T}{2}\right) + \frac{4}{j\omega^2 T}\sin\left(\frac{\omega T}{2}\right) + 2\pi k\delta(\omega) \qquad (8\text{-}49)$$

Since the signal $g(t)$ has a zero average value, k equals zero. This makes the results in (8-48) and (8-49) identical. The value of k can also be found by substituting the expression $G(j\omega)$ in (8-49) in the inverse Fourier integral $g(0)$.

Fourier transform of periodic functions

The Fourier transforms of periodic functions other than the sine and cosine functions are found by use of the shifting property stated in (8-29).

If a given periodic function $g_T(t)$ is described by $g(t)$ during the period $-T/2 < t \le T/2$, the function during $nT - T/2 < t \le nT + T/2$ is simply $g(t - nT)$. Thus the periodic function may be written

$$g_T(t) = \sum_{n=-\infty}^{\infty} g(t - nT) \qquad (8\text{-}50)$$

Taking the Fourier transform on both sides of (8-50) gives

$$G_T(j\omega) = \mathfrak{F}\Big[\sum_{n=-\infty}^{\infty} g(t - nT) \Big] = \sum_{n=-\infty}^{\infty} \mathfrak{F}[g(t - nT)] \qquad (8\text{-}51)$$

Using (8-29), expression (8-51) becomes

$$G_T(j\omega) = \sum_{n=-\infty}^{\infty} G(j\omega)e^{-jn\omega T} \qquad (8\text{-}52)$$

where $G(j\omega)$ is the Fourier transform of $g(t)$.

As a simple illustration, suppose that the signal shown in Fig. 8-11a is repeated every T sec between $t = -\infty$ and $t = +\infty$. We have the periodic sawtooth signal shown in Fig. 8-12. The Fourier transform of

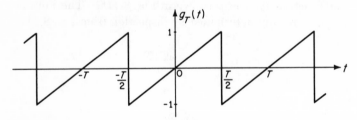

Fig. 8-12   *A periodic sawtooth signal.*

this sawtooth signal is obtained by substituting the expression (8-48) in (8-52). Thus

$$G_T(j\omega) = \sum_{n=-\infty}^{\infty} \left[-\frac{2}{j\omega} \cos\left(\frac{\omega T}{2}\right) + \frac{4}{j\omega^2 T} \sin\frac{\omega T}{2} \right] e^{-jn\omega T} \qquad (8\text{-}53)$$

8-4   LAPLACE TRANSFORMS—DEFINITIONS

It was pointed out in the preceding section that the Fourier transform integrals of many practical signals such as $\sin t$, $\cos t$, $u(t)$, t, t^2, etc., do not converge absolutely.   Although the Fourier transforms of some of these functions can be represented by delta function, strictly, they do not have any physical meaning and practical applications.

In order to handle functions of the nonconvergent type, we now consider the Fourier transform of the function $g(t)$ multiplied by a convergence function $e^{-\sigma t}$, where σ is a real number, so chosen to ensure the absolute convergence of the Fourier transform.   In other words,

$$\int_{-\infty}^{\infty} |g(t)e^{-\sigma t}| \, dt < \infty \tag{8-54}$$

The Fourier transform of $e^{-\sigma t}g(t)$ is

$$G(\sigma,j\omega) = \int_{-\infty}^{\infty} g(t)e^{-\sigma t}e^{-j\omega t} \, dt \tag{8-55}$$

Rather than consider this integral as the Fourier integral of $e^{-\sigma t}g(t)$, there is an advantage in defining it as the "two-sided Laplace transform," or the "bilateral Laplace transform," of $g(t)$.   The terms "two-sided" and "bilateral" refer to the limits of integration of (8-55) being taken from $-\infty$ to $+\infty$.   However, it is clear that, generally, the same value of σ cannot be used over the entire range of integration from $-\infty$ to $+\infty$; for σ greater than zero, the integral converges when it is evaluated at the upper limit as $t \to +\infty$, and it diverges at the lower limit as $t \to -\infty$. This means that, given $g(t)$, unless a finite value of σ can be found such that the condition of absolute convergence in (8-54) is satisfied, the two-sided Laplace transform of $g(t)$ does not exist.   For instance, if $g(t) = t$, for $-\infty < t < \infty$, in order that the integral

$$\int_{-\infty}^{0} te^{-\sigma t}e^{-j\omega t} \, dt \qquad t < 0$$

converge absolutely, σ must be less than zero.   However, the condition that

$$\int_{0}^{\infty} te^{-t} \, dt \qquad t > 0$$

be absolutely convergent requires that $\sigma > 0$.   Since these conditions on σ contradict each other, the two-sided Laplace transform of t is not defined.

Often, however, such difficulty is not encountered because one is actually interested only in the positive range of t.   For this, it is convenient to define the "one-sided Laplace transform," or the "unilateral

Laplace transform," or just the *Laplace transform*, by considering only the range of integration from 0^- to $+\infty$. We choose 0^- as the lower limit (rather than just 0 or 0^+) to include cases in which the function $g(t)$ may have a jump discontinuity or an impulse at $t = 0$. The Laplace transform of $g(t)$ is now given by

$$G(\sigma, j\omega) = \int_{0-}^{\infty} g(t)e^{-\sigma t}e^{-j\omega t} \, dt \tag{8-56}$$

where σ is to be chosen so that, as a sufficient but not necessary condition,

$$\int_{0-}^{\infty} |g(t)e^{-\sigma t}| \, dt < \infty \tag{8-57}$$

It is important to note that in the Laplace transform integral defined by (8-56), the values of $g(t)$ prior to $t = 0^-$ do not influence the evaluation of the integral. This does not really impose any serious limitations on the application of the Laplace transform, since, in the usual transient studies, time origin is taken at the instant $t = 0$ or some finite time $t > 0$.

If we let $s = \sigma + j\omega$, where s is a complex parameter, (8-56) becomes

$$G(s) = \int_{0-}^{\infty} g(t)e^{-st} \, dt \tag{8-58}$$

This integral defines the Laplace transform of $g(t)$, and is denoted by

$$G(s) = \mathcal{L}[g(t)] \tag{8-59}$$

A sufficient condition for the Laplace transform to exist follows directly from (8-57); i.e.,

$$\int_{0-}^{\infty} |g(t)e^{-\sigma t}| \, dt < \infty \tag{8-60}$$

for some finite σ. The region of the s plane in which the Laplace transform of a function exists is called the *region of absolute convergence*. The greatest lower bound of the values σ in the region of convergence is defined as the *abscissa of absolute convergence*.

We now use the following examples to illustrate the idea of the region and the abscissa of convergence and the Laplace transforms of some simple functions.

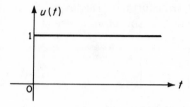

Fig. 8-13   The unit step function.

Example 8-8   Find the Laplace transform of the unit step function $u(t)$ shown in Fig. 8-13.

$$\mathcal{L}[u(t)] = \int_{0^-}^{\infty} 1 \times e^{-st} \, dt = \left[-\frac{1}{s} e^{-st} \right]_{0^-}^{\infty} \tag{8-61}$$

For $t > 0$ and if $\sigma > 0$, the upper limit, $t = \infty$, will make $e^{-st} = 0$. Thus (8-61) gives

$$\mathcal{L}[u(t)] = -\frac{1}{s} (0 - 1) = \frac{1}{s} \tag{8-62}$$

The maximum lower bound on σ is found by investigating the behavior of the integral at the upper limit $+\infty$ of the Laplace transform integral.   It is apparent in this case that the right-hand side of (8-61) will be zero at the upper limit only if the real part of s, σ is positive.   From this result we conclude that the Laplace transform of the unit step function is defined only for Re $(s) = \sigma > 0$, which is the right half of the s plane.   The abscissa of absolute convergence of $\mathcal{L}[u(t)]$ is the imaginary axis of the s plane (Fig. 8-14).

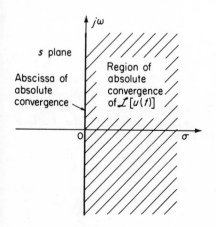

Fig. 8-14   Abscissa and region of absolute convergence of the Laplace transform of a unit step function.

Example 8-9   Find the Laplace transform of the exponential function $g(t) = e^{-at}$ for $t > 0$. First, consider the case where $a > 0$. Substituting $g(t)$ in the defining integral, we get

$$G(s) = \mathcal{L}[e^{-at}] = \int_{0^-}^{\infty} e^{-at}e^{-st}\, dt = -\left[\frac{e^{-(s+a)t}}{s+a}\right]_{0^-}^{\infty} \tag{8-63}$$

Again, investigating the behavior of $e^{-(s+a)t}$ at the upper limit of integration, we have

$$\lim_{t \to \infty} e^{-(\sigma+a)t}e^{-j\omega t} = 0$$

only if $\sigma > -a$. Therefore the abscissa of absolute convergence for $\mathcal{L}[e^{-at}]$, $a > 0$, is a straight line described by Re $(s) = -a$, and the region of convergence is to the right of this abscissa; or Re $(s) = \sigma > -a$. Now with the real part of s satisfying this convergence property, (8-63) becomes

$$G(s) = \frac{1}{s+a} \tag{8-64}$$

The function e^{-at} for $a > 0$ is sketched in Fig. 8-15, and the abscissa of convergence of its Laplace transform is shown in Fig. 8-16.

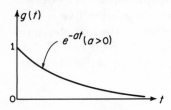

Fig. 8-15   *An exponential function.*

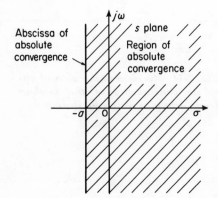

Fig. 8-16   *Abscissa and region of absolute convergence of the Laplace transform of e^{-at} $(a > 0)$.*

If a is a negative number, we let $a = -b$, where $b > 0$. Then, $g(t) = e^{bt}$ for $t > 0$. The Laplace transform of $g(t)$ is

$$G(s) = \int_{0^-}^{\infty} e^{bt} e^{-st}\, dt = \left[\frac{-e^{-(s-b)t}}{s - b}\right]_{0^-}^{\infty} \tag{8-65}$$

In this case, since the magnitude of e^{bt} increases as t approaches infinity, it is intuitively clear that, in order for $G(s)$ to converge absolutely, the convergent factor $e^{-\sigma t}$ must converge more rapidly than e^{bt} diverges as t becomes large. From the upper limit of (8-65), we see that the condition of absolute convergence of $G(s)$ is $\sigma > b$. Therefore (8-65) gives

$$G(s) = \frac{1}{s - b} \tag{8-66}$$

The function e^{bt} $(b > 0)$ and the region of convergence of its Laplace transform are shown in Figs. 8-17 and 8-18, respectively.

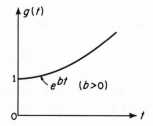

Fig. 8-17   *An exponential function.*

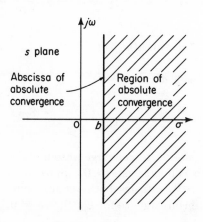

Fig. 8-18   *Region of absolute convergence of $G(s) = 1/(s - b)$.*

Example 8-10   Let us find the Laplace transform of the sine function $g(t) = \sin \omega_0 t$. By definition,

$$G(s) = \int_{0^-}^{\infty} \sin \omega_0 t e^{-st} \, dt = \int_{0^-}^{\infty} \frac{e^{j\omega_0 t} - e^{-j\omega_0 t}}{2j} e^{-st} \, dt$$

$$= \frac{1}{2j} \left[\frac{e^{-(s-j\omega_0)t}}{-(s - j\omega_0)} - \frac{e^{-(s+j\omega_0)t}}{-(s + j\omega_0)} \right]_{0^-}^{\infty} \tag{8-67}$$

We see that (8-67) converges to a finite quantity only if it becomes zero at the upper limit of integration, which requires that the real part of s be greater than zero.   Therefore the abscissa of absolute convergence is the $j\omega$ axis, and the region of absolute convergence is the entire right half of the s plane.

Completing the integration of (8-67),

$$G(s) = \frac{1}{2j} \left(\frac{1}{s - j\omega_0} - \frac{1}{s + j\omega_0} \right) = \frac{\omega_0}{s^2 + \omega_0^2} \tag{8-68}$$

Using the same procedure, it can easily be shown that the Laplace transform of $\cos \omega_0 t$ is $s/(s^2 + \omega_0^2)$, and the abscissa of absolute convergence is $\sigma = 0$.

Example 8-11   In this example we show that if σ_1 and σ_2 are the abscissas of absolute convergence of $g_1(t)$ and $g_2(t)$, respectively, the abscissa of convergence of the Laplace transform of $g_1(t) + g_2(t)$ is max (σ_1, σ_2), that is, the largest value of σ_1 and σ_2.

Suppose that $g_1(t) = e^{-2t}$ and $g_2(t) = \sin \omega_0 t$.   From the results of Examples 8-9 and 8-10, we have $\sigma_1 = -2$ and $\sigma_2 = 0$.   The Laplace transform of $g_1(t) + g_2(t)$ is

$$\mathcal{L}[g(t)] = \mathcal{L}[g_1(t) + g_2(t)] = \int_{0^-}^{\infty} (e^{-2t} + \sin \omega_0 t) e^{-st} \, dt$$

$$= \int_{0^-}^{\infty} e^{-2t} e^{-st} \, dt + \int_{0^-}^{\infty} \sin \omega_0 t e^{-st} \, dt$$

$$= \frac{1}{s + 2} + \frac{\omega_0}{s^2 + \omega_0^2} \tag{8-69}$$

The requirement on $\sigma = \text{Re}\,(s)$ for $1/(s + 2)$ to converge absolutely is $\sigma > -2$, and that for $\omega_0/(s^2 + \omega_0^2)$ to converge is $\sigma > 0$.   Since it is apparent that the latter condition, $\sigma > 0$, satisfies both requirements simultaneously, the abscissa of absolute convergence for $\mathcal{L}[g(t)]$ is $\sigma = 0$.

Example 8-12   Thus far, in the Laplace transforms we have encountered in these illustrative examples, the regions of convergence are some portions of the s plane.   However, there are functions whose Laplace transforms are convergent everywhere in the finite s plane; and there are functions whose Laplace transforms do not converge anywhere in the finite s plane, and the functions are said to be non-Laplace-transformable.

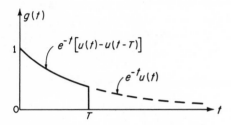

Fig. 8-19 $g(t) = e^{-t}[u(t) - u(t - T)]$.

Consider the function

$$g(t) = e^{-t}[u(t) - u(t - T)] \tag{8-70}$$

which is sketched as shown in Fig. 8-19.   The Laplace transform of $g(t)$ is given by

$$G(s) = \int_{0^-}^{\infty} e^{-t}[u(t) - u(t - T)]e^{-st}\, dt$$

$$= \int_{0^-}^{T} e^{-t}e^{-st}\, dt = \left[-\frac{1}{s+1} e^{-(s+1)t} \right]_{0^-}^{T}$$

$$= -\frac{1}{s+1} e^{-(s+1)T} + \frac{1}{s+1} \tag{8-71}$$

We notice that the integral at the upper limit is infinite only if

$$\sigma = \text{Re } (s) = -\infty$$

Therefore the abscissa of absolute convergence for $G(s)$ is $\sigma = -\infty$, and the region of convergence is $\sigma > -\infty$.

It is a simple matter to show that the function

$$g(t) = e^{t^2} \qquad t > 0 \tag{8-72}$$

Table 8-1 Table of Laplace transforms

Laplace transform $F(s)$	Time function $f(t) \quad t > 0$
1	$\delta(t)$ unit impulse function
$\dfrac{1}{s}$	$u(t)$ unit step function
$\dfrac{1}{s^2}$	t unit ramp function
$\dfrac{1}{s^{n+1}}$	$\dfrac{1}{n!}\,t^n \quad n = \text{positive integer}$
$\dfrac{1}{s+a}$	e^{-at}
$\dfrac{1}{(s+a)^2}$	te^{-at}
$\dfrac{1}{(s+a)(s+b)}$	$\dfrac{e^{-at} - e^{-bt}}{b-a}$
$\dfrac{1}{(s+a)^n}$	$\dfrac{1}{(n-1)!}\,t^{n-1}e^{-at} \quad n = \text{positive integer}$
$\dfrac{1}{s(s+a)}$	$\dfrac{1}{a}\left(1 - e^{-at}\right)$
$\dfrac{1}{s(s+a)(s+b)}$	$\dfrac{1}{ab}\left(1 - \dfrac{b}{b-a}\,e^{-at} + \dfrac{a}{b-a}\,e^{-bt}\right) \quad a \neq b$
$\dfrac{1}{s(s+a)^2}$	$\dfrac{1}{a^2}[1 - (1+at)e^{-at}]$
$\dfrac{\omega}{s^2 + \omega^2}$	$\sin \omega t$
$\dfrac{s}{s^2 + \omega^2}$	$\cos \omega t$
$\dfrac{\omega_n{}^2}{s^2 + 2\zeta\omega_n s + \omega_n{}^2}$	$\dfrac{\omega_n{}^2}{\sqrt{1-\zeta^2}}\,e^{-\zeta\omega_n t}\sin \omega_n \sqrt{1-\zeta^2}\,t$
$\dfrac{\omega_n{}^2}{s(s^2 + 2\zeta\omega_n s + \omega_n{}^2)}$	$1 + \dfrac{1}{\sqrt{1-\zeta^2}}\,e^{-\zeta\omega_n t}\sin (\omega_n \sqrt{1-\zeta^2}\,t - \phi)$ where $\phi = \tan^{-1}\dfrac{\sqrt{1-\zeta^2}}{-\zeta}$
$\dfrac{\omega_n{}^2}{s(s^2 + \omega_n{}^2)}$	$1 - \cos \omega_n t$
$\dfrac{s}{(s^2 + \omega_n{}^2)^2}$	$\dfrac{1}{2\omega_n}\,t \sin \omega_n t$
$\dfrac{1}{s^2(s+a)}$	$\dfrac{1}{a^2}(at - 1 + e^{-at})$

is not Laplace-transformable. As e^{t^2} increases more rapidly than $e^{-\sigma t}$ decreases for any finite σ, the integral of $e^{t^2}e^{-st}$ never converges for $t > 0$ for any finite σ. Fortunately, this type of non-Laplace-transformable function is rarely encountered in engineering practice, and we need not be concerned by its existence.

It is necessary to remark here that, when applying Laplace transformation, the Laplace transforms need not always be found by direct integration. In fact, the amount of work involved in finding the Laplace transforms of complicated functions via the direct-integration approach may be formidable. However, we can usually treat a complicated function $g(t)$ as an algebraic combination of several simple functions whose Laplace transforms are already known and are often tabulated, as in accompanying Table 8-1. The Laplace transform of $g(t)$ is then found by combining the transforms of these simple functions according to the theorems and properties of the Laplace transformation.

8-5 PROPERTIES AND THEOREMS OF THE LAPLACE TRANSFORMS

A complete understanding and appreciation of the usefulness of the Laplace transformation cannot be attained until its properties are known. Some of the important theorems of the Laplace transform are stated and proved in the following discussion.

1. *The Laplace transform of the product of a constant k and a function $g(t)$ is the product of k and the Laplace transform of $g(t)$; that is,*

$$\mathcal{L}[kg(t)] = kG(s) \tag{8-73}$$

where $G(s) = \mathcal{L}[g(t)]$.

Proof   By definition,

$$\mathcal{L}[kg(t)] = \int_{0^-}^{\infty} kg(t)e^{-st}\, dt = k\int_{0^-}^{\infty} g(t)e^{-st}\, dt = kG(s)$$

2. *The Laplace transform of the sum (difference) of two functions is equal to the sum (difference) of the Laplace transforms of the two functions. Therefore*

$$\mathcal{L}[g_1(t) \pm g_2(t)] = G_1(s) \pm G_2(s) \tag{8-74}$$

where $G_1(s) = \mathcal{L}[g_1(t)]$ and $G_2(s) = \mathcal{L}[g_2(t)]$.

Proof   By definition,

$$\mathcal{L}[g_1(t) \pm g_2(t)] = \int_{0^-}^{\infty} [g_1(t) \pm g_2(t)]e^{-st}\, dt$$

$$= \int_{0^-}^{\infty} g_1(t)e^{-st}\, dt \pm \int_{0^-}^{\infty} g_2(t)e^{-st}\, dt = G_1(s) \pm G_2(s)$$

3. *The Laplace transform of the first derivative of a function $g(t)$ is s times the Laplace transform of $g(t)$ minus the limit of $g(t)$ as t approaches zero from the left; i.e.,*

$$\mathcal{L}\left[\frac{dg(t)}{dt}\right] = sG(s) - \lim_{t \to 0^-} g(t) = sG(s) - g(0^-) \qquad (8\text{-}75)$$

In general, the Laplace transform of the nth derivative of $g(t)$ is

$$\mathcal{L}\left[\frac{d^n g(t)}{dt^n}\right] = s^n G(s) - \lim_{t \to 0^-}\left[s^{n-1}g(t) + s^{n-2}\frac{dg(t)}{dt} + \cdots\right.$$

$$\left. + \frac{d^{n-1}g(t)}{dt^{n-1}}\right]$$

$$= s^n G(s) - s^{n-1}g(0^-) - s^{n-2}g^{(1)}(0^-)$$

$$- \cdots - g^{(n-1)}(0^-) \quad (8\text{-}76)$$

Proof   By definition,

$$\mathcal{L}\left[\frac{dg(t)}{dt}\right] = \int_{0^-}^{\infty} \frac{dg(t)}{dt}\, e^{-st}\, dt$$

Integrating by parts with $u = e^{-st}$ and $v = g(t)$, we have

$$\mathcal{L}\left[\frac{dg(t)}{dt}\right] = \int_{0^-}^{\infty} u\, dv = [e^{-st}g(t)]_{0^-}^{\infty} - \int_{0^-}^{\infty} -se^{-st}g(t)\, dt$$

$$= sG(s) - g(0^-)$$

The general expression of (8-76) can be proved by repeated application of this procedure.

The applications of the differentiation property of the Laplace transform are illustrated by the following examples.

Example 8-13   It is pointed out in Sec. 8-4 that, since the Laplace transform integral is defined from 0^- to ∞, the behavior of the function

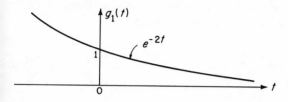

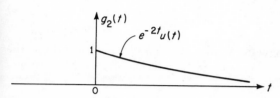

Fig. 8-20   *Two functions having the same Laplace transform.*

$g(t)$ for $t < 0$ never enters the integral and therefore is immaterial.   For this reason, the two functions shown in Fig. 8-20 have the same Laplace transform; i.e.,

$$G_1(s) = G_2(s) = \frac{1}{s + 2}$$

The derivative of $g_1(t)$ is

$$\frac{dg_1(t)}{dt} = -2e^{-2t} \qquad \text{all } t \tag{8-77}$$

Strictly, the derivative of $g_2(t)$ is not defined at $t = 0$.   However, if we admit the impulse function,

$$\frac{dg_2(t)}{dt} = -2e^{-2t}u(t) + \delta(t) \qquad \text{all } t \tag{8-78}$$

Therefore the derivative of the jump discontinuity of $g_2(t)$ at $t = 0$ has produced an impulse function at $t = 0$.   Taking the Laplace transforms of (8-77) and (8-78) gives

$$\mathcal{L}\left[\frac{dg_1(t)}{dt}\right] = \mathcal{L}[-2e^{-2t}] = \frac{-2}{s + 2} \tag{8-79}$$

$$\mathcal{L}\left[\frac{dg_2(t)}{dt}\right] = \mathcal{L}[-2e^{-2t}u(t)] + \mathcal{L}[\delta(t)] \tag{8-80}$$

The Laplace transform of the unit impulse function is found directly from the definition of the impulse function.   We have

$$\mathcal{L}[\delta(t)] = \int_{0^-}^{\infty} \delta(t)e^{-st}\,dt = [e^{-st}]_{t=0} = 1 \qquad (8\text{-}81)$$

Therefore (8-80) gives

$$\mathcal{L}\left[\frac{dg_2(t)}{dt}\right] = \frac{-2}{s+2} + 1 = \frac{s}{s+2} \qquad (8\text{-}82)$$

We now show that these same results are also obtained by use of the differentiation theorem of the Laplace transformation.   For the function $g_1(t)$, $g_1(0^-) = 1$.   From (8-75),

$$\mathcal{L}\left[\frac{dg_1(t)}{dt}\right] = \frac{s}{s+2} - 1 = \frac{-2}{s+2}$$

which agrees with the result in (8-79).
For $g_2(t)$, however, $g_2(0^-) = 0$; (8-75) gives

$$\mathcal{L}\left[\frac{dg_2(t)}{dt}\right] = \frac{s}{s+2} - 0 = \frac{s}{s+2}$$

which agrees with (8-82).
This illustrative example has brought out the importance of defining the Laplace transform integral from 0^- to ∞ instead of from 0^+ to ∞, since in the latter case the transform integral would exclude any impulse function located at the origin.
The differentiation theorem is valid for functions that are continuous or discontinuous at $t = 0$.   It is necessary only to make sure that the limit of $g(t)$ as t approaches 0^- be properly taken.

4. *The Laplace transform of the integral of a function $g(t)$ is*

$$\mathcal{L}\left(\int_0^t g(\tau)\,d\tau\right) = \frac{G(s)}{s} \qquad (8\text{-}83)$$

Proof   By definition,

$$\mathcal{L}\left(\int_0^t g(\tau)\,d\tau\right) = \int_0^{\infty}\left[\int_0^t g(\tau)\,d\tau\right]e^{-st}\,dt \qquad (8\text{-}84)$$

Integrating by parts with

$$u = \int_0^t g(\tau)\, d\tau \qquad du = g(t)\, dt$$

$$dv = e^{-st}\, dt \qquad v = -\frac{e^{-st}}{s}$$

(8-84) becomes

$$\mathcal{L}\left[\int_0^t g(\tau)\, d\tau\right] = \left[-\frac{e^{-st}}{s}\int_0^t g(\tau)\, d\tau\right]_0^\infty + \int_0^\infty \frac{e^{-st}}{s} g(t)\, dt$$

The first term on the right-hand side of the last equation is zero.   Thus

$$\mathcal{L}\left[\int_0^t g(\tau)\, d\tau\right] = \frac{G(s)}{s}$$

By repeated application of the proof of (8-83), we can generalize it for higher-order integrations.   For nth-order integration, we have

$$\mathcal{L}\left[\underbrace{\int_0^{t_1}\int_0^{t_2}\cdots\int_0^{t_n} g(\tau)\, d\tau\, dt_n \cdots dt_1}_{n}\right] = \frac{G(s)}{s^n} \tag{8-85}$$

The application of the integration properties of the Laplace transforms is now illustrated by the following example.

Example 8-14   Find the Laplace transform of $t^n u(t)$, where n is a positive integer, without using the Laplace transform integral.

Since the Laplace transform of the unit step function is $1/s$, and

$$\mathcal{L}[tu(t)] = \int_0^t u(\tau)\, d\tau$$

the Laplace transform of $tu(t)$ is given by

$$\mathcal{L}[tu(t)] = \mathcal{L}\left[\int_0^t u(\tau)\, d\tau\right] = \frac{1}{s^2} \tag{8-86}$$

Similarly,

$$\mathcal{L}[t^2 u(t)] = \mathcal{L}\left[2\int_0^t \tau u(\tau)\, d\tau\right] = \frac{2}{s}\frac{1}{s^2} = \frac{2}{s^3} \tag{8-87}$$

and

$$\mathcal{L}[t^3 u(t)] = \mathcal{L}\left[3 \int_0^t \tau^2 u(\tau)\, d\tau \right] = \frac{3!}{s^4} \tag{8-88}$$

Thus, for any positive integer n,

$$\mathcal{L}[t^n u(t)] = \frac{n!}{s^{n+1}} \tag{8-89}$$

5. *Shifting theorem (real translation)*   *The Laplace transform of a function $g(t)$ shifted to the right by T is equal to the Laplace transform of $g(t)$ multiplied by e^{-Ts}; that is,*

$$\mathcal{L}[g(t - T)u(t - T)] = G(s)e^{-Ts} \qquad T > 0 \tag{8-90}$$

where $u(t - T)$ is the unit step function shifted to the right by T, and $G(s)$ is the Laplace transform of $g(t)$.

Proof   By definition,

$$\mathcal{L}[g(t - T)u(t - T)] = \int_T^\infty g(t - T)e^{-st}\, dt \tag{8-91}$$

Letting $\tau = t - T$, (8-91) is written

$$\mathcal{L}[g(\tau)u(\tau)] = \int_0^\infty g(\tau)e^{-(T+\tau)s}\, d\tau$$

$$= e^{-Ts} \int_0^\infty g(\tau)e^{-\tau s}\, d\tau = G(s)e^{-Ts}$$

It is natural to question the validity of the shifting relationship given in (8-90) if T is negative. In other words, if $g(t)$ is defined for $t > 0$, is the following relation true?

$$\mathcal{L}[g(t - T)u(t)] = G(s)e^{-Ts} \qquad T < 0 \tag{8-92}$$

We can answer this question simply by substituting the left-hand side of (8-92) in the defining Laplace integral. We have

$$\mathcal{L}[g(t - T)u(t)] = \int_0^\infty g(t - T)e^{-st}\, dt$$

Letting $\tau = t - T$, the last integral becomes

$$\mathcal{L}[g(t - T)u(t)] = \int_{-T}^\infty g(\tau)e^{-s(\tau+T)}\, d\tau = e^{-Ts} \int_{-T}^\infty g(\tau)e^{-\tau s}\, d\tau \tag{8-93}$$

Since the right-hand side of (8-93) is not $e^{-Ts}G(s)$, Eqs. (8-92) and (8-93) are not the same in general.   In fact,

$$G(s) = \int_0^\infty g(\tau)e^{-\tau s}\,d\tau = \int_{-T}^\infty g(\tau)e^{-\tau s}\,d\tau \qquad T < 0$$

only if $g(\tau) = 0$ for $0 < \tau < -T$.   This means that expression (8-92) is correct only if $g(t) = 0$ for $0 < t < -T(T < 0)$.

The shifting theorem stated in (8-90) is one of the most important and most useful theorems in Laplace-transform applications.   Its principal use in the analysis of networks and systems is the transform representation of complex functions and signals.   The following examples illustrate the importance and the applications of the theorem.

Example 8-15   Find the Laplace transform of the rectangular pulse shown in Fig. 8-21a.

The pulse signal $g(t)$ can be considered as the sum of the two unit step functions $u(t)$ and $-u(t - T)$ as shown in Fig. 8-21b.   The Laplace

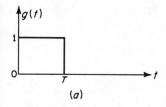

(a)

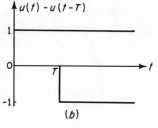

(b)

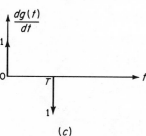

(c)

Fig. 8-21   Rectangular pulse for Example 8-15.

transform of $u(t)$ is $1/s$, and the Laplace transform of the shifted unit step function is $-1/s$ times the shifting factor e^{-Ts}. Therefore we have

$$G(s) = \mathcal{L}[u(t) - u(t - T)] = \frac{1}{s} - \frac{1}{s}e^{-Ts} = \frac{1 - e^{-Ts}}{s} \qquad (8\text{-}94)$$

The same problem can be solved using the differentiation and the shifting theorems. Differentiating the pulse signal with respect to t gives the two impulses shown in Fig. 8-21c whose Laplace transform is $1 - e^{-Ts}$. Then, from (8-75), we have

$$\mathcal{L}\left[\frac{dg(t)}{dt}\right] = sG(s) - g(0^-) = 1 - e^{-Ts}$$

Solving for $G(s)$ from the last equation, and since $g(0^-)$ is zero, we get

$$G(s) = \frac{1 - e^{-Ts}}{s}$$

Example 8-16 Find and compare the Laplace transforms of the following two functions:

$$g_1(t) = e^{-a(t-T)}u(t - T) \qquad (8\text{-}95)$$

$$g_2(t) = e^{-at}u(t - T) \qquad (8\text{-}96)$$

where T is positive.

The two signals are depicted in Fig. 8-22. It is important to note that, although $g_1(t)$ is the exponential function e^{-at} delayed by T, $g_2(t)$ does not involve any shifting; it is simply the signal e^{-at} multiplied by the delayed unit step $u(t - T)$. Thus $g_2(t) = 0$ for $t < T$. The Laplace transform of $g_1(t)$ is obtained by direct application of the shifting theorem. Since the Laplace transform of e^{-at} is $1/(s + a)$, the Laplace transform

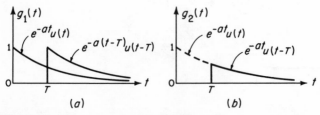

Fig. 8-22 *Two exponential signals.*

of the shifted e^{-at} is

$$G_1(s) = \frac{1}{s+a} e^{-Ts} \tag{8-97}$$

The signal $g_2(t)$ may be formed by first shifting $e^{-at}u(t)$ to the left by T, multiplying it by $u(t)$, and then shifting it back by T. This process is

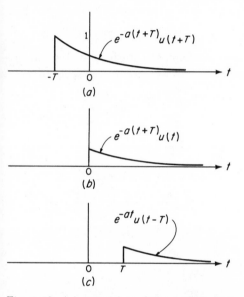

(a)

(b)

(c)

Fig. 8-23 *(a) $e^{-at}u(t)$ is shifted to the left by T. (b) The shifted e^{-at} is multiplied by $u(t)$. (c) The signal in (b) is shifted to the right by T.*

illustrated in Fig. 8-23. The Laplace transform of $e^{-a(t+T)}u(t)$ is

$$\mathcal{L}[e^{-a(t+T)}u(t)] = e^{-aT}\mathcal{L}[e^{-at}u(t)] = e^{-aT}\frac{1}{s+a}$$

Now shifting the function $e^{-a(t+T)}u(t)$ to the right by T gives

$$G_2(s) = \mathcal{L}[g_2(t)] = \mathcal{L}[e^{-at}u(t-T)] = \frac{e^{-aT}}{s+a} e^{-Ts} \tag{8-98}$$

This result can be verified by substituting $g_2(t)$ directly in the Laplace transform integral.

$$G_2(s) = \mathcal{L}[g_2(t)] = \int_{0^-}^{\infty} e^{-at}u(t - T)e^{-st}\, dt$$

$$= \int_{T^-}^{\infty} e^{-at}e^{-st}\, dt = \left[-\frac{1}{s + a}\, e^{-(s+a)t} \right]_{T^-}^{\infty}$$

$$= \frac{e^{-aT}}{s + a}\, e^{-Ts}$$

which is identical with (8-98).

Example 8-17   Determine the Laplace transform of the triangular pulse signal shown in Fig. 8-24.

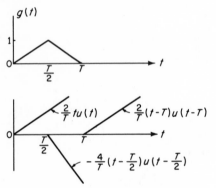

Fig. 8-24 *A triangular pulse and its decomposition into ramp signals.*

We again explore this problem using two different methods.   First, the triangular pulse is considered to be the sum of three ramp functions as shown in Fig. 8-24.   The expression for the pulse signal is given by

$$g(t) = \frac{2}{T}\, tu(t) - \frac{4}{T}\left(t - \frac{T}{2} \right) u\left(t - \frac{T}{2} \right) + \frac{2}{T}\, (t - T)u(t - T)$$

Taking the Laplace transform on both sides of the last equation, we get

$$G(s) = \frac{2}{Ts^2} - \frac{4}{Ts^2}\, e^{-Ts/2} + \frac{2}{Ts^2}\, e^{-Ts} = \frac{2}{Ts^2}\left(1 - 2e^{-Ts/2} + e^{-Ts} \right)$$

$$(8\text{-}99)$$

An alternative approach to this problem is to take the derivative of the original pulse signal with respect to t successively until impulses occur. The first and the second derivatives of $g(t)$ are shown in Fig. 8-25.   The

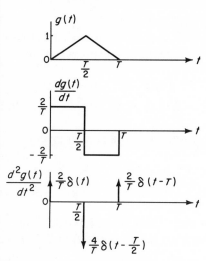

Fig. 8-25   A triangular pulse and its derivatives.

Laplace transform of $d^2g(t)/dt^2$, as obtained by inspection, is

$$\mathcal{L}\left[\frac{d^2g(t)}{dt^2}\right] = \frac{2}{T}\left(1 - 2e^{-Ts/2} + e^{-Ts}\right)$$

Using the derivative theorem, we write

$$\mathcal{L}\left[\frac{d^2g(t)}{dt^2}\right] = s^2G(s) - sg(0^-) - g^{(1)}(0^-) = \frac{2}{T}\left(1 - 2e^{-Ts/2} + e^{-Ts}\right)$$

Solving for $G(s)$ from this equation gives the same result as in (8-99) since $g(0^-)$ and $g^{(1)}(0^-)$ are zero in this case.

6. *Periodic function*   *Given a periodic function $g_T(t)$ with period T, and letting a function $g(t)$ be described by*

$$g(t) = \begin{cases} g_T(t) & 0 \leq t < T \\ 0 & \text{all other } t \end{cases}$$

then the Laplace transform of $g_T(t)$ is given by

$$G_T(s) = \frac{G(s)}{1 - e^{-Ts}} \tag{8-100}$$

where $G(s)$ is the Laplace transform of $g(t)$.

Proof   Since $g(t)$ is identical with $g_T(t)$ for the period between $t = 0$ and $t = T$ and is zero everywhere else, we can express $g_T(t)$ as

$$g_T(t) = g(t)u(t) + g(t - T)u(t - T) + g(t - 2T)u(t - 2T)$$
$$+ \cdots + g(t - kT)u(t - kT) + \cdots \tag{8-101}$$

Taking the Laplace transform on both sides of this equation gives

$$G_T(s) = G(s) + G(s)e^{-Ts} + G(s)e^{-2Ts} + \cdots + G(s)e^{-kTs} + \cdots$$
$$= G(s)(1 + e^{-Ts} + e^{-2Ts} + \cdots + e^{-kTs} + \cdots) \tag{8-102}$$

The infinite series appearing on the right-hand side of (8-102) can be written in a closed form.   Multiplying both sides of (8-102) by e^{-Ts} gives

$$e^{-Ts}G_T(s) = G(s)(e^{-Ts} + e^{-2Ts} + \cdots + e^{-(k+1)Ts} + \cdots) \tag{8-103}$$

Subtracting (8-103) from (8-102) gives

$$(1 - e^{-Ts})G_T(s) = G(s)$$

from which (8-100) is obtained.

Example 8-18   As an illustrative example of finding the Laplace transform of a periodic function, let us consider the periodic triangular wave shown in Fig. 8-26.

We notice that the waveform of this periodic signal during one period is described by the triangular pulse in Fig. 8-24, whose Laplace

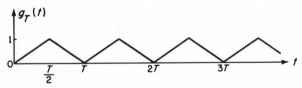

Fig. 8-26   *A periodic triangular signal.*

transform is given by (8-99).   Therefore, from (8-100), we get

$$G_T(s) = \frac{1}{1 - e^{-Ts}} \left[\frac{2}{Ts^2} (1 - 2e^{-Ts/2} + e^{-Ts}) \right]$$

$$= \frac{2}{Ts^2} \frac{1 - e^{-Ts/2}}{1 + e^{-Ts/2}}$$

Example 8-19   Find the Laplace transform of the unit impulse train shown in Fig. 8-27.   The Laplace transform of the function $g(t)$ for

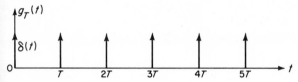

Fig. 8-27   *A unit impulse train.*

$0 \leq t < T$ is

$$\mathcal{L}[\delta(t)] = 1$$

From (8-100), we have, for the unit impulse train,

$$G_T(s) = \frac{1}{1 - e^{-Ts}}$$

Example 8-20   Find the Laplace transform of the periodic pulse train shown in Fig. 8-28.   Since the Laplace transform of the pulse signal

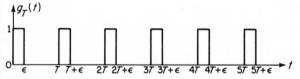

Fig. 8-28   *A periodic pulse train.*

for $0 \leq t < T$ is

$$G(s) = \frac{1 - e^{-\epsilon s}}{s}$$

using (8-100), we have

$$G_T(s) = \frac{1 - e^{-\epsilon s}}{s(1 - e^{-Ts})}$$

7. Complex translation theorem *If $G(s)$ is the Laplace transform of $g(t)$, then*

$$\mathcal{L}[e^{\mp at}g(t)] = G(s \pm a) \tag{8-104}$$

where a is a positive constant.

Proof By definition,

$$G(s \pm a) = \int_{0^-}^{\infty} e^{-(s \pm a)t}g(t)\ dt = \int_{0^-}^{\infty} e^{\mp at}g(t)e^{-st}\ dt$$
$$= \mathcal{L}[e^{\mp at}g(t)]$$

Example 8-21 Find the Laplace transform of the function $g(t) = te^{-at}$.

Since the Laplace transform of t is $1/s^2$, the Laplace transform of te^{-at}, using (8-104), is obtained by replacing s by $s + a$ in $1/s^2$. We have

$$\mathcal{L}(te^{-at}) = \mathcal{L}(t)_{s=s+a} = \frac{1}{(s + a)^2}$$

8. Multiplication by t *The Laplace transform of the product of t^n (n is a positive integer) and $g(t)$ is $(-1)^n$ times the nth derivative of the Laplace transform of $g(t)$ with respect to s; that is,*

$$\mathcal{L}[t^n g(t)] = (-1)^n \frac{d^n G(s)}{ds^n} \tag{8-105}$$

Proof By definition,

$$\frac{dG(s)}{ds} = \frac{d}{ds} \int_{0^-}^{\infty} g(t)e^{-st}\ dt = \int_{0^-}^{\infty} \frac{\partial}{\partial s}[g(t)e^{-st}]\ dt$$
$$= \int_{0^-}^{\infty} -tg(t)e^{-st}\ dt = -\mathcal{L}[tg(t)]$$

By repeated application of this property, (8-105) is obtained.

Example 8-22 The Laplace transform of the function $g(t)$ in Example 8-21 can be found by use of the multiplication-by-t theorem.

The following relationship can be written directly:

$$\mathcal{L}(te^{-at}) = -\frac{d}{ds}\mathcal{L}(e^{-at}) = -\frac{d}{ds}\left(\frac{1}{s+a}\right) = \frac{1}{(s+a)^2}$$

which is the same result as in Example 8-21. In general, we can show that

$$\mathcal{L}(t^n e^{-at}) = (-1)^n \frac{d^n}{ds^n} \mathcal{L}(e^{-at}) = \frac{n!}{(s+a)^{n+1}}$$

9. *Scale change*   *If $G(s)$ is the Laplace transform of $g(t)$, then*

$$\mathcal{L}\left[g\left(\frac{t}{a}\right)\right] = aG(as) \tag{8-106}$$

where a is a positive real number.
   Proof   By definition,

$$\mathcal{L}\left[g\left(\frac{t}{a}\right)\right] = \int_{0^-}^{\infty} g\left(\frac{t}{a}\right) e^{-st}\, dt$$

Letting $\tau = t/a$, we have

$$\mathcal{L}[g(\tau)] = \int_{0^-}^{\infty} g(\tau)e^{-a\tau s}\, da\tau = a\int_{0^-}^{\infty} g(\tau)e^{-(as)\tau}\, d\tau = aG(as)$$

10. *Initial-value theorem*   *If $g(t)$ is Laplace-transformable and has the Laplace transform $G(s)$ and if $dg(t)/dt$ is Laplace-transformable, then*

$$g(0^+) = \lim_{t\to 0+} g(t) = \lim_{s\to\infty} sG(s) \tag{8-107}$$

if the limit exists.
   Proof   The proof of the initial-value theorem makes use of the differentiation theorem stated in (8-75); i.e.,

$$\mathcal{L}\left[\frac{dg(t)}{dt}\right] = sG(s) - g(0^-)$$

Taking the limit as s approaches infinity on both sides of the last equation, we get

$$\lim_{s\to\infty} \int_{0^-}^{\infty} \frac{dg(t)}{dt} e^{-st}\, dt = \lim_{s\to\infty} [sG(s) - g(0^-)] \tag{8-108}$$

Considering that $g(t)$ may have a jump discontinuity at $t = 0$, its derivative for all t can be written

$$\frac{dg(t)}{dt} = g_1(t) + [g(0^+) - g(0^-)]\delta(t)$$

where $g_1(t)$ is finite.   Therefore (8-108) becomes

$$\lim_{s \to \infty} \int_{0^-}^{\infty} \frac{dg(t)}{dt} e^{-st}\, dt = \lim_{s \to \infty} \int_{0^-}^{\infty} g_1(t) e^{-st}\, dt$$

$$+ \lim_{s \to \infty} \int_{0^-}^{\infty} [g(0^+) - g(0^-)]\delta(t) e^{-st}\, dt \quad (8\text{-}109)$$

Since $g_1(t)$ is finite, the first term on the right side of (8-109) is zero, and thus we have

$$\lim_{s \to \infty} [sG(s) - g(0^-)] = \lim_{s \to \infty} \int_{0^-}^{\infty} [g(0^+) - g(0^-)]\delta(t) e^{-st}\, dt$$

$$= \lim_{s \to \infty} \{[g(0^+) - g(0^-)]e^{-st}\} = g(0^+) - g(0^-)$$

Therefore

$$g(0^+) = \lim_{s \to \infty} sG(s)$$

and the theorem is proved.

If $g(0^-) = g(0^+)$, the left-hand side of (8-108) vanishes, and the expression naturally leads to

$$g(0^-) = \lim_{s \to \infty} sG(s)$$

The usefulness of the initial-value theorem is that it gives the initial value of a function $g(t)$ at $t = 0^+$ or $t = 0^-$ in terms of the value of the corresponding $sG(s)$ evaluated at $s = \infty$ without performing the inverse transformation.

11. *Final-value theorem*   *If $g(t)$ is Laplace-transformable and has the Laplace transform $G(s)$, and if the zeros of the denominator of $sG(s)$ do not have positive or vanishing real parts, then*

$$\lim_{t \to \infty} g(t) = \lim_{s \to 0} sG(s) \qquad (8\text{-}110)$$

Proof   We start with the same equation as for the proof of the initial-value theorem, but only with the limit of s approaching zero instead of infinity.   We have

$$\lim_{s \to 0} \int_{0^-}^{\infty} \frac{dg(t)}{dt} e^{-st} dt = \lim_{s \to 0} sG(s) - g(0^-) \tag{8-111}$$

The left-hand side of this equation can be written

$$\lim_{s \to 0} \int_{0^-}^{\infty} \frac{dg(t)}{dt} e^{-st} dt = \int_{0^-}^{\infty} \frac{dg(t)}{dt} dt = \lim_{t \to \infty} \int_{0^-}^{t} \frac{dg(\tau)}{d\tau} d\tau$$

$$= \lim_{t \to \infty} [g(t) - g(0^-)] \tag{8-112}$$

Now equating (8-111) with (8-112) gives

$$\lim_{s \to 0} sG(s) - g(0^-) = \lim_{t \to \infty} [g(t) - g(0^-)]$$

Therefore

$$\lim_{t \to \infty} g(t) = \lim_{s \to 0} sG(s) \tag{8-113}$$

The final-value theorem is very useful in networks and systems analysis since it gives the final value of a function or a signal from the behavior of its Laplace transform evaluated at $s = 0$.   However, before applying the theorem to any function $G(s)$, we must first make sure that all the zeros of the denominator of $sG(s)$ lie in the left half of the s plane.   If any of the zeros is found on the imaginary axis or in the right half of the s plane, the final-value theorem becomes invalid.   The following numerical examples should illustrate these important points.

Example 8-23   Given

$$G(s) = \frac{5}{s(s^2 + 2s + 3)} \tag{8-114}$$

Find the final value of $g(t)$.

Since the roots of the denominator polynomial of $sG(s)$ are at $s = -1$ and $s = -2$, which are all in the left half of the s plane, the final-value theorem is valid for this case.   Substituting (8-114) in (8-113), we get

$$\lim_{t \to \infty} g(t) = \lim_{s \to 0} sG(s) = \lim_{s \to 0} \frac{5}{s^2 + 2s + 3} = \frac{5}{3}$$

Example 8-24   The Laplace transform of the function

$$g(t) = \sin \omega_0 t$$

is

$$G(s) = \frac{\omega_0}{s^2 + \omega_0^2}$$

The two roots of $s^2 + \omega_0^2 = 0$ lie on the $j\omega$ axis of the s plane, and thus the final-value theorem is invalid for this case.   In fact, we know that the value of $\sin \omega_0 t$ fluctuates between $+1$ and -1, and no final value can be defined for the function.   However, if we apply the theorem erroneously, we should get

$$\lim_{t \to \infty} \sin \omega_0 t = \lim_{s \to 0} \frac{s\omega_0}{s^2 + \omega_0^2} = 0$$

12. *Real multiplication (complex convolution)*   *If $g_1(t)$ and $g_2(t)$ are both Laplace-transformable, having Laplace transforms $G_1(s)$ and $G_2(s)$, respectively, the Laplace transform of the product, $g_1(t)g_2(t)$, is given by*

$$\mathcal{L}[g_1(t)g_2(t)] = \frac{1}{2\pi j} \int_{c-j\infty}^{c+j\infty} G_1(p)G_2(s - p)\, dp \tag{8-115}$$

for $\sigma > \max (\sigma_1, \sigma_2, \sigma_1 + \sigma_2)$ and $\sigma_1 < c < \sigma - \sigma_2$, where c is a real constant; $\sigma = Re(s)$; σ_1 and σ_2 are the abscissas of absolute convergence of $g_1(t)$ and $g_2(t)$, respectively; and p is a dummy variable of integration.   Since $g_1(t)$ and $g_2(t)$ are basically interchangeable, the real multiplication theorem can also be written

$$\mathcal{L}[g_1(t)g_2(t)] = \frac{1}{2\pi j} \int_{c-j\infty}^{c+j\infty} G_2(p)G_1(s - p)\, dp \tag{8-116}$$

But the condition on c should be changed accordingly to $\sigma_2 < c < \sigma - \sigma_1$. Expressions (8-115) and (8-116) represent the complex convolution integral of $g_1(t)$ and $g_2(t)$, and are often denoted by $G_1(s) * G_2(s)$, meaning "$G_1(s)$ convolves into $G_2(s)$."   In other words, multiplication in the real domain corresponds to a convolution process in the complex domain.

Proof   By definition,

$$\mathcal{L}[g_1(t)g_2(t)] = \int_{0-}^{\infty} g_1(t)g_2(t)e^{-st}\, dt \tag{8-117}$$

In order that this Laplace transform integral converge absolutely, the real part of s, σ must be greater than the largest value of σ_1, σ_2, and $\sigma_1 + \sigma_2$; that is, $\sigma > \max(\sigma_1, \sigma_2, \sigma_1 + \sigma_2)$.

We may write $g_1(t)$ as an inverse Laplace-transform relationship,

$$g_1(t) = \frac{1}{2\pi j} \int_{c-j\infty}^{c+j\infty} G_1(p) e^{pt} \, dp \tag{8-118}$$

In order to avoid confusion with the complex variable s, the dummy variable p is used in the last integral. To ensure the convergence of this inverse transform integral, the value of c must be greater than σ_1, the abscissa of convergence of $G_1(s)$. Substituting (8-118) in (8-117), we obtain

$$\mathcal{L}[g_1(t)g_2(t)] = \frac{1}{2\pi j} \int_{c-j\infty}^{c+j\infty} G_1(p) \, dp \int_{0-}^{\infty} g_2(t) e^{-(s-p)t} \, dt$$

But since

$$\int_{0-}^{\infty} g_2(t) e^{-(s-p)t} \, dt = G_2(s-p)$$

for

$$\text{Re}\,(s-p) > \sigma_2 \qquad \text{or} \qquad \text{Re}\,(p) < \text{Re}\,(s) - \sigma_2 = \sigma - \sigma_2$$

we have

$$\mathcal{L}[g_1(t)g_2(t)] = \frac{1}{2\pi j} \int_{c-j\infty}^{c+j\infty} G_1(p)G_2(s-p) \, dp$$

for

$$\sigma = \text{Re}\,(s) > \max(\sigma_1, \sigma_2, \sigma_1 + \sigma_2)$$

and

$$\sigma_1 < \text{Re}\,(p) = c < \sigma - \sigma_2$$

Expression (8-116) can be proved in the same way.

Since the right-hand side of (8-115) is a line integral with the path of integration along the straight line $\text{Re}\,(p) = c$, from $-\infty$ to $+\infty$, the first step in the application of the real-multiplication theorem is the determination of the proper value of c once $g_1(t)$ and $g_2(t)$ are given. We shall illustrate the method of finding c in the following example.

Example 8-25 Given $g_1(t) = e^{-t}u(t)$ and $g_2(t)e^{-2t}u(t)$, determine the range in which Re $(p) = c$ may lie in order for the line integral of $\mathcal{L}[g_1(t)g_2(t)]$ to converge absolutely.

The abscissas of absolute convergence for $g_1(t)$ and $g_2(t)$ are $\sigma_1 = -1$ and $\sigma_2 = -2$, respectively. Therefore, from the $\sigma > \max(\sigma_1, \sigma_2, \sigma_1 + \sigma_2)$ requirement, we have $\sigma > -1$, which means that the real part of s must be greater than -1. The region of absolute convergence of $\mathcal{L}[g_1(t)g_2(t)]$ in the s plane is shown in Fig. 8-29a. Let us arbitrarily choose $\sigma = 0$.

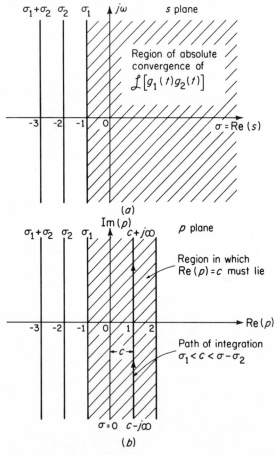

Fig. 8-29 Region of convergence and line of integration for Example 8-25.

Then $\sigma - \sigma_2 = 0 - (-2) = 2$; the line of integration representing Re $(p) = c$ should lie in the strip bounded by $\sigma_1 = -1$ and $\sigma - \sigma_2 = 2$ (Fig 8-29b).

A well-known method of evaluating a line integral depends on the use of contour integration and the calculus of residues in complex-variable theory.

13. *Complex multiplication (real convolution)* *If the functions $g_1(t)$ and $g_2(t)$ are Laplace-transformable and have the Laplace transforms $G_1(s)$ and $G_2(s)$, respectively, then*

$$G_1(s)G_2(s) = \mathcal{L} \int_{0^-}^{t} g_1(t - \tau)g_2(\tau) \, d\tau \qquad (8\text{-}119)$$

Expression (8-119) is called the real convolution integral and is denoted by $g_1(t) * g_2(t)$, meaning "$g_1(t)$ convolves into $g_2(t)$."

Proof Let the right-hand side of (8-119) be represented by $g(t)$; that is,

$$g(t) = \int_{0^-}^{t} g_1(t - \tau)g_2(\tau) \, d\tau \qquad (8\text{-}120)$$

Then, by definition,

$$G(s) = \int_{0^-}^{\infty} \int_{0^-}^{t} g_1(t - \tau)g_2(\tau)e^{-st} \, d\tau \, dt \qquad (8\text{-}121)$$

Let us assume that $g_1(\tau)$ and $g_2(\tau)$ have the arbitrary waveforms as shown in Fig. 8-30. The construction of $g_1(t - \tau)g_2(\tau)$ from $g_1(\tau)$ and $g_2(\tau)$ is also illustrated by two steps as shown in Fig. 8-30. We see that the process involves, first, inverting $g_1(\tau)$ with respect to τ, and then shifting it to the right by t; the resulting function, $g_1(t - \tau)$, is then multiplied by $g_2(\tau)$. Note that no matter what exact forms $g_1(\tau)$ and $g_2(\tau)$ may have, so long as $g_1(\tau)$ is defined only for $\tau > 0$, $g_1(t - \tau)g_2(\tau)$ is always zero for $\tau > t$. For this reason, we may change the upper limit of the inner integral of (8-121) from t to ∞. We have

$$G(s) = \int_{0^-}^{\infty} \int_{0^-}^{\infty} g_1(t - \tau)g_2(\tau)e^{-st} \, d\tau \, dt$$

$$= \int_{0^-}^{\infty} g_2(\tau) \, d\tau \int_{0^-}^{\infty} g_1(t - \tau)e^{-st} \, dt \qquad (8\text{-}122)$$

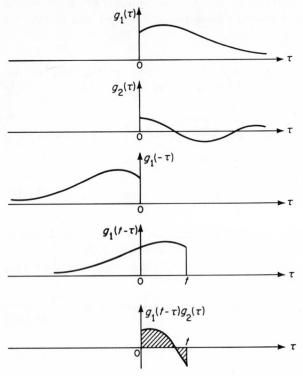

Fig. 8-30 Graphical interpretation of the process of real convolution.

Letting $u = t - \tau$, Eq. (8-122) becomes

$$G(s) = \int_{0^-}^{\infty} g_2(\tau) \, d\tau \int_{-\tau}^{\infty} g_1(u)e^{-us}e^{-\tau s} \, du \qquad (8\text{-}123)$$

Since $g(u) = g(t - \tau)$ is zero for $u < 0$ (or $\tau > t$), the lower limit of the inner integral of (8-123) can again be changed from $-\tau$ to 0. We now have

$$G(s) = \int_{0^-}^{\infty} g_2(\tau)e^{-\tau s} \, d\tau \int_{0^-}^{\infty} g_1(u)e^{-us} \, du = G_1(s)G_2(s) \qquad (8\text{-}124)$$

Thus the theorem is proved.

Figure 8-30 gives a graphical interpretation of the real convolution process. We see that the right-hand side of (8-119) is equal to the area under the $g_1(t - \tau)g_2(\tau)$ curve. This suggests a graphical method of evaluating the convolution integral, which involves inverting and shifting. In fact, the convolution integral can be defined for functions that are non-Laplace-transformable, although the proof presented above does imply that $g_1(t)$ and $g_2(t)$ must be transformable. A proof of the convolution integral without using the Laplace transformation is presented in Sec. 11-2 in conjunction with the discussion of the impulse responses and transfer functions of linear systems.

In this section we have presented and proved some of the important theorems and properties of the Laplace transforms. For the purpose of quick reference, these theorems are given in Table 8-2.

TABLE 8-2   *Important theorems and properties of the Laplace transforms*

1.	Multiplication by a constant	$\mathcal{L}[kg(t)] = kG(s)$
2.	Sum or difference	$\mathcal{L}[g_1(t) \pm g_2(t)] = G_1(s) \pm G_2(s)$
3.	Differentiation in time	$\mathcal{L}\left[\dfrac{d^n g(t)}{dt^n}\right] = s^n G(s) - s^{n-1}g(0^-) - s^{n-2}g^{(1)}(0^-)$ $- \cdots - g^{(n-1)}(0^-)$
4.	Integration in time	$\mathcal{L}\left[\displaystyle\int_{0^-}^{t_1}\int_{0^-}^{t_2}\cdots\int_{0^-}^{t_n} g(\tau)\, d\tau\, dt \cdots dt_1\right] = \dfrac{G(s)}{s^n}$
5.	Shifting theorem (real translation)	$\mathcal{L}[g(t - T)u(t - T)] = e^{-Ts}G(s) \qquad T > 0$ $\mathcal{L}[g(t - T)u(t)] = e^{-Ts}G(s) \qquad \text{if } g(t) = 0 \text{ for}$ $\qquad\qquad\qquad\qquad\qquad t < -T,\ T < 0$
6.	Periodic function $g_T(t)$	$G_T(s) = \dfrac{G(s)}{1 - e^{-Ts}} \qquad G(s) = \mathcal{L}[g(t)]$ $g(t) = g_T(t) \qquad 0 \le t < T$ $\qquad\ = 0 \qquad\quad \text{all other } t$
7.	Complex translation	$\mathcal{L}[e^{\mp at}g(t)] = G(s \pm a)$
8.	Multiplication by t	$\mathcal{L}[t^n g(t)] = (-1)^n \dfrac{d^n G(s)}{ds^n}$
9.	Scale change	$\mathcal{L}\left[g\left(\dfrac{t}{a}\right)\right] = aG(as) \qquad a > 0$
10.	Initial-value theorem	$\displaystyle\lim_{t \to 0^+} g(t) = \lim_{s \to \infty} sG(s) = \lim_{s \to \infty} s\int_{0^-}^{\infty} g(t)e^{-st}\, dt$
11.	Final-value theorem	$\displaystyle\lim_{t \to \infty} g(t) = \lim_{s \to 0} sG(s) \qquad \text{if zeros of denominator}$ $\text{of } sG(s) \text{ are all in left half of } s \text{ plane}$

TABLE 8-2   *Important theorems and properties of the Laplace transforms* (*continued*)

---

12. Real multiplication (complex convolution)

$$\mathcal{L}[g_1(t)g_2(t)] = \frac{1}{2\pi j} \int_{c-j\infty}^{c+j\infty} G_1(p)G_2(s-p)\,dp$$
$$= G_1(s) * G_2(s)$$
$$\sigma > \max\,(\sigma_1, \sigma_2, \sigma_1 + \sigma_2)$$
$$\sigma_1 < c < \sigma - \sigma_2$$
$$\mathcal{L}[g_1(t)g_2(t)] = \frac{1}{2\pi j} \int_{c-j\infty}^{c+j\infty} G_2(p)G_1(s-p)\,dp$$
$$= G_2(s) * G_1(s)$$
$$\sigma > \max\,(\sigma_1, \sigma_2, \sigma_1 + \sigma_2)$$
$$\sigma_2 < c < \sigma - \sigma_1$$

13. Complex multiplication (real convolution)

$$g_1(t) * g_2(t) = \mathcal{L}^{-1}[G_1(s)G_2(s)]$$
$$= \int_{0-}^{t} g_1(t-\tau)g_2(\tau)\,d\tau$$
$$= \int_{0-}^{t} g_2(t-\tau)g_1(\tau)\,d\tau$$
$$= g_2(t) * g_1(t)$$
$$g_1(t) \text{ and } g_2(t) = 0 \text{ for } t < 0$$

8-6   INVERSE LAPLACE TRANSFORMATION

The process of going from the complex Laplace domain to the real domain is described as *inverse Laplace transformation*. The inverse transform is usually needed as the final step in solving a physical problem using the Laplace-transform method. The advantage of the Laplace transformation is that, by its use, one shifts from an integral-differential equation in the real domain to an algebraic relationship in the complex s domain. After the solution has been obtained in the s domain, it must be reverted to the time domain by the use of the inverse transformation.

The inverse Laplace transform is defined as

$$\mathcal{L}^{-1}[G(s)] = g(t) = \text{inverse Laplace transform of } G(s) \qquad (8\text{-}125)$$

and

$$g(t) = \frac{1}{2\pi j} \int_{c-j\infty}^{c+j\infty} G(s)e^{st}\,ds \qquad (8\text{-}126)$$

where c is a real number greater than the abscissa of absolute convergence of $G(s)$. This inverse transform integral is obtained directly from the

Fourier integral of (8-21).   The derivation of the integral is left to the student as an exercise.

The inverse transform integral of (8-126) should not be confused with the complex convolution integral appearing in (8-115), although at first glance they may appear to be similar.

The simplest way of obtaining $g(t)$ from its Laplace transform $G(s)$ is to use a Laplace-transform table.   However, when a transform table is not available, the integral of (8-126) may be evaluated using the method of contour integration and the theorem of residues.

In general, the Laplace transforms encountered in physical problems can be classified as *rational* and *irrational functions*.   The first type is defined as a quotient of two polynomials, and is usually found in lumped-parameter systems.   The second type is often characterized by transcendental functions or others having an infinite number of singularities with periodic characteristics or with distributed parameters such as in transmission lines or waveguides.

When $G(s)$ is an algebraic rational function of s, its inverse Laplace transform may be obtained by means of partial fraction expansion. $G(s)$ may be written as a quotient of two polynomials, i.e.,

$$G(s) = \frac{P(s)}{Q(s)} \tag{8-127}$$

where $P(s)$ and $Q(s)$ are polynomials of s with real coefficients.

In general, $G(s)$ can be expanded by partial fraction expansion into the following form:

$$G(s) = \frac{P(s)}{Q(s)} = K_0 + K_1 s + K_2 s^2 + \cdots + \frac{K_{s1}}{s - s_1} + \frac{K_{s2}}{s - s_2}$$

$$+ \cdots + \frac{K_{sn}}{s - s_n} + \frac{A_1}{s - s_i} + \frac{A_2}{(s - s_i)^2} + \cdots + \frac{A_r}{(s - s_i)^r} \tag{8-128}$$

where $s_1, s_2, \ldots, s_n$ are the n simple poles of $G(s)$ and s_i represents an rth-order pole.   Therefore the partial fraction expansion of $G(s)$ generally involves the following three types of terms.

Polynomial

$$K_0 + K_1 s + K_2 s^2 + \cdots \tag{8-129}$$

These terms will be present if the order of $Q(s)$ is not greater than that of

$P(s)$. The constants $K_0, K_1, K_2, \ldots$ are determined by performing long division on $G(s)$.

Example 8-26   Given

$$G(s) = \frac{s^3 + 4s^2 + 4s + 5}{s^2 + 3s + 2} \tag{8-130}$$

Since the order of the denominator polynomial is not greater than that of the numerator, a long-division process must first be performed, as follows:

$$
\begin{array}{r}
s + 1 \\
s^2 + 3s + 2 \overline{)s^3 + 4s^2 + 4s + 5} \\
\underline{s^3 + 3s^2 + 2s} \\
s^2 + 2s + 5 \\
\underline{s^2 + 3s + 2} \\
-s + 3
\end{array}
$$

Therefore (8-130) is written

$$G(s) = s + 1 + \frac{-s + 3}{s^2 + 3s + 2} \tag{8-131}$$

and $K_0 = 1$, $K_1 = 1$. We must point out that the complete partial fraction expansion of (8-130) is not yet accomplished; only the polynomial part of $G(s)$ is carried out.

Simple poles

If $G(s)$ has n simple poles at $s = s_k$, where $k = 1, 2, \ldots, n$, the partial-fraction-expanded terms which correspond to these poles are given by

$$\frac{K_{s1}}{s - s_1} + \frac{K_{s2}}{s - s_2} + \cdots + \frac{K_{sn}}{s - s_n} \tag{8-132}$$

The coefficients $K_{s1}, K_{s2}, \ldots, K_{sn}$ are determined from the relationship

$$K_{sk} = [(s - s_k)G(s)]_{s=s_k} \tag{8-133}$$

where $k = 1, 2, \ldots, n$.

For instance, in order to complete the partial fraction expansion of (8-131), the expression is written

$$G(s) = s + 1 + \frac{-s + 3}{(s + 1)(s + 2)}$$

$$= s + 1 + \frac{K_{s1}}{s + 1} + \frac{K_{s2}}{s + 2} \tag{8-134}$$

Then, according to (8-133),

$$K_{s1} = [(s + 1)G(s)]_{s=-1}$$

$$= \left[(s + 1)^2 + \frac{-s + 3}{s + 2} \right]_{s=-1} = 4 \tag{8-135}$$

Also

$$K_{s2} = [(s + 2)G(s)]_{s=-2}$$

$$= \left[(s + 1)(s + 2) + \frac{-s + 3}{s + 1} \right]_{s=-2} = -5 \tag{8-136}$$

Therefore the complete partial fraction expansion of (8-130) is

$$G(s) = s + 1 + \frac{4}{s + 1} - \frac{5}{s + 2} \tag{8-137}$$

Once the coefficients $K_{s1}, K_{s2}, \ldots, K_{sn}$ are determined, the inverse Laplace transform of the first-order term is easily obtained. Since

$$\mathcal{L}^{-1} \left[\frac{K_{sk}}{s - s_k} \right] = K_{sk}e^{s_k t}$$

we can write

$$\mathcal{L}^{-1} \left[\frac{K_{sk}}{s - s_k} \right] = [(s - s_k)G(s)e^{st}]_{s=s_k} \tag{8-138}$$

Example 8-27   Consider the function

$$G(s) = \frac{\omega_n^2}{s^2 + 2\zeta\omega_n s + \omega_n^2} \tag{8-139}$$

If $0 < \zeta < 1$, the function has two complex poles which are conjugates of each other.   Letting $\alpha = \zeta\omega_n$ and $\omega = \omega_n \sqrt{1 - \zeta^2}$, $G(s)$ is written

$$G(s) = \frac{\omega_n{}^2}{(s + \alpha + j\omega)(s + \alpha - j\omega)} \tag{8-140}$$

Applying (8-138), the inverse Laplace transform of (8-140) is written

$$g(t) = [G(s)(s + \alpha + j\omega)]_{s=-\alpha-j\omega}e^{(-\alpha-j\omega)t}$$
$$+ [G(s)(s + \alpha - j\omega)]_{s=-\alpha+j\omega}e^{(-\alpha+j\omega)t} \tag{8-141}$$

Therefore

$$g(t) = \frac{\omega_n{}^2}{2j\omega} \left[e^{(-\alpha+j\omega)t} - e^{(-\alpha-j\omega)t} \right]$$

$$= \frac{\omega_n}{\sqrt{1 - \zeta^2}} e^{-\zeta\omega_n t} \sin \omega_n \sqrt{1 - \zeta^2}\, t \qquad t > 0 \tag{8-142}$$

Multiple-order poles

When $G(s)$ has a pole of order r at $s = s_i$, its partial fraction expansion at the pole is given by

$$\frac{A_1}{s - s_i} + \frac{A_2}{(s - s_i)^2} + \cdots + \frac{A_r}{(s - s_i)^r} \tag{8-143}$$

The coefficients $A_1, A_2, \ldots, A_r$ are determined from

$$A_k = \frac{1}{(k - 1)!} \frac{\partial^{k-1}[(s - s_i)^k G(s)]}{\partial s^{k-1}} \Bigg|_{s = s_k} \tag{8-144}$$

for $k = 1, 2, \ldots, r$.   Notice that (8-144) also includes the simple-pole case; i.e., when $k = 1$, the expression reverts to the same form as (8-133).
The inverse Laplace transform of the terms in (8-143) can be written

$$g(t) = \sum_{k=1}^{r} \frac{1}{(k - 1)!} \frac{\partial^{k-1}[(s - s_i)^k G(s) e^{st}]}{\partial s^{k-1}} \Bigg|_{s = s_k} \tag{8-145}$$

Example 8-28   Consider the function

$$G(s) = \frac{1}{s^2(s + 1)(s + 2)} \tag{8-146}$$

Using (8-138) and (8-145), the inverse Laplace transform of this function is written

$$
\begin{aligned}
g(t) &= \frac{\partial}{\partial s}\left[s^2 G(s)e^{st}\right]_{s=0} + \left[(s+1)G(s)\right]_{s=-1}e^{-t} + \left[(s+2)G(s)\right]_{s=-2}e^{-2t} \\
&= \frac{\partial}{\partial s}\left[\frac{e^{st}}{s^2+3s+2}\right]_{s=0} + e^{-t} - \frac{1}{4}e^{-2t} \qquad t > 0 \\
&= \left[\frac{te^{st}(s^2+3s+2)+(2s+3)e^{st}}{(s^2+3s+2)^2}\right]_{s=0} + e^{-t} - \frac{1}{4}e^{-2t} \\
&= \frac{1}{2}t + \frac{3}{4} + e^{-t} - \frac{1}{4}e^{-2t} \qquad t > 0 \qquad\qquad (8\text{-}147)
\end{aligned}
$$

PROBLEMS

8-1 Find the Fourier transforms for the functions shown in Fig. P8-1. Some of the transform expressions for these functions may not be defined for $\omega = 0$. How do you propose to find these $F(0)$?

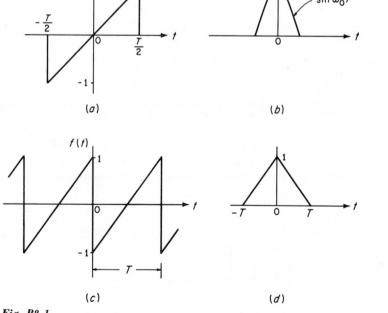

Fig. P8-1

8-2   Find the Fourier transforms of the functions shown in Fig. P8-2.

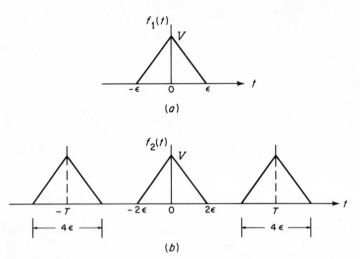

(a)

(b)

Fig. P8-2

8-3   Find the Fourier transform of the function shown in Fig. P8-3.

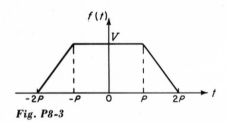

Fig. P8-3

8-4   The plot of the Fourier transform of a time function $f(t)$ is shown in Fig. P8-4. Find $f(t)$.

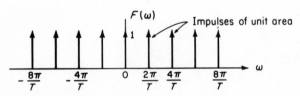

Fig. P8-4

8-5 Which of the following functions are Laplace-transformable?   Find the abscissa of absolute convergence of the transformable functions.

(a) $f(t) = u(t)$ unit step function
(b) $f(t) = \sin at$
(c) $f(t) = t^2$
(d) $f(t) = e^{at}$ $a > 0$
(e) $f(t) = t^n$
(f) $f(t) = te^{-at}$ $a > 0$
(g) $f(t) = e^{t^2}$

8-6 Find the Laplace transform for the following function:

$$f(t) = \begin{cases} 0 & t < 5 \\ 10t - 50 & 5 < t < 10 \\ -20t + 200 & 10 < t < 15 \\ 0 & t > 15 \end{cases}$$

8-7 Find the Laplace transform of a half-wave rectified sine wave with original frequency $\omega = \omega_0$.

8-8 Find the Laplace transform of the function shown in Fig. P8-5.

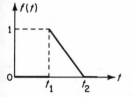

Fig. P8-5

8-9 Find the Laplace transform of

$$f(t) = t^2 u(t - a)   a > 0$$

where $u(t)$ is the unit step function.

8-10 Prove that

$$\mathcal{L}\left[\frac{f(t)}{t}\right] = \int_s^\infty F(s)\, ds$$

where $F(s) = \mathcal{L}[f(t)]$.

8-11 Find the Laplace transform of the function shown in Fig. P8-6.

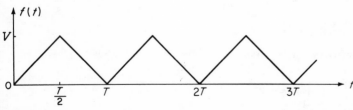

Fig. P8-6

8-12 Solve for $f(t)$ from the following equation, using the Laplace transformation:

$$t\frac{df(t)}{dt} - f(t) = 0$$

8-13 Find the Laplace transform of

$$f(t) = t\cos(\omega t + \phi) \qquad \omega = \text{const and } \phi = \text{const}$$

8-14 Find the Laplace transform of the periodic function shown in Fig. P8-7.

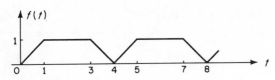

Fig. P8-7

8-15 Solve the following differential equation, using the Laplace-transform method:

$$2\frac{d^2f(t)}{dt^2} + \frac{df(t)}{dt} - f(t) = 0$$

The initial conditions are $f(0) = 1$ and $f'(0) = 1$.

8-16 Prove that

$$\int_{-\infty}^{0} f(t)e^{-st}\,dt = \mathcal{L}[f(-t)]_{s=-s}$$

where $f(t)$ is defined for $t < 0$.

8-17 Let

$$f_T(t) = \begin{cases} f(t) & 0 < t \le T \\ 0 & t > T \end{cases}$$

and let $F_T(s) = \mathcal{L}[f_T(t)]$.   Find the Laplace transform of $f(t)$ in terms of $F_T(t)$.

8-18 The Laplace transform of $f(t)$ is given by $F(s)$.   Find the Laplace transform of the function $f(-t)$ for $t < 0$ in terms of $F(s)$.

8-19 Derive the inverse Laplace transform integral from the Fourier transform integral given in (8-21).

8-20 Find the inverse Laplace transform for the following functions:

(a) $G(s) = \dfrac{se^{-2s}}{s^2 + 2s + 5}$

(b) $G(s) = \dfrac{5}{s^2(s + 1)^2}$

8-21 Find the inverse Laplace transforms of the following functions:

(a) $F(s) = \dfrac{s}{(s + 1)(s + 2)}$

(b) $F(s) = \dfrac{1}{s^3(s + 1)}$

8-22   Draw pictures to illustrate the graphical interpretation of the convolution of $f_1(t)$ and $f_2(t)$; that is, $f_1(t) * f_2(t)$, where

$$f_1(t) = e^{-at}u(t)$$
$$f_2(t) = tu(t)$$

8-23   Given

$$F_1(s) = \frac{1}{s + 3} \quad \text{and} \quad F_2(s) = \frac{5}{s^2 + 4}$$

Find the inverse Laplace transform of $F_1(s)F_2(s)$, using the convolution integral. Do not solve the integral.

8-24   Given

$$g_1(t) = e^{-t} \sin tu(t) \quad \text{and} \quad g_2(t) = e^{-3t}u(t)$$

Determine the range of Re $(p) = c$ so that the line integral of $\mathcal{L}[g_1(t)g_2(t)]$ in (8-116) converges absolutely.

8-25   Given $f_1(t)$ and $f_2(t)$ as shown in Fig. P8-8. Find the waveform for $f(t) = f_1(t) * f_2(t)$. Check your answer using the Laplace transform method.

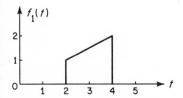

Fig. P8-8

BIBLIOGRAPHY

1   Wylie, Jr., C. R.: "Advanced Engineering Mathematics," 3d ed., McGraw-Hill Book Company, New York, 1966.
2   LePage, W. R.: "Complex Variables and the Laplace Transform for Engineers," McGraw-Hill Book Company, New York, 1961.

ADDITIONAL REFERENCES

Aseltine, J. A.: "Transform Method in Linear System Analysis," McGraw-Hill Book Company, New York, 1958.
Goldberg, R. R.: "Fourier Transforms," Cambridge University Press, New York, 1961.
Papoulis, A.: "The Fourier Integral and Its Applications," McGraw-Hill Book Company, New York, 1962.
Van der Pol, B., and H. Bremmer: "Operational Calculus and the Two-sided Laplace Transform," Cambridge University Press, New York, 1955.
Widder, D. V.: "The Laplace Transform," Princeton University Press, Princeton, N.J., 1941.

NINE

NETWORK ANALYSIS
BY LAPLACE TRANSFORMS

9-1 SOLUTION OF ORDINARY DIFFERENTIAL EQUATIONS WITH CONSTANT COEFFICIENTS BY LAPLACE TRANSFORMS

The main advantage of the Laplace-transform method is that it effects a shift from an integral-differential equation with constant coefficients in the real domain to an algebraic equation in the complex domain; and after the transform of the solution has been obtained in the complex domain by using laws of algebra, the desired solution is obtained with the aid of the inverse transform. This implies, simply, that when the transform method is used, the solution of differential equations becomes, essentially, an algebraic one. Further, in solving a differential equation with constant coefficients by the classical methods, the total solution, usually comprising two separate parts known as the particular integral and the complementary function, is thus obtained in two operations. With the Laplace-transform method, however, the total solution is obtained in one operation.

284

As a simple example, consider the linear differential equation with constant coefficients

$$\frac{d^2x}{dt^2} + 3\frac{dx}{dt} + 2x = 3 \tag{9-1}$$

The initial conditions of x are assumed to be

$$\frac{dx}{dt}(0^+) = \dot{x}(0^+) = 0 \quad \text{and} \quad x(0^+) = -1$$

Taking the Laplace transform on both sides of (9-1) and using the theorem on derivatives in (8-76), the transformed equation is

$$s^2X(s) - sx(0^+) - \dot{x}(0^+) + 3sX(s) - 3x(0^+) + 2X(s) = \frac{3}{s} \tag{9-2}$$

Here the initial value at $t = 0^+$ is used since it is the same as at 0^-. Substituting the values of $\dot{x}(0^+)$ and $x(0^+)$ in (9-2) and solving for $X(s)$, we get

$$X(s) = \frac{-s^2 - 3s + 3}{s(s^2 + 3s + 2)} = \frac{-s^2 - 3s + 3}{s(s + 1)(s + 2)} \tag{9-3}$$

The inverse Laplace transform of $X(s)$, as obtained using the technique described in Sec. 8-6, is

$$x(t) = \left[\frac{-s^2 - 3s + 3}{(s + 1)(s + 2)}\right]_{s=0} + \left[\frac{-s^2 - 3s + 3}{s(s + 2)}e^{-t}\right]_{s=-1}$$
$$+ \left[\frac{-s^2 - 3s + 3}{s(s + 1)}e^{-2t}\right]_{s=-2} \qquad t > 0$$

or

$$x(t) = (\tfrac{3}{2} - 5e^{-t} + \tfrac{5}{2}e^{-2t})u(t) \tag{9-4}$$

The first term on the right-hand side of the solution is the *particular integral;* in this case, it is also the steady-state solution, which is due to the nonhomogeneous part of the equation.   It is also possible to arrive at this steady-state solution by applying the final-value theorem to (9-3). Therefore

$$\lim_{t \to \infty} x(t) = \lim_{s \to \infty} sX(s) = \lim_{s \to \infty} \frac{-s^2 - 3s + 3}{(s + 1)(s + 2)} = \frac{3}{2}$$

The last two exponential terms in (9-4) are called the *complementary function*. They represent the transient part of the solution, which becomes zero as time approaches infinity.

From this simple illustrative example we see that the Laplace-transform method has at least the following features:

1 The total solution is obtained in one operation.
2 The initial conditions are incorporated at the outset of the solution steps.

The Laplace-transform method of solving ordinary linear differential equations with constant coefficients illustrated by the foregoing example is entirely general and can be applied to differential equations of any order. When dealing with integral-differential equations, the theorem on integration, as well as the theorem on differentiation, must be used.

The application of the Laplace transforms to linear networks and systems becomes straightforward once the networks or systems are represented by integral-differential equations.

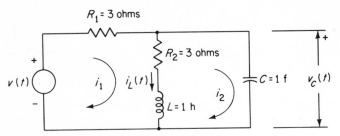

Fig. 9-1   An electric network.

As an illustrative example of a network problem, let us consider the network shown in Fig. 9-1.   The loop equations according to the assigned loop currents are written as follows:

$$v(t) = (R_1 + R_2)i_1(t) + L\frac{di_1(t)}{dt} - R_2i_2(t) - L\frac{di_2(t)}{dt} \qquad (9\text{-}5)$$

$$0 = -R_2i_1(t) - L\frac{di_1(t)}{dt} + R_2i_2(t) + L\frac{di_2(t)}{dt}$$

$$+ \frac{1}{C}\int_{0^+}^{t} i_2(\tau)\,d\tau + v_c(0^+) \qquad (9\text{-}6)$$

Taking the inverse Laplace transform on both sides of these loop equations, we get

$$V(s) = (R_1 + R_2)I_1(s) + LsI_1(s) - Li_1(0^+) - R_2I_2(s)$$
$$- LsI_2(s) + Li_2(0^+) \quad (9\text{-}7)$$

$$0 = -R_2I_1(s) - LsI_1(s) + Li_1(0^+) + R_2I_2(s) + LsI_2(s)$$
$$- Li_2(0^+) + \frac{1}{Cs}I_2(s) + \frac{v_c(0^+)}{s} \quad (9\text{-}8)$$

Rearranging terms, these equations become

$$V(s) + L[i_1(0^+) - i_2(0^+)] = (R_1 + R_2 + Ls)I_1(s) - (R_2 + Ls)I_2(s)$$
$$(9\text{-}9)$$

$$- L[i_1(0^+) - i_2(0^+)] - \frac{v_c(0^+)}{s} = -(R_2 + Ls)I_1(s)$$
$$+ \left(R_2 + Ls + \frac{1}{Cs}\right)I_2(s) \quad (9\text{-}10)$$

Substituting the values of the network parameters in these transformed equations, we get

$$V(s) + i_L(0^+) = (s + 6)I_1(s) - (s + 3)I_2(s) \quad (9\text{-}11)$$

$$-i_L(0^+) - \frac{v_c(0^+)}{s} = -(s + 3)I_1(s) + \left(s + 3 + \frac{1}{s}\right)I_2(s) \quad (9\text{-}12)$$

where $i_1(0^+) - i_2(0^+)$ has been replaced by $i_L(0^+)$, which is the initial current in the inductor L.

Now $I_1(s)$ and $I_2(s)$ can be solved from (9-11) and (9-12), using Cramer's rule or matrix algebra.   With Cramer's rule, we have

$$I_1(s) = \frac{\begin{vmatrix} V(s) + i_L(0^+) & -(s+3) \\ -i_L(0^+) - \dfrac{v_c(0^+)}{s} & s + 3 + \dfrac{1}{s} \end{vmatrix}}{\begin{vmatrix} s + 6 & -(s+3) \\ -(s+3) & s + 3 + \dfrac{1}{s} \end{vmatrix}}$$

$$= \frac{[V(s) + i_L(0^+)](s + 3 + 1/s) + (s + 3)[-i_L(0^+) - v_c(0^+)/s]}{(s + 6)(s + 3 + 1/s) - (s + 3)^2}$$

$$= \frac{[V(s) + i_L(0^+)](s^2 + 3s + 1) + (s + 3)[-i_L(0^+)s - v_c(0^+)]}{3s^2 + 10s + 6}$$
$$(9\text{-}13)$$

$$I_2(s) = \frac{\begin{vmatrix} s+6 & V(s) + i_L(0^+) \\ -(s+3) & -i_L(0^+) - \dfrac{v_c(0^+)}{s} \end{vmatrix}}{\begin{vmatrix} s+6 & -(s+3) \\ -(s+3) & s+3+\dfrac{1}{s} \end{vmatrix}}$$

$$= \frac{(s+6)[-i_L(0^+)s - v_c(0^+)] + (s+3)[V(s) + i_L(0^+)]}{3s^2 + 10s + 6}$$

$$(9\text{-}14)$$

With the matrix notation, (9-11) and (9-12) are written

$$\begin{bmatrix} V(s) + i_L(0^+) \\ -i_L(0^+) - \dfrac{v_c(0^+)}{s} \end{bmatrix} = \begin{bmatrix} s+6 & -(s+3) \\ -(s+3) & \left(s+3+\dfrac{1}{s}\right) \end{bmatrix} \begin{bmatrix} I_1(s) \\ I_2(s) \end{bmatrix} \quad (9\text{-}15)$$

The solutions of $I_1(s)$ and $I_2(s)$ are obtained by matrix inversion. Thus

$$\begin{bmatrix} I_1(s) \\ I_2(s) \end{bmatrix} = \begin{bmatrix} s+6 & -(s+3) \\ -(s+3) & s+3+\dfrac{1}{s} \end{bmatrix}^{-1} \begin{bmatrix} V(s) + i_L(0^+) \\ -i_L(0^+) - \dfrac{v_c(0^+)}{s} \end{bmatrix} \quad (9\text{-}16)$$

or

$$\begin{bmatrix} I_1(s) \\ I_2(s) \end{bmatrix} = \frac{1}{\Delta} \begin{bmatrix} s+3+\dfrac{1}{s} & s+3 \\ s+3 & s+6 \end{bmatrix} \begin{bmatrix} V(s) + i_L(0^+) \\ -i_L(0^+) - \dfrac{v_c(0^+)}{s} \end{bmatrix} \quad (9\text{-}17)$$

where $\Delta = (s+6)(s+3+1/s) - (s+3)^2$.

It is easy to see that (9-17) is the matrix representation of the two equations (9-13) and (9-14).

The currents $i_1(t)$ and $i_2(t)$ are obtained for $v(t) = Vu(t)$ or $V(s) = V/s$ by applying the inverse Laplace transform to $I_1(s)$ and $I_2(s)$, respectively. We have

$$i_1(t) = \frac{V}{6} u(t) + [0.178V + 0.19i_L(0^+) - 0.42v_c(0^+)]e^{-0.788t}u(t)$$

$$+ [-0.012V - 0.19i_L(0^+) + 0.087v_c(0^+)e^{-2.54t}]u(t) \quad (9\text{-}18)$$

$$i_2(t) = [0.42V + 0.45i_L(0^+) - 0.99v_c(0^+)e^{-0.788t}]u(t)$$

$$+ [-0.087V - 1.45i_L(0^+) + 0.657v_c(0^+)e^{-2.54t}]u(t) \quad (9\text{-}19)$$

The details of the inverse transformation are left to the student as an exercise.

The voltage across the capacitor for $t \geq 0$ can be obtained from

$$v_c(t) = \frac{1}{C} \int_{0^+}^{t} i_2(\tau) \, d\tau + v_c(0^+) \tag{9-20}$$

Substituting $i_2(t)$ from (9-19) in (9-20), we get

$$v_c(t) = 0.5Vu(t) + [-0.534V - 0.57i_L(0+) + 1.25v_c(0^+)]e^{-0.788t}u(t)$$
$$+ [0.034V + 0.57i_L(0+) - 0.25v_c(0^+)]e^{-2.54t}u(t) \tag{9-21}$$

9-2   SOLUTION OF STATE EQUATIONS (CONTINUOUS - DATA) BY LAPLACE TRANSFORMS

The general solution of the state equations of a continuous-data system has been obtained in Sec. 5-4 using a classical method.   In this section, we obtain the solution of the state equations by means of the Laplace-transform method.

Let us consider that the dynamics of an nth-order linear time-invariant system with m independent inputs are represented by the vector-matrix state equation

$$\frac{d\mathbf{x}(t)}{dt} = \mathbf{A}\mathbf{x}(t) + \mathbf{B}\mathbf{r}(t) \tag{9-22}$$

where

$$\mathbf{x}(t) = \begin{bmatrix} x_1(t) \\ x_2(t) \\ \cdot \\ \cdot \\ \cdot \\ x_n(t) \end{bmatrix} \qquad \mathbf{r}(t) = \begin{bmatrix} r_1(t) \\ r_2(t) \\ \cdot \\ \cdot \\ \cdot \\ r_m(t) \end{bmatrix}$$

$\mathbf{A}$ is an $n \times n$ square matrix, and $\mathbf{B}$ is an $n \times m$ matrix.

Taking the Laplace transform on both sides of (9-22) yields†

$$s\mathbf{X}(s) = \mathbf{A}\mathbf{X}(s) + \mathbf{B}\mathbf{R}(s) + \mathbf{x}(0^+) \tag{9-23}$$

† Taking the Laplace transform of a matrix is equivalent to taking the Laplace transform of each element of the matrix.

where $\mathbf{x}(0^+)$ denotes the initial-state vector $\mathbf{x}(t)$ evaluated at $t = 0^+$. Note that the state equations, being first-order differential equations, require the use of only the theorem on the Laplace transform of the first derivative of a function.

Solving for $\mathbf{X}(s)$ in (9-23), we have

$$\mathbf{X}(s) = (s\mathbf{I} - \mathbf{A})^{-1}\mathbf{x}(0^+) + (s\mathbf{I} - \mathbf{A})^{-1}\mathbf{B}\mathbf{R}(s) \tag{9-24}$$

where $\mathbf{I}$ is the unit matrix, and $(s\mathbf{I} - \mathbf{A})^{-1}$ denotes the matrix inverse of $s\mathbf{I} - \mathbf{A}$. We can show that the following identity is true:

$$(s\mathbf{I} - \mathbf{A})^{-1} = \frac{\mathbf{I}}{s} + \frac{\mathbf{A}}{s^2} + \frac{\mathbf{A}^2}{s^3} + \cdots + \frac{\mathbf{A}^n}{s^n} + \cdots \tag{9-25}$$

The proof may be easily carried out by premultiplying both sides of the equation by $s\mathbf{I} - \mathbf{A}$. Now the inverse Laplace transform of $(s\mathbf{I} - \mathbf{A})^{-1}$ is obtained by taking the inverse Laplace transform of the right-hand side of (9-25). Therefore

$$\mathcal{L}^{-1}[(s\mathbf{I} - \mathbf{A})^{-1}] = \mathbf{I} + \mathbf{A}t + \frac{1}{2!}\mathbf{A}^2 t^2 + \cdots + \frac{1}{n!}\mathbf{A}^n t^n + \cdots \tag{9-26}$$

The right-hand side of (9-26) is recognized to be the state-transition matrix of $\mathbf{A}$. Thus

$$\mathcal{L}^{-1}[(s\mathbf{I} - \mathbf{A})^{-1}] = e^{\mathbf{A}t} = \mathbf{\Phi}(t) \tag{9-27}$$

Substituting (9-27) in the inverse Laplace transform of (9-24) gives

$$\mathbf{x}(t) = \mathbf{\Phi}(t)\mathbf{x}(0^+) + \mathcal{L}^{-1}[(s\mathbf{I} - \mathbf{A})^{-1}\mathbf{B}\mathbf{R}(s)] \tag{9-28}$$

The last term in (9-28) represents the inverse Laplace transform of the product of two transformed functions, which calls for the use of the real convolution integral in (8-119). Thus

$$\mathbf{x}(t) = \mathbf{\Phi}(t)\mathbf{x}(0^+) + \int_0^t \mathbf{\Phi}(t - \tau)\mathbf{B}\mathbf{r}(\tau)\,d\tau \tag{9-29}$$

which is the solution of (9-22) between the time interval $\tau = 0^+$ and $\tau = t > 0$, when the initial state $\mathbf{x}(0^+)$ and the input $\mathbf{r}(\tau)$ for $\tau \geq 0$ are given. It is apparent that (9-29) is identical with the solution obtained earlier, in (5-94).   The state-transition equation for any initial time t_0 is derived as described in (5-95) to (5-97).

It is important to point out that the Laplace-transform method of evaluating the state-transition matrix is easier to carry out than the infinite-series method since it involves only taking the inverse Laplace transform of $(s\mathbf{I} - \mathbf{A})^{-1}$.

As an illustrative example, let us consider analyzing the network of Fig. 9-1, using the method just described.   The state equations of the network in normal form are

$$\frac{di_L(t)}{dt} = v_c(t) - 3i_L(t) \tag{9-30}$$

$$\frac{dv_c(t)}{dt} = \frac{v(t)}{3} - i_L(t) - \frac{v_c(t)}{3} \tag{9-31}$$

Taking the Laplace transform on both sides of these state equations yields

$$sI_L(s) - i_L(0^+) = V_c(s) - 3I_L(s) \tag{9-32}$$

$$sV_c(s) - v_c(0^+) = \frac{V(s)}{3} - I_L(s) - \frac{V_c(s)}{3} \tag{9-33}$$

Ordinarily, the solutions of $i_L(t)$ and $v_c(t)$ are obtained by solving for $I_L(s)$ and $V_c(s)$ from these transformed state equations, and then taking the inverse Laplace transformation.   However, the state-transition equation (9-29) represents a more direct way of obtaining the solutions for the network.

From (9-30) and (9-31), the $\mathbf{A}$ and $\mathbf{B}$ matrices of the network are obtained as

$$\mathbf{A} = \begin{bmatrix} -3 & 1 \\ -1 & -\frac{1}{3} \end{bmatrix} \qquad \mathbf{B} = \begin{bmatrix} 0 \\ \frac{1}{3} \end{bmatrix}$$

and

$$s\mathbf{I} - \mathbf{A} = \begin{bmatrix} s & 0 \\ 0 & s \end{bmatrix} - \begin{bmatrix} -3 & 1 \\ -1 & -\frac{1}{3} \end{bmatrix} = \begin{bmatrix} s+3 & -1 \\ 1 & s+\frac{1}{3} \end{bmatrix} \tag{9-34}$$

The matrix inverse of $s\mathbf{I} - \mathbf{A}$ is

$$(s\mathbf{I} - \mathbf{A})^{-1} = \frac{1}{(s+3)(s+\frac{1}{3})+1} \begin{bmatrix} s+\frac{1}{3} & 1 \\ -1 & s+3 \end{bmatrix} \tag{9-35}$$

and

$$\mathcal{L}^{-1}[(s\mathbf{I} - \mathbf{A})^{-1}] = \mathbf{\Phi}(t)$$
$$= \begin{bmatrix} -0.26e^{-0.788t} + 1.26e^{-2.54t} & 0.57e^{-0.788t} - 0.57e^{-2.54t} \\ -0.57e^{-0.788t} + 0.57e^{-2.54t} & 1.26e^{-0.788t} - 0.26e^{-2.54t} \end{bmatrix} \quad (9\text{-}36)$$

Also

$$(s\mathbf{I} - \mathbf{A})^{-1}\mathbf{BR}(s)$$

$$= \frac{1}{(s+3)(s+\frac{1}{3})+1} \begin{bmatrix} s + \frac{1}{3} & 1 \\ -1 & s+3 \end{bmatrix} \begin{bmatrix} 0 \\ \frac{1}{3} \end{bmatrix} [V(s)]$$

$$= \frac{1}{(s+0.788)(s+2.54)} \begin{bmatrix} \frac{1}{3} \\ \dfrac{s+3}{3} \end{bmatrix} \begin{bmatrix} \dfrac{V}{s} \end{bmatrix}$$

$$= \begin{bmatrix} \dfrac{V}{3s(s+0.788)(s+2.54)} \\ \dfrac{V(s+3)}{3s(s+0.788)(s+2.54)} \end{bmatrix} \quad (9\text{-}37)$$

The inverse Laplace transform of $(s\mathbf{I} - \mathbf{A})^{-1}\mathbf{BR}(s)$ is readily obtained as

$$\mathcal{L}^{-1}[(s\mathbf{I} - \mathbf{A})^{-1}\mathbf{BR}(s)] = \begin{bmatrix} \dfrac{V}{6} - 0.24Ve^{-0.788t} + 0.075Ve^{-2.54t} \\ \dfrac{V}{2} + 0.0344e^{-0.788t} - 0.534e^{-2.54t} \end{bmatrix}$$
$$(9\text{-}38)$$

Thus, from (9-29), we have, for $t_0^+ = 0^+$,

$$\mathbf{x}(t) = \begin{bmatrix} i_L(t) \\ v_c(t) \end{bmatrix}$$

$$= \begin{bmatrix} -0.26e^{-0.788t} + 1.26e^{-2.54t} & 0.57e^{-0.788t} - 0.57e^{-2.54t} \\ -0.57e^{-0.788t} + 0.57e^{-2.54t} & 1.26e^{-0.788t} - 0.26e^{-2.54t} \end{bmatrix} \begin{bmatrix} i_L(0^+) \\ v_c(0^+) \end{bmatrix}$$

$$+ \begin{bmatrix} \dfrac{V}{6} - 0.24Ve^{-0.788t} + 0.075e^{-2.54t} \\ \dfrac{V}{2} + 0.0344e^{-0.788t} - 0.534e^{-2.54t} \end{bmatrix} \quad (9\text{-}39)$$

This result can be checked easily with the results (9-18) to (9-21).

9-3 TRANSFORM NETWORKS

From the preceding sections we realize that the Laplace-transform method of solving linear systems and networks involves, essentially, the following four steps:

1 Write the system or network equations in the time domain, using the loop analysis, node analysis, or the state-variable analysis.
2 Take the Laplace transforms of the time-domain equations.
3 Solve for the desired variables in the complex Laplace domain.
4 Take the inverse Laplace transforms of the unknown variables.

Since electric networks and systems generally contain such elements as resistors, inductors, and capacitors, whose mathematical descriptions have been standardized, it is possible to simplify the analysis procedure outlined above.   In other words, we demonstrate below that it is possible to write down the equations directly in the Laplace domain in the same way as the time-domain ones.   This simplified procedure relies on the use of the *transform networks*, which are described in the following discussion.

Transform network of an inductor

Consider the inductor L shown in Fig. 9-2.   The voltage-current relationship in loop- and state-equation form is

$$v(t) = L\frac{di(t)}{dt} \qquad\qquad I(s) = \frac{Li(0)}{L} + \frac{\frac{V}{s}}{L} \qquad (9\text{-}40)$$

Taking the Laplace transform on both sides of (9-40) yields

$$V(s) = sLI(s) + Li(0^+) \qquad 5 + I(s)L(s) + Li(0) = 0 \qquad (9\text{-}41)$$

$$I_s = i(0^+) + \frac{\frac{V}{s}}{L}$$

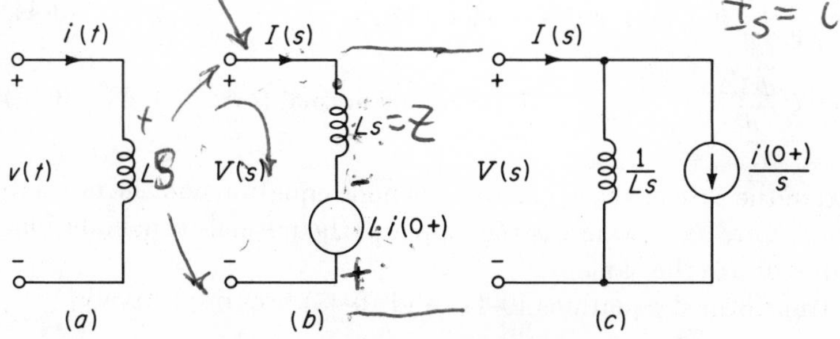

Fig. 9-2   Transform networks of an inductor. (a) Inductor. (b) Loop or normal-form transform network. (c) Node transform network.

Whereas (9-40) represents a voltage relationship in the time domain, (9-41) may be regarded as a voltage equation in the Laplace domain. The equation can be interpreted as follows: The voltage $V(s)$ is equal to the sum of a voltage drop $sLI(s)$ caused by the current $I(s)$ flowing through the "impedance" sL and a voltage source of strength $-Li(0^+)$. Therefore (9-41) is represented by a network configuration featuring an impedance connected in series with a voltage source as shown in Fig. 9-2b. Notice that the polarity of the voltage source $Li(0^+)$ is so assigned that the sign in front of $Li(0^+)$ in (9-41) is negative. The network configuration shown in Fig. 9-2b is defined as the *loop*, or the *normal-form*, *transform network* of an inductor.

For node analysis, the voltage-current relationship is given by

$$i(t) = \frac{1}{L} \int_{0^+}^{t} v(\tau) \, d\tau + i(0^+) \tag{9-42}$$

Taking the Laplace transform on both sides of (9-42) yields

$$I(s) = \frac{V(s)}{Ls} + \frac{i(0^+)}{s} \tag{9-43}$$

The node transform network of an inductor consists of a current source of strength $i(0^+)/s$ connected in parallel with an admittance $1/Ls$. The transform network for node analysis is shown in Fig. 9-2c.

Transform networks of a capacitor

For the capacitor C shown in Fig. 9-3a, the voltage-current relationships in loop form and node or normal form are

$$v(t) = \frac{1}{C} \int_{0^+}^{t} i(\tau) \, d\tau + v(0^+) \qquad \text{loop form} \tag{9-44}$$

$$i(t) = C \frac{dv(t)}{dt} \qquad \text{node or normal form} \tag{9-45}$$

Note that, in the case of the capacitor, the node equation and the normal-form equation are alike, whereas the loop and the normal-form equations for an inductor are the same.

The transformed equations (9-44) and (9-45) are, respectively,

$$V(s) = \frac{I(s)}{Cs} + \frac{v(0^+)}{s} \qquad \text{loop form} \tag{9-46}$$

and

$$I(s) = CsV(s) - Cv(0^+) \qquad \text{node or normal form} \qquad (9\text{-}47)$$

The transform networks of the capacitor are shown in Fig. 9-3.

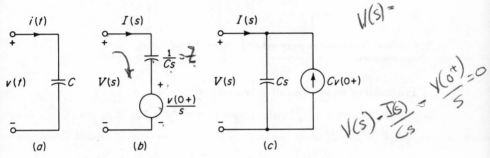

Fig. 9-3   Transform networks of a capacitor. (a) Capacitor. (b) Loop transform network. (c) Node or normal-form transform network.

Transform networks of a resistor

Since the functional form of the voltage-current relationship of a resistor in the time domain is the same as that in the Laplace domain, but now the transforms of currents and voltages occur, the transform network of R is identical with the time-domain configuration.   The voltage and current quantities of the transform network are designated by $V(s)$ and $I(s)$, respectively (Fig. 9-4).

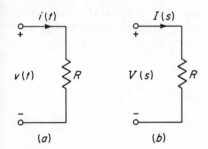

Fig. 9-4   Transform network of a resistor. (a) Resistor. (b) Loop, node, and normal-form transform network.

Transform networks of voltage and current sources

As shown in Fig. 9-5, the transform networks of voltage and current sources are the same as their time-domain counterparts, since

$$V(s) = \mathcal{L}[v(t)] \qquad \text{and} \qquad I(s) = \mathcal{L}[i(t)]$$

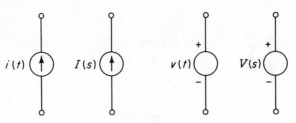

Fig. 9-5 *Transform networks of current and voltage sources.*

Transform networks of a transformer

For the transformer circuit shown in Fig. 9-6a, the loop equations in the time domain are

$$v_1(t) = L_1 \frac{di_1(t)}{dt} \pm M \frac{di_2(t)}{dt} \tag{9-48}$$

$$v_2(t) = \pm M \frac{di_1(t)}{dt} + L_2 \frac{di_2(t)}{dt} \tag{9-49}$$

Taking the Laplace transforms of this set of equations, we get

$$V_1(s) = L_1 s I_1(s) \pm M s I_2(s) - L_1 i_1(0^+) \mp M i_2(0^+) \tag{9-50}$$

$$V_2(s) = \pm M s I_1(s) + L_2 s I_2(s) - L_2 i_2(0^+) \mp M i_1(0^+) \tag{9-51}$$

where plus and minus signs are used in front of M to indicate variations in winding orientations of the transformer.   The two transform equations (9-50) and (9-51) are represented by the transform network shown in Fig. 9-6b.   Since only L and M are involved in the transformer shown, the normal-form transform network is the same as that shown in Fig. 9-6b.

Based on (2-29) and (2-30), the node equations of the transformer are written

$$i_1(t) = \Gamma_1 \int_{0^+}^{t} v_1(\tau)\, d\tau \mp \Gamma_M \int_{0^+}^{t} v_2(\tau)\, d\tau + i_1(0^+) \tag{9-52}$$

$$i_2(t) = \mp \Gamma_M \int_{0^+}^{t} v_1(\tau)\, d\tau + \Gamma_2 \int_{0^+}^{t} v_2(\tau)\, d\tau + i_2(0^+) \tag{9-53}$$

Taking the Laplace transforms on both sides of these equations, we get

$$I_1(s) = \frac{\Gamma_1 V_1(s)}{s} \mp \frac{\Gamma_M V_2(s)}{s} + \frac{i_1(0^+)}{s} \tag{9-54}$$

$$I_2(s) = \mp \frac{\Gamma_M V_1(s)}{s} + \frac{\Gamma_2 V_2(s)}{s} + \frac{i_2(0^+)}{s} \tag{9-55}$$

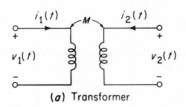

(a) Transformer

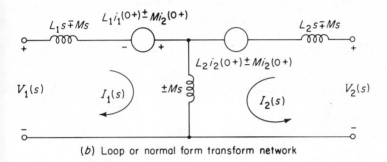

(b) Loop or normal form transform network

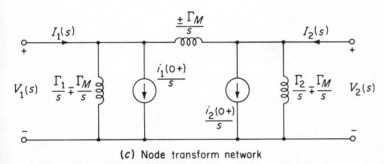

(c) Node transform network

Fig. 9-6   Transform networks of a transformer.

These node-transform equations are portrayed by the transform network shown in Fig. 9-6c.

We see from the foregoing developments that the transform-network equivalent of a network is obtained by replacing each electric element by its corresponding transform-network element. For loop analysis, the loop transform equivalents are used, and for node analysis the node transform equivalents are used. Since the network equations in the normal form are a mixture of loop and node equations, both loop and node transform equivalents are needed for the state-variable analysis.

Example 9-1   Find the transform network in loop form, node form, and normal form for the network shown in Fig. 9-7a.

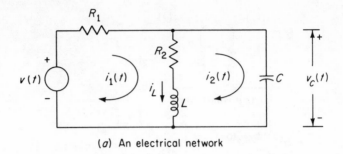

(a) An electrical network

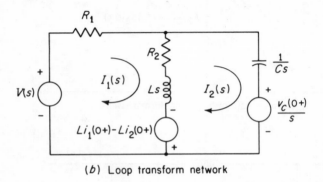

(b) Loop transform network

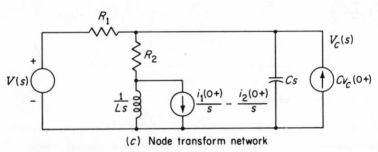

(c) Node transform network

Fig. 9-7   Transform networks for Example 9-1.

Replacing the circuit elements of the network by their corresponding transform equivalents, we obtain the loop and node transform networks as shown in Fig. 9-7b and c, respectively.   It is apparent that the transformed loop equations can be written directly from the loop transform network using Kirchhoff's voltage law.   Similarly, the transformed node equations are written directly from Fig. 9-7c using Kirchhoff's current law.   In the state-variable approach, since the voltage across L and the current in C are the state variables, the loop equivalent of L and the node equivalent of C are used.   Thus the transform network of the network in Fig. 9-7a for state-variable analysis is as shown in Fig. 9-8.   Notice that

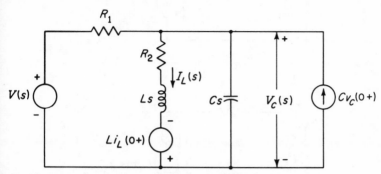

Fig. 9-8   Transform network for state-variable analysis (normal form) of the network in Fig. 9-7a.

the inductor L is replaced by its loop transform equivalent.   The transformed network equations of the network in normal form are written directly from Fig. 9-8.   Writing the voltage drop across the impedance Ls as a function of the state variables $I_L(s)$ and $V_c(s)$, we have

$$LsI_L(s) = V_c(s) - R_2I_L(s) + Li_L(0^+) \qquad (9\text{-}56)$$

Writing the current through the capacitor as a function of the state variables, we get

$$CsV_c(s) = \frac{V(s)}{R_1} - \frac{V_c(s)}{R_1} - I_L(s) + Cv_c(0^+) \qquad (9\text{-}57)$$

9-4   APPLICATIONS OF THE TRANSFORM NETWORKS

In this section we present examples to demonstrate the usefulness of the transform networks in solving network problems.   Emphasis is placed mainly on networks with switching operations.

Example 9-2   As our first example, consider the network shown in Fig. 9-9a.   The switch S is switched from a neutral position to position a at $t = 0$.   Clearly, at $t = 0$, the initial current in the inductor is zero. At $t = T$ sec, the switch is moved from position a to position b.   Determine the current $i_L(t)$ using the Laplace-transform method.

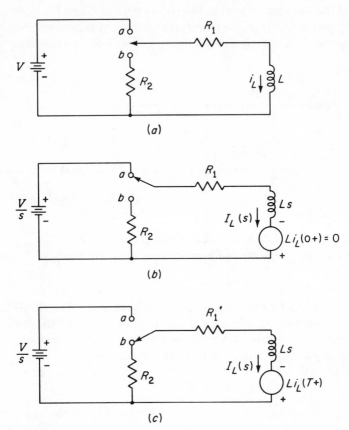

Fig. 9-9 *Networks for Example 9-2. (a) Network. (b)*
Transform network for $0 \leq t < T$. (c) Transform network
for $t \geq T$.

The transform network of the original network for the time interval $0^+ \leq t < T$ is depicted in Fig. 9-9b. The transformed state-transition equation is written directly from Fig. 9-9b.

$$LsI_L(s) = \frac{V}{s} - R_1I_L(s) + Li_L(0^+) \tag{9-58}$$

Solving for $I_L(s)$, and since $i_L(0^+)$ is zero, we get

$$I_L(s) = \frac{V}{R_1s(1 + Ls/R_1)} \tag{9-59}$$

The inverse Laplace transform of $I_L(s)$ is

$$i_L(t) = \frac{V}{R_1}(1 - e^{-R_1 t/L}) \qquad 0 \leq t < T \tag{9-60}$$

At $t = T^+$, the switch is moved from position a to position b. Substituting $t = T^+$ in (9-60) yields

$$i_L(T^+) = \frac{V}{R_1}(1 - e^{-R_1 T^+/L}) \tag{9-61}$$

which is the initial inductor current at $t = T^+$. Now the transform equivalent network for $t > T$ is shown in Fig. 9-9c. Notice that the equivalent-voltage source has a voltage strength of $Li_L(T^+)$, which corresponds to an impulse in the time domain. The state-transition equation of the network for $t > T$ is written from Fig. 9-9c:

$$LsI_L(s) = Li_L(T^+) - (R_1 + R_2)I_L(s)$$
$$= \frac{VL}{R_1}(1 - e^{-R_1 T^+/L}) - (R_1 + R_2)I_L(s) \tag{9-62}$$

Solving for $I_L(s)$ from (9-62), we have

$$I_L(s) = \frac{V}{R_1}(1 - e^{-R_1 T^+/L})\frac{1}{s + (R_1 + R_2)/L} \tag{9-63}$$

The inverse Laplace transform of $I_L(s)$ is

$$i_L(t) = \frac{V}{R_1}(1 - e^{-R_1 T^+/L})e^{-(R_1+R_2)(t-T)/L} \qquad t > T \tag{9-64}$$

The complete waveform for $i_L(t)$ for $t > 0$ is sketched in Fig. 9-10. We see that, if the switch were not switched from position a to position b, the current $i_L(t)$ would reach the value V/R_1 as its final value. After the

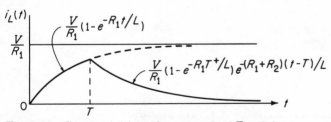

Fig. 9-10 *Current $i_L(t)$ in the network of Fig. 9-9.*

switch is switched to position b, the current $i_L(t)$ approaches zero with a time constant of $L/(R_1 + R_2)$.

We should not be puzzled by the equivalent-voltage generator in the transform network of Fig. 9-9c. Since the equivalent transform voltage of the generator is $Li_L(T^+)$, the time-domain equivalent is an impulse voltage. Thus the current caused by this impulsive voltage eventually has to die out as time approaches infinity.

Example 9-3   As a second example, consider the network shown in Fig. 9-11a. The switch S_1 is closed at $t = 0$. The initial voltage across the capacitor is assumed to be zero. After S_1 is closed for T sec, the switch S_2 is closed. Determine the voltage $v_c(t)$ for $t > 0$ using the Laplace-transform method.

The transform network for the time duration $0 < t < T$ is shown in Fig. 9-11b. The node transform equivalent of the capacitor is used as

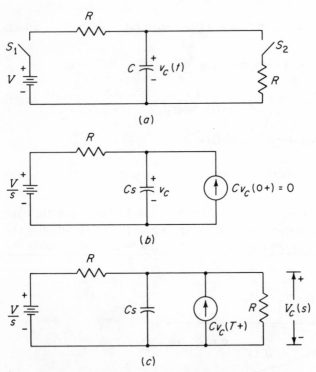

(a)

(b)

(c)

Fig. 9-11 Networks for Example 9-3. (a) Network.
(b) Transform network for $0 < t < T$. (c) Transform
network for $t > T$.

required by the state-transition method.   Writing the current through Cs as the algebraic sum of the other currents, we have

$$CsV_c(s) = \frac{V}{Rs} - \frac{V_c(s)}{R} + Cv_c(0^+)$$ (9-65)

Solving for $V_c(s)$ from this expression, and since $v_c(0^+)$ is zero, we have

$$V_c(s) = \frac{V}{s(1 + RCs)}$$ (9-66)

The inverse transform of $V_c(s)$ is, simply,

$$v_c(t) = V(1 - e^{-t/RC}) \qquad 0 < t < T$$ (9-67)

Thus the capacitor voltage rises exponentially toward V volts with a time constant of RC.   At $t = T$ sec, the switch S_2 is closed, and S_1 remains closed.   The transform network for $t > T$ is shown in Fig. 9-11c.   The initial voltage on the capacitor at $t = T^+$ is obtained by substituting $t = T^+$ in (9-67); then we have

$$v_c(T^+) = V(1 - e^{-T^+/RC})$$ (9-68)

The state-transition equation in the Laplace domain for $t > T$ is obtained by equating the capacitor current to the algebraic sum of the other currents in the transform network of Fig. 9-11c.   Therefore

$$CsV_c(s) = \frac{V}{Rs} - \frac{V_c(s)}{R} - \frac{V_c(s)}{R} + Cv_c(T^+)$$ (9-69)

Solving for $V_c(s)$ from this expression, we get

$$V_c(s) = \frac{V}{2s(1 + RCs/2)} + \frac{v_c(T^+)}{(s + 2/RC)}$$ (9-70)

The inverse transform of $V_c(s)$ is

$$v_c(t) = \left[\frac{V}{2}(1 - e^{-2(t-T)/RC}) + v_c(T^+)e^{-2(t-T)/RC}\right]u(t - T)$$ (9-71)

where $v_c(T^+)$ is defined in (9-68).   When t approaches infinity, $v_c(t)$ approaches $V/2$.   This result may be obtained by letting t approach infinity in (9-71) or by applying the final-value theorem to (9-70).   Substituting $v_c(T^+)$ from (9-68) in (9-71) and simplifying, we have

$$v_c(t) = \left[\frac{V}{2} + V(\tfrac{1}{2} - e^{-T/RC})e^{-2(t-T)/RC}\right]u(t - T)$$ (9-72)

which represents an exponential decay if $e^{-T/RC} > \frac{1}{2}$ and an exponential rise if $e^{-T/RC} < \frac{1}{2}$. The waveforms of $v_c(t)$ for $t > 0$ are sketched in Fig. 9-12 for two possible cases.

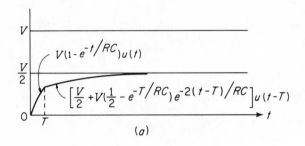

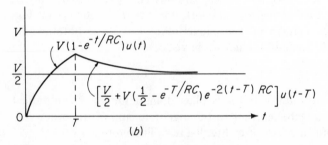

Fig. 9-12   Voltage waveforms of the network in Example 9-3. (a) $e^{-T/RC} < \frac{1}{2}$. (b) $e^{-T/RC} > \frac{1}{2}$.

Example 9-4   Consider the network shown in Fig. 9-13a. The ideal current source is a step function of I amp. The initial current in L and the initial voltage across C at $t = 0$ are denoted by $i_L(0^+)$ and $v_c(0^+)$, respectively. Determine the final value of the capacitor voltage $v_c(t)$ when time approaches infinity by means of the Laplace-transform method.

Actually, the final-value problem can be solved simply by inspection of the network shown in Fig. 9-13a. In the steady state, the inductor acts as a short circuit and the capacitor acts as an open circuit; thus the current $i(t)$ is divided between R_1 and R_2. We easily observe that

$$\lim_{t \to \infty} v_c(t) = \frac{R_1 R_2}{R_1 + R_2} I \tag{9-73}$$

However, we use this example to demonstrate the method of the transform networks. Furthermore, we show that the final value of $v_c(t)$ is completely independent of the initial states $i_L(0^+)$ and $v_c(0^+)$.

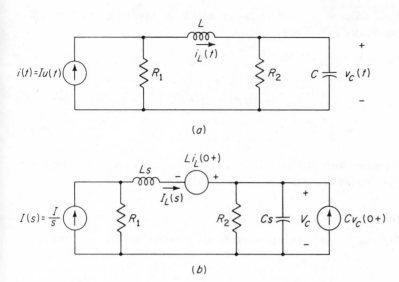

Fig. 9-13   Networks for Example 9-4.   (a) Network.   (b) Normal-
form transform network.

The normal-form transform network is drawn as shown in Fig. 9-13b.
The inductor current $I_L(s)$ and the capacitor voltage $V_c(s)$ are designated
as the state variables.   Therefore only these two variables and the input
$I(s)$ can appear in the normal-form state equations.   First, we write the
voltage across the inductor as the difference between the voltage across
R_1 and $Li_L(0^+) + V_c(s)$.   We have

$$LsI_L(s) = I(s) - I_L(s)R_1 + Li_L(0^+) - V_c(s) \qquad (9\text{-}74)$$

Next, the current in the capacitor is equated with the difference between
$I_L(s) + Cv_c(0^+)$ and the current through R_2.   Thus

$$CsV_c(s) = I_L(s) + Cv_c(0^+) - \frac{V_c(s)}{R_2} \qquad (9\text{-}75)$$

Solving for $V_c(s)$ in (9-74) and (9-75), we get

$$V_c(s) = \frac{R_1I(s) + (R_1 + Ls)Cv_c(0^+) + Li_L(0^+)}{1 + (R_1 + Ls)(Cs + 1/R_2)} \qquad (9\text{-}76)$$

For a step-function input, $I(s) = I/s$; (9-76) becomes

$$V_c(s) = I\frac{R_1 + s(R_1 + Ls)Cv_c(0^+) + Lsi_L(0^+)}{s[LCs^2 + (R_1C + L/R_2)s + 1 + R_1/R_2]} \qquad (9\text{-}77)$$

The final value of $v_c(t)$ may be obtained by applying the final-value theorem to (9-77).   Thus

$$\lim_{t \to \infty} v_c(t) = \lim_{s \to 0} sV_c(s)$$

$$= \lim_{s \to 0} I \frac{R_1 + s(R_1 + Ls)Cv_c(0^+) + sLi_L(0^+)}{LCs^2 + (R_1C + L/R_2)s + 1 + R_1/R_2}$$

$$= \frac{R_1R_2}{R_1 + R_2} I \qquad (9\text{-}78)$$

which agrees with (9-73).   It is also interesting to find out that this result is constant for any initial state $i_L(0^+)$ and $v_c(0^+)$.

PROBLEMS

9-1   Draw the loop transform networks for the networks shown in Fig. P9-1.

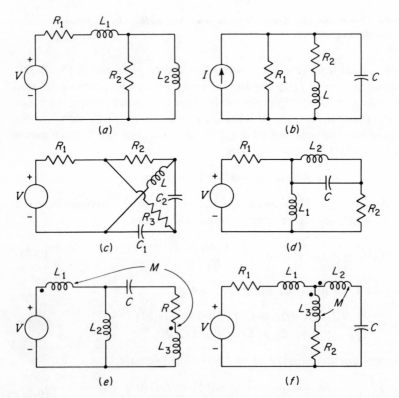

Fig. P9-1

9-2 Draw the node transform networks for the networks shown in Fig. P9-1.

9-3 Draw the normal-form transform networks for the networks shown in Fig. P9-1.

9-4 For the network shown in Fig. P9-2, determine $v_1(t)$ and $v_2(t)$ and sketch the voltage waveforms. Use the Laplace-transform method. $R = 10$ ohms, $L = 10^{-5}$ henry. Assume that all initial conditions are zero.

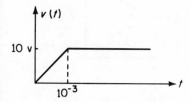

Fig. P9-2

9-5 Determine $v(t)$ for $t > 0$. What is $v_c(0+)$? (See Fig. P9-3.) $R = 10$ ohms, $i_L(t) = 10e^{-t/2}$ $(t \geq 0)$, $i_c(t) = 5e^{-t/2}$ $(t \geq 0)$, $L = 1$ henry.

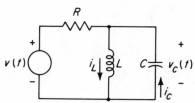

Fig. P9-3

9-6 In the network shown in Fig. P9-4, the switch S is closed at $t = T$ sec. Determine the expression for $v_0(t)$ for $t > 0$ and sketch the waveform of $v_0(t)$. Assume that, before the switch is closed, the network has not reached its steady state. $v(t) = u(t)$, and assume $v_0(0^+) = 0$.

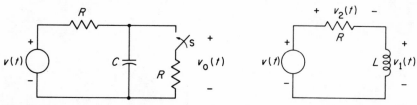

Fig. P9-4

9-7   Find the state-transition matrices for the networks shown in Fig. P9-5 by means of the Laplace-transform method.

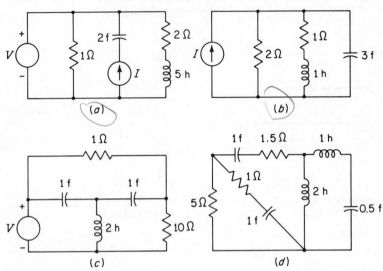

Fig. P9-5

9-8   Given the state equations of a physical system as

$$\begin{bmatrix} \dot{x}_1(t) \\ \dot{x}_2(t) \end{bmatrix} = \begin{bmatrix} -2 & -3 \\ -1 & -2 \end{bmatrix} \begin{bmatrix} x_1(t) \\ x_2(t) \end{bmatrix}$$

find the state-transition matrix $\Phi(t)$ by means of the Laplace-transform method.

TEN

THE z TRANSFORMATION

10-1 DEFINITION OF THE z TRANSFORMATION

It has been shown that Laplace transformation is a powerful tool for solving linear differential equations. However, it proved to be an awkward and ineffective method when used directly to solve difference equations such as (5-112) and (5-114). Furthermore, since $x(kT)$ represents the value of $x(t)$ at $t = kT$, it is just a number; therefore the meaning of $\mathcal{L}[x(kT)]$ is not clear. The Laplace transform of $x(kT)$ is not $x(kT)/s$, since, although $x(kT)$ is a constant, it cannot be regarded as a step function with amplitude $x(kT)$. Therefore a new and separate mathematical description of a discrete-data system must be established before the transform method can be utilized to its full advantage.

Let us investigate the sequence $x(0)$, $x(T)$, $x(2T)$, . . . , $x(kT)$, . . . , which can be considered either as associated with sending the signal $x(t)$ through an ideal sampler,[1] i.e., a sampler with zero sampling

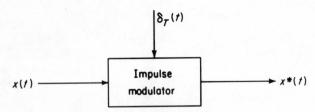

duration (Fig. 10-1), or with the product of $x(t)$ and the unit impulse train $\delta_T(t)$ in an impulse modulator[1] (Fig. 10-2). The ideal sampler shown in Fig. 10-1 is a switch which closes for zero duration once every

$x(t) \longrightarrow \times_T \longrightarrow x^*(t)$

Fig. 10-1   The ideal sampler.

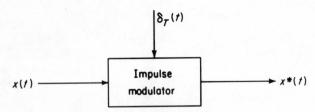

Fig. 10-2   The impulse modulator.

T sec.   The impulse modulator shown in Fig. 10-2 produces the product $x(t)\,\delta_T(t)$, where $\delta_T(t)$ is given by

$$\delta_T(t) = \sum_{k=0}^{\infty} \delta(t - kT) \tag{10-1}$$

Therefore the signal $x^*(t)$, obtained by either process, is written

$$x^*(t) = x(t)\delta_T(t) = x(t) \sum_{k=0}^{\infty} \delta(t - kT) \tag{10-2}$$

Since

$$x(t)\delta(t - kT) = x(kT)\delta(t - kT) \tag{10-3}$$

Eq. (10-2) can be written

$$x^*(t) = \sum_{k=0}^{\infty} x(kT)\delta(t - kT) \tag{10-4}$$

and when expanded gives

$$x^*(t) = x(0)\delta(t) + x(T)\delta(t - T) + \cdots$$
$$+ x(kT)\delta(t - kT) + \cdots \tag{10-5}$$

which is a time display of the original sequence $x(kT)$. A significant fact about this impulse-train description of the sequence is that the values of $x(t)$ at $t = kT$ are represented by the strength (or area) of the impulse located at $t = kT$. The magnitude of the impulse function is always infinite, of course.

Now it is possible to take the Laplace transform of the function in (10-4), and we have

$$\mathcal{L}[x^*(t)] = X^*(s) = \sum_{k=0}^{\infty} x(kT)e^{-kTs} \tag{10-6}$$

This is a key expression for transform analysis of discrete-data systems. Let us consider a simple numerical example of the application of (10-6). Consider

$$x(t) = e^{-t} \tag{10-7}$$

Substituting (10-7) in (10-6) gives

$$X^*(s) = \mathcal{L}\left[\sum_{k=0}^{\infty} e^{-kT}\delta(t - kT)\right] = \sum_{k=0}^{\infty} e^{-kT}e^{-kTs}$$

$$= \sum_{k=0}^{\infty} e^{-k(s+1)T} \tag{10-8}$$

or

$$X^*(s) = 1 + e^{-T(s+1)} + e^{-2T(s+1)} + \cdots \tag{10-9}$$

Multiplying both sides of (10-9) by $e^{-(s+1)T}$ and subtracting the result from (10-9), we get

$$(1 - e^{-(s+1)T})X^*(s) = 1 \qquad \text{if } |e^{-(s+1)T}| < 1$$

Therefore

$$X^*(s) = \frac{1}{1 - e^{-(s+1)T}} \tag{10-10}$$

The result of this simple illustration showed that the Laplace transform of a sampled function is usually a transcendental function of s. One of the disadvantages of this type of function is that inverse Laplace transforms are difficult to obtain, especially in complex cases. We recall that one of the advantages of the Laplace-transform method is that the transformed expressions are usually algebraic equations, thus making the equations much easier to manipulate. Another advantage of the algebraic transform equations is that the inverse transform can be obtained in a straightforward manner.

The z transformation is introduced to overcome the aforementioned difficulty. Although the z transform can be derived purely from a mathematical basis using the Stieljes integral,[7] at least from the engineering viewpoint, we can regard it purely as a step in changing the transformed expression into an algebraic equation. The z transform is defined as

$$z = e^{Ts} \tag{10-11}$$

where T is the sampling period, which is the interval between two consecutive impulses of a sampled signal. With this change in variable, (10-6) becomes

$$X^*(s) \Big|_{z=e^{Ts}} = \sum_{k=0}^{\infty} x(kT)z^{-k} \tag{10-12}$$

We define $X(z)$ as the z transform of $x(t)$, so that

$$X(z) = \mathsf{Z}[x(t)] = X^*(s) \Big|_{z=e^{Ts}} = \sum_{k=0}^{\infty} x(kT)z^{-k} \tag{10-13}$$

Therefore, taking the z transform of a function $x(t)$ implies the following three operations:

1   Sampling the function $x(t)$ with an ideal sampler with sampling period T, getting $x^*(t)$
2   Taking the Laplace transform of $x^*(t)$, that is, $\mathcal{L}[e^*(t)] = E^*(s)$
3   Replacing e^{Ts} by z in $E^*(s)$, which gives $E(z)$

From (10-10), the z transform of e^{-t} is written

$$\mathsf{Z}[e^{-t}] = \frac{1}{1 - e^{-1}z^{-1}} = \frac{z}{z - e^{-1}} = \frac{z}{z - 0.368} \qquad T = 1 \tag{10-14}$$

The z transform of well-known functions can be obtained using the definition of (10-13). A short list of z transforms is given in Table 10-1.

TABLE 10-1   Table of one-sided z transforms

Time function $f(t)$	Laplace transform $F(s)$	z-transform $F(z)$
Unit impulse $\delta(t)$	1	1
Unit step $u(t)$	$\dfrac{1}{s}$	$\dfrac{z}{z-1}$
t	$\dfrac{1}{s^2}$	$\dfrac{Tz}{(z-1)^2}$
t^2	$\dfrac{2}{s^3}$	$\dfrac{T^2z(z+1)}{(z-1)^3}$
t^n	$\dfrac{n!}{s^{n+1}}$	$\displaystyle\lim_{a\to 0}\dfrac{(-1)^n\partial^n}{\partial a^n}\dfrac{z}{z-e^{-aT}}$
e^{-at}	$\dfrac{1}{s+a}$	$\dfrac{z}{z-e^{-aT}}$
$a^{t/T}$	$\dfrac{1}{s-(1/T)\ln a}$	$\dfrac{z}{z-a}$
te^{-at}	$\dfrac{1}{(s+a)^2}$	$\dfrac{Tze^{-aT}}{(z-e^{-aT})^2}$
$\sin \omega t$	$\dfrac{\omega}{s^2+\omega^2}$	$\dfrac{z\sin \omega T}{z^2-2z\cos \omega T+1}$
$\cos \omega t$	$\dfrac{s}{s^2+\omega^2}$	$\dfrac{z(z-\cos \omega T)}{z^2-2z\cos \omega T+1}$
$e^{-at}\sin \omega t$	$\dfrac{\omega}{(s+a)^2+\omega^2}$	$\dfrac{ze^{-aT}\sin \omega T}{z^2-2ze^{-aT}\cos \omega T+e^{-2aT}}$
$e^{-at}\cos \omega t$	$\dfrac{s+a}{(s+a)^2+\omega^2}$	$\dfrac{z^2-ze^{-aT}\cos \omega T}{z^2-2ze^{-aT}\cos \omega T+e^{-2aT}}$

The inverse z transform

The process of obtaining $x(kT)$ from $X(z)$ is termed the *inverse z transformation*. Since $X(z)$ is defined as the z transform of $x(t)$, we should expect the inverse z transform of $X(z)$ to be $x(t)$. However, since $X(z)$ carries only partial information of $x(t)$, the inverse z transform of $X(z)$

is not necessarily $x(t)$. This points to the fact that the inverse z transform from $X(z)$ to $x(t)$ is not unique. In fact, if $X(z)$ is the z transform of $x(t)$, any function that has the same values as $x(t)$ at $t = kT$, $k = 0$, $1, 2, \ldots$, also satisfies as an inverse z transform of $X(z)$.

The inverse z transform of $X(z)$ is denoted by

$$\mathcal{Z}^{-1}[X(z)] = \text{inverse } z \text{ transform of } X(z) = x(kT) \tag{10-15}$$

In general, there are three ways of carrying out the inverse z-transform operation, as follows.

Series expansion

The values of $x(kT)$ for $k = 0, 1, 2, \ldots$ are obtained from $X(z)$ simply by expanding $X(z)$ into a power series of z^{-1}. Expanding (10-13), we get

$$X(z) = x(0) + x(T)z^{-1} + x(2T)z^{-2} + \cdots \tag{10-16}$$

Clearly, the coefficient of the z^{-k} term represents the value of $x(t)$ at $t = kT$. Therefore, given $X(z)$, it can be expanded into a power series in z^{-1}, and $x(kT)$ for $k = 0, 1, 2, \ldots$ are obtained from the coefficients of the power series.

Example 10-1   Find the inverse z transform of

$$X(z) = \frac{z}{(z - 0.368)}$$

by power-series expansion.

Expanding the right-hand side of $X(z)$ into a power series of z^{-1} by continued division, we get

$$X(z) = 1 + e^{-1}z^{-1} + e^{-2}z^{-2} + e^{-3}z^{-3} + \cdots + e^{-k}z^{-k} + \cdots \tag{10-17}$$

Inspection of the coefficients of this power series reveals that $x(kT) = e^{-k}$.

Example 10-2   Find the inverse z transform of

$$X(z) = \frac{0.632z}{z^2 - 1.368z + 0.368} \tag{10-18}$$

by expanding $X(z)$ into a power series in z^{-1}.

Expanding $X(z)$, we have

$$X(z) = 0.632z^{-1} + 0.864z^{-2} + 0.95z^{-3} + 0.982z^{-4} + \cdots \quad (10\text{-}19)$$

which means that $x(0) = 0$, $x(T) = 0.632$, $x(2T) = 0.864$, $x(3T) = 0.95$, $x(4T) = 0.982$, ...

Partial fraction expansion

Just as in the Laplace-transform method, the inverse z transform can be carried out by means of the partial fraction expansion and the z-transform table. However, an important point to keep in mind is that the partial fraction expansion must be performed on the function $X(z)/z$, rather than on $X(z)$, since, as observed from the z-transform table, all the basic z-transform expressions have a z in the numerator. In other words, the function $X(z)/z$ should first be expanded by partial fraction expansion into the following form:

$$\frac{X(z)}{z} = \frac{A_1}{z + a_1} + \frac{A_2}{z + a_2} + \frac{A_3}{z + a_3} + \cdots \quad (10\text{-}20)$$

and then the inverse z transform of $X(z)$ is given by

$$x(kT) = Z^{-1}[X(z)] = Z^{-1}\left[\frac{A_1z}{z + a_1} + \frac{A_2z}{z + a_2} + \frac{A_3z}{z + a_3} + \cdots\right] \quad (10\text{-}21)$$

Example 10-3   Find the inverse z transform of

$$X(z) = \frac{0.632z}{z^2 - 1.368z + 0.368} \quad (10\text{-}22)$$

by partial fraction expansion.

Expanding $X(z)/z$, we get

$$\frac{X(z)}{z} = \frac{-1}{z - 0.368} + \frac{1}{z - 1} \quad (10\text{-}23)$$

Therefore

$$X(z) = \frac{z}{z - 1} - \frac{z}{z - 0.368} \quad (10\text{-}24)$$

From the z-transform table, we have

$$x(kT) = 1 - e^{-k} \tag{10-25}$$

When $k = 0, 1, 2, \ldots$ are substituted into $x(kT)$, it can be shown that the result in (10-25) agrees with that of Example 10.2.

Inversion formula

An inversion formula is available for the inverse z transformation. We recall that the inversion formula for the Laplace transform in (8-126) is

$$\mathcal{L}^{-1}[X(s)] = x(t) = \frac{1}{2\pi j} \int_{c-j\infty}^{c+j\infty} X(s)e^{st}\, ds$$

where c must be greater than the abscissa of convergence of $X(s)$. Similarly, for the z transform, the inversion integral can be written

$$\mathcal{Z}^{-1}[X(z)] = x(kT) = \frac{1}{2\pi j} \oint_{\Gamma} X(z)z^{k-1}\, dz \tag{10-26}$$

where Γ is a circular path with radius large enough to enclose all the poles of $X(z)z^{n-1}$. The proof of this inversion integral is given in the literature,[1] and is not given here. It is to be noted that the contour integral on the right-hand side of (10-26) can be evaluated by using the residue method.

Example 10-4   Find the inverse z transform of

$$X(z) = \frac{0.632z}{z^2 - 1.368z + 0.368} \tag{10-27}$$

by means of the inversion formula of (10-26).

Substituting $X(z)$ into (10-26), we have

$$x(kT) = \frac{1}{2\pi j} \oint \frac{0.632z}{(z-1)(z-0.368)}\, z^{k-1}\, dz \tag{10-28}$$

From the theorem of the residues, expression (10-28) is written

$$x(kT) = \sum \text{residues of } \frac{0.632}{(z-1)(z-0.368)}\, z^k$$

$$\text{at poles } z = 1 \text{ and } z = 0.368 \tag{10-29}$$

Evaluating the residues in (10-29), we get

$$x(kT) = \frac{0.632}{1 - 0.368}\,(1)^k + \frac{0.632}{0.368 - 1}\,(0.368)^k$$
$$= 1 - (0.368)^k = 1 - e^{-k} \tag{10-30}$$

which agrees with the results obtained in Examples 10-2 and 10-3.

10-2 SOME PROPERTIES OF THE z TRANSFORMS

To facilitate the applications of the z transformation, a number of the important properties of the z transforms are discussed below. Most of these properties can be proved simply by means of the definitions of the z transformation. The details of the proofs are available in the literature.[1-4]

Multiplication by a constant

$$\mathcal{Z}[af(t)] = aF(z) \tag{10-31}$$

where a is a constant.

Linearity

$$\mathcal{Z}[f_1(t) \pm f_2(t)] = F_1(z) \pm F_2(z) \tag{10-32}$$

Right shift (time delay)

$$\mathcal{Z}[f(t - nT)u(t - nT)] = z^{-n}F(z) \tag{10-33}$$

where n is a positive integer.

Equation (10-33) states that the z transform of a function $f(t)u(t)$ which is shifted to the right or delayed by nT, where n is a positive integer, is equal to z^{-n} times the z transform of $f(t)$. Notice that this property is analogous to the shifting theorem of the Laplace transformation (8-90).

Left shift (time advance)

$$\mathcal{Z}[f(t + nT)u(t)] = z^n\left[F(z) - \sum_{k=0}^{n-1} f(kT)z^{-k}\right] \tag{10-34}$$

where n is a positive integer. This expression is analogous to (8-92), which is the Laplace transform of a time function shifted to the left by nT. Since the difference equations deal directly with functions such as $f(t + nT)$ and $f(t - nT)$, the shifting properties of the z transformation are the key relationships for the transform solution of difference equations.

Multiplication by $e^{\mp at}$

$$\mathrm{Z}[e^{\mp at}f(t)] = F(ze^{\pm aT}) \tag{10-35}$$

This property is useful when finding the z transforms of functions such as $e^{-3t}\sin \omega t$, $e^{-5t}t^2$, and others.

Initial-value theorem

$$\lim_{t \to 0} f^*(t) = \lim_{k \to 0} f(kT) = \lim_{z \to \infty} F(z) \tag{10-36}$$

if the limit exists.

This theorem is analogous to the initial-value theorem for Laplace transforms (8-107).

Final-value theorem

$$\lim_{t \to \infty} f^*(t) = \lim_{k \to \infty} f(kT) = \lim_{z \to 1} (1 - z^{-1})F(z) \tag{10-37}$$

if $(1 - z^{-1})F(z)$ does not have any pole which lies outside the unit circle $|z| = 1$ in the z plane.

Like the final-value theorem for Laplace transforms (8-110), Eq. (10-37) is very useful in determining the steady-state responses of discrete-data systems. As a simple illustration, let us evaluate the final value of the response $x(kT)$ of the function in Example 10-2 as k goes to infinity. Since the poles of the function

$$X(z) = \frac{0.632z}{z^2 - 1.368z + 0.368} \tag{10-38}$$

are at $z = 1$ and $z = 0.368$, $(1 - z^{-1})X(z)$ becomes

$$(1 - z^{-1})X(z) = \frac{0.632}{z - 0.368} \tag{10-39}$$

which does not have any pole outside the unit circle $|z| = 1$ in the z plane. Therefore the final-value theorem is applicable to this function, and

(10-37) gives

$$\lim_{k \to \infty} x(kT) = \lim_{z \to 1} \frac{0.632}{z - 0.368} = 1 \tag{10-40}$$

which is the expected result.

10-3 z-TRANSFORM SOLUTION OF DISCRETE STATE EQUATIONS

The discrete dynamic equations

$$\mathbf{x}[(k + 1)T] = \mathbf{A}\mathbf{x}(kT) + \mathbf{B}\mathbf{r}(kT) \tag{10-41}$$

$$\mathbf{y}(kT) = \mathbf{C}\mathbf{x}(kT) + \mathbf{D}\mathbf{r}(kT) \tag{10-42}$$

can be solved by means of the z-transform method.   Taking the z transform on both sides of (10-41) yields

$$z\mathbf{X}(z) - z\mathbf{x}(0^+) = \mathbf{A}\mathbf{X}(z) + \mathbf{B}\mathbf{R}(z) \tag{10-43}$$

Solving for $\mathbf{X}(z)$ from (10-43), we get

$$\mathbf{X}(z) = (z\mathbf{I} - \mathbf{A})^{-1}z\mathbf{x}(0^+) + (z\mathbf{I} - \mathbf{A})^{-1}\mathbf{B}\mathbf{R}(z) \tag{10-44}$$

which has an inverse z transform,

$$\mathbf{x}(kT) = \mathcal{Z}^{-1}[(z\mathbf{I} - \mathbf{A})^{-1}z]\mathbf{x}(0^+) + \mathcal{Z}^{-1}[(z\mathbf{I} - \mathbf{A})^{-1}\mathbf{B}\mathbf{R}(z)] \tag{10-45}$$

Comparing this result with that of (5-121), we arrive at the following identities:

$$\mathbf{A}^k = \mathcal{Z}^{-1}[(z\mathbf{I} - \mathbf{A})^{-1}z] \tag{10-46}$$

and

$$\sum_{i=0}^{k-1} \mathbf{A}^{k-i-1}\mathbf{B}\mathbf{r}(iT) = \mathcal{Z}^{-1}[(z\mathbf{I} - \mathbf{A})^{-1}\mathbf{B}\mathbf{R}(z)] \tag{10-47}$$

To prove (10-46), taking the z transform on both sides of the equation, we get

$$\mathcal{Z}[\mathbf{A}^k] = (z\mathbf{I} - \mathbf{A})^{-1}z = \sum_{k=0}^{\infty} \mathbf{A}^k z^{-k}$$

$$= \mathbf{I} + \mathbf{A}z^{-1} + \mathbf{A}^2 z^{-2} + \cdots \tag{10-48}$$

Therefore

$$(z\mathbf{I} - \mathbf{A})^{-1}z = \mathbf{I} + \mathbf{A}z^{-1} + \mathbf{A}^2z^{-2} + \cdots \tag{10-49}$$

Premultiplying both sides of the last equation by $(z\mathbf{I} - \mathbf{A})$ yields

$$z = (z\mathbf{I} - \mathbf{A})(\mathbf{I} + \mathbf{A}z^{-1} + \mathbf{A}^2z^{-2} + \cdots) = z \tag{10-50}$$

Expression (10-47) is verified also by taking the z transform on both sides of the equation.   Therefore

$$\mathcal{Z}\Big[\sum_{i=0}^{k-1} \mathbf{A}^{k-i-1}\mathbf{Br}(iT) \Big] = \sum_{k=0}^{\infty} \sum_{i=0}^{k-1} \mathbf{A}^{k-i-1}\mathbf{Br}(iT)z^{-k}$$

$$= \sum_{k=0}^{\infty} z^{-k+i} \sum_{i=0}^{k-1} \mathbf{A}^{k-i-1}\mathbf{Br}(iT)z^{-i}$$

$$= \sum_{k=0}^{\infty} z^{-k+i}\mathbf{A}^{k-i-1}\mathbf{BR}(z) \tag{10-51}$$

Since

$$\sum_{k=0}^{\infty} z^{-k+i+1}\mathbf{A}^{k-i-1} = \sum_{k=0}^{\infty} z^{-k}\mathbf{A}^k = \mathcal{Z}[\mathbf{A}^k] \tag{10-52}$$

for the exponent of $\mathbf{A}$ cannot be negative, (10-51) is finally written

$$\mathcal{Z}\Big[\sum_{i=0}^{k-1} \mathbf{A}^{k-i-1}\mathbf{Br}(iT) \Big] = z^{-1}\mathcal{Z}[\mathbf{A}^k]\mathbf{BR}(z) = (z\mathbf{I} - \mathbf{A})^{-1}\mathbf{BR}(z) \tag{10-53}$$

The matrix $\mathbf{A}^k$ can be written $\mathbf{\Phi}(kT)$, and is called the *discrete state-transition matrix*.   Then the *discrete state-transition equation* of (10-41) becomes

$$\mathbf{x}(kT) = \mathbf{\Phi}(kT)\mathbf{x}(0^+) + \sum_{i=0}^{k-1} \mathbf{\Phi}[(k - i - 1)T]\mathbf{Br}(iT) \tag{10-54}$$

A general form of the discrete state-transition equation with initial state given at $t = t_0 = nT$, where n is a positive integer less than k, can be obtained directly from (10-54). Given the input $\mathbf{r}$ for $t \geq nT$ and the initial state $\mathbf{x}(nT)$, the state-variable vector at $t = (k + n)T$ for $k > n$ is

$$\mathbf{x}[(k + n)T] = \mathbf{\Phi}(kT)\mathbf{x}(nT)$$

$$+ \sum_{i=0}^{k-1} \mathbf{\Phi}[(k - i - 1)T]\mathbf{Br}(i + n)T \tag{10-55}$$

This general form of the state-transition equation is useful for the analysis of discrete-data systems with time delays. The proof of this expression is given as an exercise for the student.

Example 10-5   Consider the difference equation given in (5-124):

$$y[(k + 2)T] - 0.503y[(k + 1)T] + 0.0497y(kT) = kT \qquad (10\text{-}56)$$

We solve this equation following the z-transform method described above. Using the results for **A** and **B** in (5-130), we have

$$(z\mathbf{I} - \mathbf{A}) = \begin{bmatrix} z & -1 \\ 0.0497 & z - 0.503 \end{bmatrix} \qquad (10\text{-}57)$$

and

$$(z\mathbf{I} - \mathbf{A})^{-1} = \frac{1}{z^2 - 0.503z + 0.0497} \begin{bmatrix} z - 0.503 & 1 \\ -0.0497 & z \end{bmatrix} \qquad (10\text{-}58)$$

From (10-46), the discrete state-transition matrix is

$$\mathbf{A}^k = \mathbf{\Phi}(kT) = \mathcal{Z}^{-1}[(z\mathbf{I} - \mathbf{A})^{-1}z]$$

$$= \mathcal{Z}^{-1} \begin{bmatrix} \dfrac{-0.58z}{z - 0.368} + \dfrac{1.58z}{z - 0.135} & \dfrac{4.28z}{z - 0.368} - \dfrac{4.28z}{z - 0.135} \\[2ex] \dfrac{-2.13z}{z - 0.368} + \dfrac{2.13z}{z - 0.135} & \dfrac{1.58z}{z - 0.368} - \dfrac{0.58z}{z - 0.135} \end{bmatrix}$$

$$(10\text{-}59)$$

Thus

$$\mathbf{\Phi}(kT) = \begin{bmatrix} -0.58e^{-k} + 1.58e^{-2k} & 4.28e^{-k} - 4.28e^{-2k} \\ -2.13e^{-k} + 2.13e^{-2k} & 1.58e^{-k} - 0.58e^{-2k} \end{bmatrix} \qquad (10\text{-}60)$$

Substituting $\mathbf{\Phi}(kT)$ from (10-60) in (10-45) yields

$$\mathbf{x}(kT) = \begin{bmatrix} -0.58e^{-k} + 1.58e^{-2k} & 4.28e^{-k} - 4.28e^{-2k} \\ -2.13e^{-k} + 2.13e^{-2k} & 1.58e^{-k} - 0.58e^{-2k} \end{bmatrix} \begin{bmatrix} x_1(0) \\ x_2(0) \end{bmatrix}$$

$$+ \sum_{i=0}^{k-1} \begin{bmatrix} 4.28e^{-(k-i-1)} - 4.28e^{-2(k-i-1)} \\ 1.58e^{-(k-i-1)} - 0.58e^{-2(k-i-1)} \end{bmatrix} iT \qquad (10\text{-}61)$$

For $x_1(0) = 1$, $x_2(0) = 0$, and $T = 1$,

$$\mathbf{x}(kT) = \begin{bmatrix} -0.58e^{-k} + 1.58e^{-2k} \\ -2.13e^{-k} + 2.13e^{-2k} \end{bmatrix}$$

$$+ \sum_{i=0}^{k-1} \begin{bmatrix} 4.28e^{-(k-i-1)} - 4.28e^{-2(k-i-1)} \\ 1.58e^{-(k-i-1)} - 0.58e^{-2(k-i-1)} \end{bmatrix} i \qquad (10\text{-}62)$$

and

$$y(kT) = \mathbf{C}\mathbf{x}(kT) = x_1(kT)$$

$$= -0.58e^{-k} + 1.58e^{-2k} + \sum_{i=0}^{k-1} [4.28e^{-(k-i-1)} - 4.28e^{-2(k-i-1)}]i$$

$$(10\text{-}63)$$

$$y(0) = x_1(0) = 1 \qquad\qquad\qquad k = 0$$
$$y(T) = x_2(0) = -0.213 + 0.213 = 0 \qquad k = 1$$

These results agree with the given initial conditions.

$$y(2T) = -0.0783 + 0.0286 = -0.0497 \qquad\qquad\qquad k = 2$$
$$y(3T) = -0.0286 + 0.00356 + 4.28(0.368 - 0.135) = 0.975 \quad k = 3$$

. . . .

The values obtained for $y(2T)$ and $y(3T)$ again check with the results obtained earlier, in Example 5-1.

PROBLEMS

10-1   Find the z transforms for the following functions:

(a) $G(s) = \dfrac{5}{s(s+2)}$

(b) $G(s) = \dfrac{1}{s^2(s+1)}$

(c) $G(s) = \dfrac{s+1}{s(s+2)}$

10-2   The transfer function of a discrete-data system is

$$\frac{C(z)}{R(z)} = \frac{z+1}{4z(z-0.5)}$$

Write the dynamic equations for the system.

10-3   The transfer function of a linear discrete-data system is

$$\frac{C(z)}{R(z)} = \frac{1 + 2z^{-1}}{1 + z^{-1} + 3z^{-2} + 2z^{-3}}$$

Write the discrete state equations for the system.

10-4   Prove the following shifting property of the *z* transform:

$$\mathcal{Z}[f(t + nT)u(t)] = z^n \left[F(z) - \sum_{k=0}^{n-1} f(kT)z^{-k} \right]$$

where n is a positive integer.

10-5   Prove that

$$\mathcal{Z}[e^{\mp at}f(t)] = F(ze^{\pm aT})$$

10-6   Prove the initial-value theorem for *z* transforms.

$$\lim_{k \to 0} f(kT) = \lim_{z \to \infty} F(z)$$

10-7   Solve $y(k + 2) + 3y(k + 1) - 2y(k) = 1$ by *z* transform. $y(1) = 1$ and $y(0) = 0$.

BIBLIOGRAPHY

1   Kuo, B. C.: "Analysis and Synthesis of Sampled-data Control Systems," Prentice-Hall, Inc., Englewood Cliffs, N.J., 1963.
2   Ragazzini, J. R., and G. F. Franklin: "Sampled-data Control Systems," McGraw-Hill Book Company, New York, 1958.
3   Tou, J. T.: "Digital and Sampled-data Control Systems," McGraw-Hill Book Company, New York, 1959.
4   Lindorff, D. P.: "Theory of Sampled-data Control Systems," John Wiley & Sons, Inc., New York, 1965.
5   Levy, H., and F. Lessman: "Finite Difference Equations," The Macmillan Company, New York, 1961.
6   Zadeh, L. A., and C. A. Desoer: "Linear System Theory," McGraw-Hill Book Company, New York, 1963.
7   Helm, H. A.: The Z-transformation, *Bell System Tech. J.*, vol. 38, pp. 177–196, January, 1959.
8   Ragazzini, J. R., and L. A. Zadeh: The Analysis of Sampled-data Systems, *Trans. AIEE*, vol. 71, pt. 2, pp. 225–234, 1952.
9   Kuo, B. C.: Analysis and Design of Sampled-data Systems via State Transition Flow Graphs, *Proc. Natl. Electron. Conf.*, 1962, pp. 28–39.

ADDITIONAL REFERENCES

Freeman, H.: "Discrete-time Systems," John Wiley & Sons, Inc., New York, 1965.
Jury, E. I.: "Sampled-data Control Systems," John Wiley & Sons, Inc., New York, 1958.

ELEVEN

TRANSFER FUNCTIONS AND IMPULSE RESPONSES OF LINEAR SYSTEMS

11-1 INTRODUCTION

Thus far we have shown that a dynamic system or network can be described by state variables and state equations. Another method of describing a linear dynamic system or network is to make use of the input-output relations. In this second method, a linear dynamic system is modeled by a *transfer function*, which is defined as the ratio of the Laplace transform of the output to the Laplace transform of the input, with all initial conditions assumed to be zero. In the state-variable analysis, the starting point is the system of state equations, and interest is focused on the state-transition equation and the time response of the system. The transfer-function concept is relatively old and more conventional, and its emphasis is on the frequency response and the pole-zero studies of a system. In a broad sense, a transfer function can be considered a generalized gain between a pair of input and output variables of a system. It

324

resembles the description of the input-output relation of an electronic amplifier by a voltage gain or amplification.

Since, usually, a number of variables of a system can be identified as outputs, and in fact, any variable which can be directly observed is an output, and further, from a signal-flow-graph viewpoint, any noninput node is an output node, it generally requires several transfer functions to describe a given system completely.

Some of the important questions raised in this chapter are: (1) What are the relationships between the state equations and the transfer function? (2) What is an impulse response and its relations to the state equations and the transfer functions? (3) What role does the signal flow graph play in the transfer-function analysis?

11-2   TRANSFER FUNCTIONS AND IMPULSE RESPONSES OF LINEAR TIME - INVARIANT SYSTEMS

Assuming that a given dynamic system has the following properties, i.e., (1) the system is linear and time-invariant, and (2) all initial conditions of the system are zero,† then *the transfer function of the system for an input and output pair is defined as the ratio of the Laplace transform of the output to the Laplace transform of the input.* Consider that the input-output relation of the system is described by the following nth-order differential equation:

$$\frac{d^n y}{dt^n} + a_1 \frac{d^{n-1} y}{dt^{n-1}} + a_2 \frac{d^{n-2} y}{dt^{n-2}} + \cdots + a_{n-1} \frac{dy}{dt} + a_n y = b_0 \frac{d^m r}{dt^m}$$

$$+ b_1 \frac{d^{m-1} r}{dt^{m-1}} + \cdots + b_{m-1} \frac{dr}{dt} + b_m r \quad (11\text{-}1)$$

where
$$y = \text{output variable}$$
$$r = \text{input variable}$$
$$a \text{ and } b = \text{constant coefficients}$$
$$m \text{ and } n = \text{positive integers}$$

Taking the Laplace transform on both sides of (11-1) and assuming zero initial conditions, we get

$$(s^n + a_1 s^{n-1} + a_2 s^{n-2} + \cdots + a_{n-1} s + a_n) Y(s) = (b_0 s^m + b_1 s^{m-1}$$

$$+ \cdots + b_{m-1} s + b_m) R(s)$$

† In transfer-function relationships, the actual initial conditions of the system need not be, and may not be, zero.

Therefore the transfer function of the system between r and y is

$$G(s) = \frac{Y(s)}{R(s)} = \frac{b_0 s^m + b_1 s^{m-1} + \cdots + b_{m-1} s + b_m}{s^n + a_1 s^{n-1} + a_2 s^{n-2} + \cdots + a_{n-1} s + a_n} \quad (11\text{-}2)$$

We should repeat here that a physical system usually has more than one measurable output, but one transfer function can be defined between only one pair of input and output. For a system with more than one input variable, a transfer function is defined between one input and one output at a time, with all the other inputs set to zero.

Since the coefficient a's and b's in (11-1) depend solely on the dynamic characteristics of the system, expression (11-2) shows that the transfer function is a description of the property of the system elements only, and is completely independent of the type of excitation and the initial conditions. However, transfer functions are not defined for nonlinear systems. In general, the dynamic behavior of a nonlinear system depends on the excitations as well as the initial conditions. This is why the transfer-function concept is invalid for nonlinear systems.

Relation between transfer function and impulse response

The transformed quantities in (11-2) can be written

$$Y(s) = G(s)R(s) \quad (11\text{-}3)$$

which is a typical cause-and-effect relationship. The signal-flow-graph representation of (11-3) is shown in Fig. 11-1.

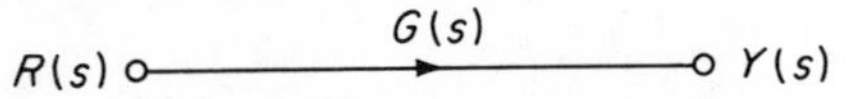

$$R(s) \circ \xrightarrow{\quad G(s) \quad} \circ Y(s)$$

Fig. 11-1   Signal-flow-graph representation of a transfer function.

In the analysis problem the transfer function is found from the system's differential equation in the manner shown in (11-2), and the input $R(s)$ is given; the output time response is obtained by taking the inverse Laplace transform of $Y(s)$ in (11-3).

Now let us consider a special case where the input $r(t)$ is the unit impulse function $\delta(t)$ whose Laplace transform is unity. From (11-3), the transformed output becomes

$$Y(s) = G(s) \quad (11\text{-}4)$$

whose inverse transform expression is

$$y(t) = g(t) \tag{11-5}$$

The function $g(t)$ is the inverse Laplace transform of $G(s)$, and is called the *impulse response*, or *weighting function*, of the linear system. An interesting significance of the impulse response is thus established. The development in (11-4) and (11-5) clearly shows that *the Laplace transform of the impulse response gives a function in s identical with that of the transfer function* $G(s)$. In fact, this statement is also an alternative definition of the transfer function. This exposition also has a practical significance in that the description of a linear system may be effected by exciting the system with an impulse function and measuring the output response. In practice, although a true impulse cannot be generated physically, a pulse signal with a very narrow width (much less than the significant time constant of the system) usually provides a suitable approximation.

It would seem that the feasibility of (11-3) depends upon the existence of $G(s)$ and $R(s)$. However, in practice, one cannot always ensure that $r(t)$ and $g(t)$ are Laplace-transformable. It is quite possible that $r(t)$ and $g(t)$ are available only in the form of experimental data and that no analytic expression can be obtained for $R(s)$ and $G(s)$. Under such circumstances, in order to make a transfer-function study of the system, we have no alternative but to work with the time functions $r(t)$ and $g(t)$.

The problem confronting us now is that, given $r(t)$ and $g(t)$, which are all identically zero for $t < 0$, how do we find $y(t)$ without using the Laplace transformation and (11-3)? The problem can be solved by means of the real convolution integral theorem stated in (8-120). The theorem states that, if $Y(s) = G(s)R(s)$, then $y(t)$ is given by

$$y(t) = g(t) * r(t) = \int_{0^-}^{t} g(t - \tau)r(\tau)\,d\tau$$
$$= \int_{0^-}^{t} r(t - \tau)g(\tau)\,d\tau \tag{11-6}$$

We show below that the real convolution theorem can be proved without using the Laplace transformation. Let us assume that the signal $r(t)$ shown in Fig. 11-2a is applied as an input to a linear system. The impulse response of the system is denoted by $g(t)$. In Fig. 11-2 the input r is denoted as a function of τ, which is a dummy variable. This is necessary since the ordinary time variable t is considered to be a fixed quantity in the process. Also, for all practical purposes, we assume that r extends from $-\infty$ to $+\infty$ in time. In Fig. 11-2b the signal $r(\tau)$ is approximated by a sequence of flat-topped pulses; the pulses all have a pulsewidth of $\Delta\tau$, and are placed next to each other. When $\Delta\tau$ approaches zero as a limit, these pulses become a sequence of impulses, and the impulse at time $k\,\Delta\tau$ has a strength of $\Delta\tau\,r(k\,\Delta\tau)$, which is the area of the pulse at $\tau = k\,\Delta\tau$. The approximation by impulses also implies that, as $\Delta\tau$ approaches zero, k must be increased to infinity, so that the value of $k\,\Delta\tau$

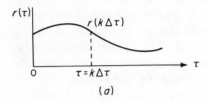

(a)

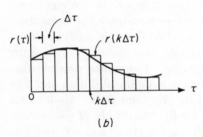

(b)

Fig. 11-2 (a) *Input signal of a linear system.* (b) *Input signal represented by a sum of rectangular pulses.*

stays constant and is equal to τ in the limit. Now when an impulse of strength $\Delta\tau\,r(k\,\Delta\tau)$ is applied to the system at $\tau = k\,\Delta\tau$, the response of the system is

$$x(t) = \Delta\tau\,r(k\,\Delta\tau)g(t - k\,\Delta\tau) \qquad t > k\,\Delta\tau \tag{11-7}$$

When all the pulses between $\tau = 0$ and $\tau = \infty$ are considered, the total response of the system is obtained by means of the principle of superposition. Therefore

$$y(t) = \lim_{\substack{\Delta\tau\to 0 \\ N\to\infty}} \sum_{k=0}^{N} r(k\,\Delta\tau)g(t - k\,\Delta\tau)$$

which in the limit becomes the integral

$$y(t) = \int_0^\infty r(\tau)g(t - \tau)\,d\tau \tag{11-8}$$

Since $g(\tau) = 0$ for all $\tau < 0$, which implies that $g(t - \tau) = 0$ for $\tau > t$, the convolution integral of (11-8) becomes

$$y(t) = \int_0^t r(\tau)g(t - \tau)\, d\tau \tag{11-9}$$

11-3 RELATIONSHIP BETWEEN STATE EQUATION AND THE IMPULSE RESPONSE

We have shown that there are two different ways of describing linear dynamic systems: (1) by means of state variables and dynamic equations of the form

$$\frac{d\mathbf{x}}{dt} = \mathbf{Ax} + \mathbf{Br} \tag{11-10}$$

$$\mathbf{y} = \mathbf{Cx} + \mathbf{Dr} \tag{11-11}$$

where $\mathbf{x}$ denotes the state variables (state vector), $\mathbf{y}$ is the output vector, and $\mathbf{r}$ is the input vector; (2) by means of the input-output relations—the impulse responses and the transfer functions.   In matrix form,

$$\mathbf{Y}(s) = \mathbf{G}(s)\mathbf{R}(s) \qquad \text{transfer function} \tag{11-12}$$

$$\mathbf{y}(t) = \int_0^t \mathbf{r}(\tau)\mathbf{g}(t - \tau)\, d\tau \qquad \text{impulse response} \tag{11-13}$$

Since these two approaches provide valid descriptions of a physical system, they must be closely related.   Taking the Laplace transform on both sides of (11-10), we have

$$s\mathbf{X}(s) = \mathbf{AX}(s) + \mathbf{BR}(s) + \mathbf{x}(0^+) \tag{11-14}$$

Solving for $\mathbf{X}(s)$ in (11-14) gives

$$\mathbf{X}(s) = (s\mathbf{I} - \mathbf{A})^{-1}\mathbf{x}(0^+) + (s\mathbf{I} - \mathbf{A})^{-1}\mathbf{BR}(s) \tag{11-15}$$

Substituting from (11-15) in the transformed version of (11-11), we get

$$\mathbf{Y}(s) = \mathbf{C}(s\mathbf{I} - \mathbf{A})^{-1}\mathbf{x}(0^+) + \mathbf{C}(s\mathbf{I} - \mathbf{A})^{-1}\mathbf{BR}(s) + \mathbf{DR}(s) \tag{11-16}$$

Since the transfer function is defined with zero initial conditions, $\mathbf{x}(0^+) = \mathbf{0}$, Eq. (11-16) becomes

$$\mathbf{Y}(s) = \mathbf{C}(s\mathbf{I} - \mathbf{A})^{-1}\mathbf{BR}(s) + \mathbf{DR}(s) \tag{11-17}$$

Comparing (11-17) with (11-12), we see that these two expressions are identical only when

$$\mathbf{G}(s) = \mathbf{C}(s\mathbf{I} - \mathbf{A})^{-1}\mathbf{B} + \mathbf{D} \qquad (11\text{-}18)$$

Therefore the impulse function is

$$\begin{aligned}\mathbf{g}(t) &= \mathcal{L}^{-1}[\mathbf{C}(s\mathbf{I} - \mathbf{A})^{-1}\mathbf{B} + \mathbf{D}] \\ &= \mathbf{C}\boldsymbol{\Phi}(t)\mathbf{B} + \mathbf{D}\delta(t) \qquad t \geq 0\end{aligned} \qquad (11\text{-}19)$$

and

$$\mathbf{g}(t) = \mathbf{0} \qquad\qquad t < 0$$

Thus, given the state-equation description of a linear system, its impulse-response matrix is readily obtained from (11-19). The reverse process, however, is not so simple. In other words, given the impulse-response matrix $\mathbf{g}(\tau)$ of a linear system, how do we find the matrices $\mathbf{A}$, $\mathbf{B}$, $\mathbf{C}$, and $\mathbf{D}$? It is apparent by inspecting (11-19) that, since the right-hand side of the expression consists of the product of three matrices, $\mathbf{C}$, $\boldsymbol{\Phi}(t)$, and $\mathbf{B}$, given $\mathbf{g}(\tau)$, finding the state equations is not an easy task. The determination of the state equations of a system from its impulse-response matrix is sometimes called the process of *identification*. However, this problem is beyond the scope of this text.

An illustrative example determining the impulse-response matrix from the state equations of a system is given below.

Example 11-1   Consider the network shown in Fig. 11-3, which has been discussed in Sec. 9-1. Let us assign the output variables as the voltages across the network elements R_1, R_2, L, and C. The state variables are i_L and v_c. The state equations of the network that correspond

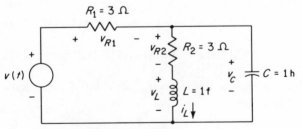

Fig. 11-3   An electric network.

to (11-10) are given by (9-30) and (9-31), and are repeated in the following matrix form:

$$\begin{bmatrix} \dfrac{dx_1(t)}{dt} \\[2mm] \dfrac{dx_2(t)}{dt} \end{bmatrix} = \begin{bmatrix} \dfrac{di_L(t)}{dt} \\[2mm] \dfrac{dv_c(t)}{dt} \end{bmatrix} = \begin{bmatrix} -3 & 1 \\ -1 & -\tfrac{1}{3} \end{bmatrix} \begin{bmatrix} i_L(t) \\ v_c(t) \end{bmatrix} + \begin{bmatrix} 0 \\ \tfrac{1}{3} \end{bmatrix} [v(t)] \qquad (11\text{-}20)$$

The output matrix equation that corresponds to (11-11) is

$$\begin{bmatrix} y_1(t) \\ y_2(t) \\ y_3(t) \\ y_4(t) \end{bmatrix} = \begin{bmatrix} v_{R1}(t) \\ v_{R2}(t) \\ v_L(t) \\ v_c(t) \end{bmatrix} = \begin{bmatrix} 0 & -1 \\ 3 & 0 \\ -3 & 1 \\ 0 & 1 \end{bmatrix} \begin{bmatrix} i_L(t) \\ v_c(t) \end{bmatrix} + \begin{bmatrix} 1 \\ 0 \\ 0 \\ 0 \end{bmatrix} [v(t)] \qquad (11\text{-}21)$$

which is written by direct inspection of the network in Fig. 11-3. The matrices **A**, **B**, **C**, and **D** are readily defined by the dynamic equations (11-20) and (11-21).

Now we proceed to find the four impulse responses, using (11-19). These impulse responses are between $v(t)$ and each of the four outputs v_{R1}, v_{R2}, v_L, and v_c. Let these impulses responses be denoted by $g_1(t)$, $g_2(t)$, $g_3(t)$, and $g_4(t)$, respectively. Then, from (11-19), the impulse-response matrix is

$$\mathbf{g}(t) = \begin{bmatrix} g_1(t) \\ g_2(t) \\ g_3(t) \\ g_4(t) \end{bmatrix} = \mathbf{C\Phi}(t)\mathbf{B} + \mathbf{D}\delta(t) \qquad t > 0 \qquad (11\text{-}22)$$

The state-transition matrix $\mathbf{\Phi}(t)$ is the inverse Laplace transform of $(s\mathbf{I} - \mathbf{A})^{-1}$, or $e^{\mathbf{A}t}$, and its expression for the network of Fig. 11-3 was given in Sec. 9-1; Eq. (11-22) becomes

$$\mathbf{g}(t) = \begin{bmatrix} 0 & -1 \\ 3 & 0 \\ -3 & 1 \\ 0 & 1 \end{bmatrix}$$

$$\begin{bmatrix} -0.26e^{-0.788t} + 1.26e^{-2.54t} & 0.57e^{-0.788t} - 0.57e^{-2.54t} \\ -0.57e^{-0.788t} + 0.57e^{-2.54t} & 1.26e^{-0.788t} - 0.26e^{-2.54t} \end{bmatrix} \begin{bmatrix} 0 \\ \tfrac{1}{3} \end{bmatrix}$$

$$+ \begin{bmatrix} 1 \\ 0 \\ 0 \\ 0 \end{bmatrix} \delta(t) \qquad (11\text{-}23)$$

Carrying out the matrix multiplication, the last equation becomes

$$
\mathbf{g}(t) = \begin{bmatrix} -0.42e^{-0.788t} + 0.087e^{-2.54t} \\ 0.57e^{-0.788t} - 0.57e^{-2.54t} \\ -0.15e^{-0.788t} + 0.48e^{-2.54t} \\ 0.42e^{-0.788t} - 0.087e^{-2.54t} \end{bmatrix} + \begin{bmatrix} \delta(t) \\ 0 \\ 0 \\ 0 \end{bmatrix} \tag{11-24}
$$

Reiterating the actual meaning of this impulse-response matrix, when a unit impulse function $\delta(t)$ is applied as the input $v(t)$ to the network of Fig. 11-3, the output matrix is given by

$$
\begin{bmatrix} v_{R1}(t) \\ v_{R2}(t) \\ v_L(t) \\ v_c(t) \end{bmatrix} = \begin{bmatrix} -0.42e^{-0.788t} + 0.087e^{-2.54t} + \delta(t) \\ 0.57e^{-0.788t} - 0.57e^{-2.54t} \\ -0.15e^{-0.788t} + 0.48e^{-2.54t} \\ 0.42e^{-0.788t} - 0.087e^{-2.54t} \end{bmatrix} \tag{11-25}
$$

Taking the Laplace transform of (11-24) gives the transfer-function matrix

$$
\mathbf{G}(s) = \begin{bmatrix} G_1(s) \\ G_2(s) \\ G_3(s) \\ G_4(s) \end{bmatrix} = \begin{bmatrix} \dfrac{-0.42}{s + 0.788} + \dfrac{0.087}{s + 2.54} + 1 \\ \dfrac{0.57}{s + 0.788} + \dfrac{-0.57}{s + 2.54} \\ \dfrac{-0.15}{s + 0.788} + \dfrac{0.48}{s + 2.54} \\ \dfrac{0.42}{s + 0.788} + \dfrac{-0.087}{s + 2.54} \end{bmatrix} \tag{11-26}
$$

where $G_1(s) = V_{R1}(s)/V(s)$
$G_2(s) = V_{R2}(s)/V(s)$
$G_3(s) = V_L(s)/V(s)$
$G_4(s) = V_c(s)/V(s)$

11-4   TRANSFER FUNCTIONS OF LINEAR NETWORKS AND SYSTEMS

A linear system or network may have many different transfer functions, depending on the choice of the input and output variables.   In electric networks, since the input and output signals may be voltages or currents, the transfer functions may assume the form of an impedance, admittance, voltage ratio, or current ratio.   Similarly, transfer functions of mechanical systems may assume the forms of force/velocity, velocity/force, force/force, velocity/velocity, and others involving displacements.   In a very broad sense, the transfer function can be regarded as a cause-and-effect relationship between two specific variables such as illustrated by the signal flow graph of Fig. 11-1.   If we bear in mind the concept of cause and effect, the understanding of the significance of the transfer functions will be greatly enhanced.

Because of the various ways of describing a linear dynamic system, there are at least two different ways of finding the transfer functions from the system equations: (1) If the system is described by an ordinary differential equation as in (11-1), the transfer function of the system is given by (11-2).   (2) If the system is described by the dynamic equations (11-10) and (11-11), the transfer function is found by taking the Laplace transform of $\mathbf{g}(t)$ in (11-19), which is (11-18).

The various forms of transfer functions of an electric network are defined as shown in Fig. 11-4.   For instance, in Fig. 11-4a, the quotient $V_i(s)/I_i(s)$ is defined as the *driving-point impedance function* between the terminals i-i'.   In this case, the current source $I_i(s)$ acts as the *cause* (input), and the voltage appearing across the terminals i-i' is regarded as the *effect* (output).   Hence

$$\text{Driving-point impedance function } Z_{ii}(s) = \frac{V_i(s)}{I_i(s)} \qquad (11\text{-}27)$$

We must add here that $Z_{ii}(s)$ is measured with all other external sources (should there be any) replaced by their internal impedances.   We also note that the driving-point functions involve only two terminals, or a one-terminal pair of the network, whereas the other transfer functions require the use of a two-terminal pair,† or four terminals.

Let us illustrate by examples the derivation of the transfer functions of some linear time-invariant systems.

Example 11-2   Find the driving-point impedance function between points 1-1' of the circuit shown in Fig. 11-5.   When the driving-point impedance is desired, we consider that a current source $I_1(s)$ is applied to the circuit between points 1 and 1', and the voltage response between 1-1' is measured.   The transform network with the current-source excitation is drawn in Fig. 11-6.   According to the definition, the initial condition of the circuit is assumed to be zero.   Thus the driving-point impedance is given by

$$Z_{11}(s) = \frac{V_1(s)}{I_1(s)} = R_1 + Ls + \frac{R_2}{1 + R_2 Cs} \qquad (11\text{-}28)$$

† In the literature, a one-terminal-pair network is often referred to as a "one-port," and a two-terminal-pair as a "two-port."

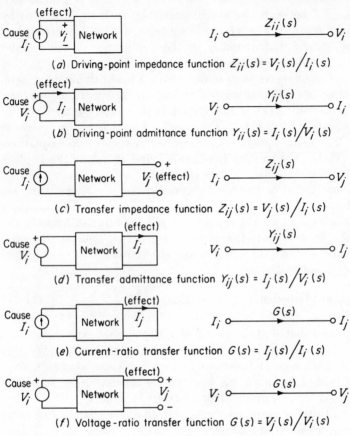

(a) Driving-point impedance function $Z_{ii}(s) = V_i(s)/I_i(s)$

(b) Driving-point admittance function $Y_{ii}(s) = I_i(s)/V_i(s)$

(c) Transfer impedance function $Z_{ij}(s) = V_j(s)/I_i(s)$

(d) Transfer admittance function $Y_{ij}(s) = I_j(s)/V_i(s)$

(e) Current-ratio transfer function $G(s) = I_j(s)/I_i(s)$

(f) Voltage-ratio transfer function $G(s) = V_j(s)/V_i(s)$

Fig. 11-4   Definitions of transfer functions of electric networks and systems.

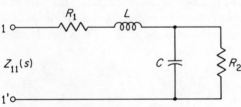

Fig. 11-5   Network for Example 11-2.

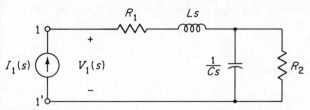

*Fig. 11-6   Transform network of the network in Fig.
11-5 with a current-source excitation.*

Example 11-3   Use the signal-flow-graph method to find the
following quantities for the network shown in Fig. 11-7:

1   The voltage-ratio transfer function $V_{out}(s)/V_{in}(s)$
2   The open-circuit driving-point impendance $Z_{ii}(s)$
3   The open-circuit transfer impedance $Z_{oi}(s)$

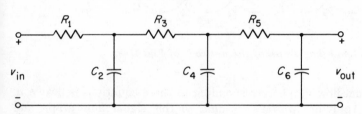

Fig. 11-7   Ladder network for Example 11-3.

First, let us draw the transform network with zero initial conditions,
and assign branch currents and node voltages to the network as shown in
Fig. 11-8.   Using the cause-and-effect relationship, a set of independent

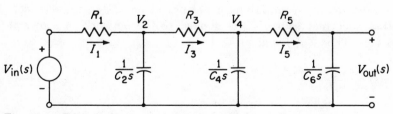

Fig. 11-8   Transform network for the network in Fig. 11-7.

network equations involving the assigned variables are written as follows:

$$I_1(s) = [V_{in}(s) - V_2(s)]G_1$$

$$V_2(s) = [I_1(s) - I_3(s)] \frac{1}{C_2 s}$$

$$I_3(s) = [V_2(s) - V_4(s)]G_3$$

$$V_4(s) = [I_3(s) - I_5(s)] \frac{1}{C_4 s}$$

$$I_5(s) = [V_4(s) - V_{out}(s)]G_5$$

$$V_{out}(s) = I_5(s) \frac{1}{C_6 s}$$

where $G_1 = 1/R_1$, $G_3 = 1/R_3$, and $G_5 = 1/R_5$.

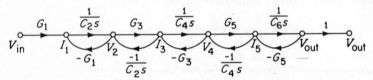

Fig. 11-9   *A signal flow graph of the network of Fig. 11-8.*

The signal flow graph corresponding to these equations is drawn in Fig. 11-9. Applying Mason's formula to this signal flow graph and simplifying, we have

$$\frac{V_{out}(s)}{V_{in}(s)} = \frac{G_1 G_3 G_5}{\begin{aligned} C_2 C_4 C_6 s^3 &+ [(G_1 + G_3)C_4 C_6 + (G_3 + G_5)C_2 C_6 + G_5 C_2 C_4]s^2 \\ &+ [G_1 G_3 C_6 + G_1 G_5 C_6 + G_1 G_5 C_4 + G_3 G_5 (C_2 + C_4 + C_6)]s \\ &+ G_1 G_3 G_5 \end{aligned}}$$

$$(11\text{-}29)$$

In order to obtain the driving-point impedance $Z_{ii}(s)$, we must consider that a current source I_{in} is applied to the network as shown in Fig. 11-10. Then $Z_{ii}(s)$ is given by

$$Z_{ii}(s) = \frac{V_1(s)}{I_{in}(s)} \qquad (11\text{-}30)$$

In this case, the voltage across the input terminal, $V_1(s)$, is considered the output variable. The network equations corresponding to the net-

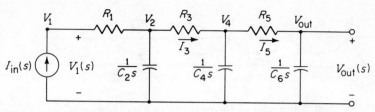

Fig. 11-10 *Transform network of the network in Example 11-3 with a current source applied at the input.*

work of Fig. 11-10 are

$$V_1(s) = R_1 I_{in}(s) + V_2(s)$$

$$V_2(s) = [I_{in}(s) - I_3(s)]\frac{1}{C_2 s}$$

$$I_3(s) = [V_2(s) - V_4(s)]G_3$$

$$V_4(s) = [I_3(s) - I_5(s)]\frac{1}{C_4 s}$$

$$I_5(s) = [V_4(s) - V_6(s)]G_5$$

$$V_{out}(s) = I_5(s)\frac{1}{C_6 s}$$

The signal flow graph for these equations is drawn in Fig. 11-11. Evaluating the gain between I_{in} and V_1, we get

$$Z_{ii}(s) = R_1 + \frac{C_4 C_6 s^2 + [(G_3 + G_5)C_6 + G_5 C_4]s + G_3 G_5}{s[C_2 C_4 C_6 s^2 + (G_3 C_4 C_6 + G_3 C_2 C_6 + G_5 C_2 C_6 + G_5 C_2 C_4)s + G_3 G_5(C_2 + C_4 + C_6)]} \qquad (11\text{-}31)$$

The transfer impedance $Z_{oi}(s)$ is found by considering that $V_{out}(s)$ is the output node on the signal flow graph of Fig. 11-11; we have

$$Z_{oi}(s) = \frac{V_{out}(s)}{I_{in}(s)}$$

$$= \frac{G_3 G_5}{s[C_2 C_4 C_6 s^2 + (G_3 C_4 C_6 + G_3 C_2 C_6 + G_5 C_2 C_6 + G_5 C_2 C_4)s + G_3 G_5(C_2 + C_4 + C_6)]} \qquad (11\text{-}32)$$

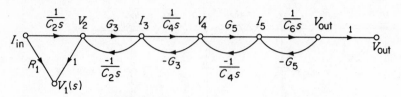

Fig. 11-11   *A signal flow graph of the network in Fig. 11-10.*

11-5   THE CHARACTERISTIC EQUATION

The characteristic equation plays an important role in the study of the dynamic behavior of a linear system.   The significance of the characteristic equation is best illustrated by the following numerical example.

Let us refer to the circuit diagram of Fig. 11-12a.   The circuit is characterized by a pentode vacuum tube and *RLC* elements.   In Fig.

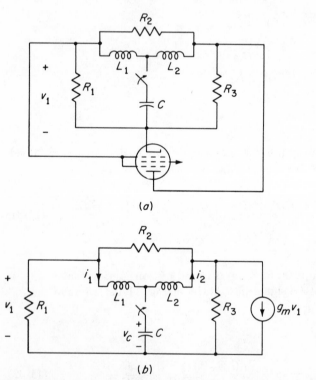

(a)

(b)

Fig. 11-12   (a) *An RLC network with vacuum tube.*
(b) *Current-source equivalent circuit.*

11-12b the tube is replaced by its linear-incremental current-source equivalent circuit.   The plate resistance of the pentode is normally high, and thus is neglected when it is considered to be in parallel to R_3 in the equivalent circuit.

As the first part of our analysis, we assume that the tube is not energized and g_m is zero.   At $t = 0^+$, the switch is closed; the network equations with $g_m = 0$ are

$$C \frac{dv_c}{dt} = i_1 - i_2 \tag{11-33}$$

$$L_1 \frac{di_1}{dt} = - \frac{(R_1 + R_3)R_1}{R_1 + R_2 + R_3} i_1 + \frac{R_1 R_3}{R_1 + R_2 + R_3} i_2 - v_c \tag{11-34}$$

$$L_2 \frac{di_2}{dt} = \frac{R_1 R_2}{R_1 + R_2 + R_3} i_1 - \frac{(R_1 + R_2)R_3}{R_1 + R_2 + R_3} i_2 + v_c \tag{11-35}$$

Substituting the values of the circuit parameters in Eqs. (11-33) to (11-35), we have

$$\frac{dv_c}{dt} = i_1 - i_2 \tag{11-36}$$

$$\frac{di_1}{dt} = -\tfrac{2}{3}i_1 + \tfrac{1}{3}i_2 - v_c \tag{11-37}$$

$$\frac{di_2}{dt} = \tfrac{1}{3}i_1 - \tfrac{2}{3}i_2 + v_c \tag{11-38}$$

Taking the Laplace transforms on both sides of these three equations and solving for $V_c(s)$, $I_1(s)$, and $I_2(s)$, we get

$$V_c(s) = \frac{\dfrac{1}{s}\left(1 + \dfrac{4}{3s} + \dfrac{3}{9s^2}\right)}{\Delta} v_c(0^+) = \frac{\dfrac{1}{9s^3}(9s^2 + 12s + 3)}{\Delta} \tag{11-39}$$

$$I_1(s) = \frac{-\dfrac{1}{s^2}\left(1 + \dfrac{1}{3s}\right) + \dfrac{1}{3s^3}}{\Delta} = \frac{-\dfrac{3s + 1}{3s^3}}{\Delta} \tag{11-40}$$

$$I_2(s) = \frac{-\dfrac{1}{3s^3} + \dfrac{1}{s^2}\left(s + \dfrac{2}{3s}\right)}{\Delta} = \frac{\dfrac{3s + 1}{3s^3}}{\Delta} = -I_1(s) \tag{11-41}$$

and

$$\Delta = \frac{3s^3 + 4s^2 + 7s + 2}{3s^3} \tag{11-42}$$

Substituting Δ in $V_c(s)$, $I_1(s)$, and $I_2(s)$, we have

$$V_c(s) = \frac{9s^2 + 12s + 3}{3(3s^3 + 4s^2 + 7s + 2)} = \frac{3s^2 + 4s + 1}{3s^3 + 4s^2 + 7s + 2} \tag{11-43}$$

$$I_1(s) = \frac{-(3s + 1)}{3s^3 + 4s^2 + 7s + 2} \tag{11-44}$$

$$I_2(s) = \frac{3s + 1}{3s^3 + 4s^2 + 7s + 2} \tag{11-45}$$

Solving for the roots of the numerator and the denominator polynomials in (11-43), we find that $V_c(s)$ can be reduced to

$$V_c(s) = \frac{s + 1}{s^2 + s + 2} \tag{11-46}$$

It is merely a coincidence that identical terms of $s + 0.333$ are found in both the numerator and the denominator of (11-43), resulting in the direct cancellation of these terms. Similarly, $I_1(s)$ and $I_2(s)$ are simplified to

$$I_1(s) = -I_2(s) = \frac{-1}{s^2 + s + 2} \tag{11-47}$$

Let us now compute the current $i_2(t)$ for $t \geq 0$ when the switch is closed as $t = 0$ and $v_c(0^+) = 1$ volt. Taking the inverse Laplace transform on both sides of (11-47), we obtain

$$i_2(t) = 0.748e^{-0.5t} \sin 1.34t \tag{11-48}$$

The waveform of $i_2(t)$ is illustrated in Fig. 11-13 as a function of time. Two important remarks may be made in regard to this plot of $i_2(t)$: (1) The waveform is commonly known as a *damped sinusoid* since it is the product of a decaying exponential and a sinusoid; (2) the magnitude of $i_2(t)$ converges to zero as time approaches infinity. The waveform for $i_1(t)$ is just the negative (inverse) of that of $i_2(t)$. We can show by taking the inverse Laplace transform of $V_c(s)$ that the waveform of $v_c(t)$ for $t \geq 0$ is also a damped sinusoid. In fact, we can show that the responses

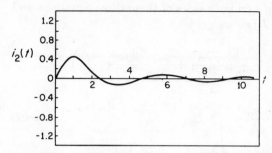

Fig. 11-13   *Waveform of the current* $i_2(t)$ *for* $t \geq 0$ *(switch is closed at* $t = 0$*) in the circuit of Fig. 11-12a, with* $g_m = 0$ *and the indicated initial conditions.*

$i_1(t)$, $i_2(t)$, and $v_c(t)$ of the passive network in Fig. 11-12*b* will always converge to zero for large t for any finite initial conditions on i_1, i_2, and v_c. When time approaches infinity, the two inductors L_1 and L_2 act as short circuits; the equivalent circuit of the passive network for $t = \infty$ is shown in Fig. 11-14. It is apparent that, under this condition, the capacitor

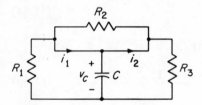

Fig. 11-14   *The network in Fig. 11-12 with* $g_m = 0$ *and* $t = \infty$.

voltage v_c will discharge through R_1 and R_3 until v_c becomes zero. Also, $i_1(\infty)$ and $i_2(\infty)$ are equal to zero. The statements made above are also true for other positive values of R_1, R_2, and R_3.

As our next step, we energize the vacuum tube in the circuit of Fig. 11-12*a*, and the latter becomes an active circuit. The network equations as written from Fig. 11-12*b* are

$$\frac{dv_c}{dt} = i_1 - i_2 \tag{11-49}$$

$$\frac{di_1}{dt} = -\tfrac{2}{3}i_1 + \tfrac{1}{3}i_2 - v_c - \frac{g_m}{3}\left(\frac{di_1}{dt} + v_c\right) \tag{11-50}$$

$$\frac{di_2}{dt} = \tfrac{1}{3}i_1 - \tfrac{2}{3}i_2 + v_c + \frac{2g_m}{3}\left(\frac{di_1}{dt} + v_c\right) \tag{11-51}$$

Taking the Laplace transforms on both sides of these three equations and solving for $V_c(s)$, $I_1(s)$, and $I_2(s)$, we get

$$V_c(s) = \frac{\dfrac{1}{s}\left(1 + \dfrac{2}{3s} + \dfrac{2}{3s} - \dfrac{1}{9s^2} + \dfrac{4}{9s^2} + \dfrac{g_m}{3} - \dfrac{2g_m}{9s} + \dfrac{2g_m}{9s}\right)}{\Delta}$$

$$= \frac{3s^2 + 4s + 1 + g_m s^2}{3s^2 \Delta} \tag{11-52}$$

$$I_1(s) = \frac{-\left(1 + \dfrac{g_m}{3}\right)\dfrac{1}{s^2}\left(1 + \dfrac{2}{3s}\right) + \left(1 + \dfrac{2g_m}{3}\right)\dfrac{1}{3s^3}}{\Delta}$$

$$= \frac{-(3s + 1) - g_m s}{3s^2 \Delta} \tag{11-53}$$

$$I_2(s) = \frac{-\left(1 + \dfrac{g_m}{3}\right)\dfrac{1}{3s^3} + \left(1 + \dfrac{2g_m}{3}\right)\dfrac{1}{s^2}\left(1 + \dfrac{g_m}{3} + \dfrac{2}{3s}\right) - \dfrac{2g_m}{3s^2}\left(1 + \dfrac{g_m}{3}\right)}{\Delta}$$

$$= \frac{(3s + 1) + g_m(s + 1)}{3s^3 \Delta} \tag{11-54}$$

where

$$\Delta = \frac{3s^3 + 4s^2 + 7s + 2 + g_m(s^3 + 2s + 1)}{3s^3} \tag{11-55}$$

After simplification, $V_c(s)$, $I_1(s)$, and $I_2(s)$ become

$$V_c(s) = \frac{3s^2 + 4s + 1 + g_m s^2}{3s^3 + 4s^2 + 7s + 2 + g_m(s^3 + 2s + 1)} \tag{11-56}$$

$$I_1(s) = \frac{-(3s + 1) - g_m s}{3s^3 + 4s^2 + 7s + 2 + g_m(s^3 + 2s + 1)} \tag{11-57}$$

$$I_2(s) = \frac{(3s + 1) + g_m(s + 1)}{3s^3 + 4s^2 + 7s + 2 + g_m(s^3 + 2s + 1)} \tag{11-58}$$

We notice that, when $g_m = 0$, these three equations revert to (11-43), (11-44), and (11-45), respectively. We shall now investigate the effects of the addition of an active element (tube) to the passive network. Basically, we are interested in finding out the significant difference between the responses of a passive network and an active network.

We have indicated (although we have not proved) that when $g_m = 0$, the responses i_1, i_2, and v_c of the passive network due to any arbitrary initial conditions will decay to zero as time approaches infinity. We can further show that if the passive network is subjected to any external excitation in the form of a voltage source or a current source, as long as the magnitude of the excitation does not increase without bound, the responses also will not increase without bound. Now with the vacuum tube inserted in the circuit, let us first demonstrate the effect by letting $g_m = 6.425$. The reason for the particular choice of g_m will become apparent after the computation of the responses is carried out. Also, the objective of this example precludes any consideration of the realistic selection of the network parameters. To demonstrate the effects of g_m, it is necessary to compute only one of the responses i_1, i_2, or v_c. Substituting $g_m = 6.425$ in $I_2(s)$ of (11-58) yields

$$I_2(s) = \frac{9.425s + 7.425}{9.425s^3 + 4s^2 + 19.85s + 8.425} \tag{11-59}$$

which can be written

$$I_2(s) = \frac{0.788(1 + 1.27s)}{(s + 0.424)(s^2 + 2.106)} \tag{11-60}$$

After partial fraction expansion, $I_2(s)$ becomes

$$I_2(s) = \frac{0.16}{s + 0.424} + \frac{-(1.5s - 10.06)0.106}{s^2 + 2.106} \tag{11-61}$$

Taking the inverse Laplace transform of $I_2(s)$, we have

$$i_2(t) = 0.159e^{-0.424t} + 0.743 \sin (1.45t - 12.3°) \tag{11-62}$$

The response of $i_2(t)$ is shown in Fig. 11-15 as a function of time. The transient part of $i_2(t)$ is strictly due to the exponential term in (11-59), which eventually goes to zero as time approaches infinity. The steady-state response of $i_2(t)$ is a perfect sine wave. Similarly, we can show that $i_1(t)$ and $v_c(t)$ will have sinusoidal steady-state responses.

The illustration in Fig. 11-15 points out the interesting fact that, when an active element is inserted in the passive network, the responses exhibit a self-sustained sinusoidal oscillation for $g_m = 6.425$. Theoretically, at least, if g_m is held at this value and if all the other network and tube parameters are also held at their fixed values, the circuit acts as an oscillator. In practice, however, it is impossible to hold this operating condition at all times in this linear circuit, since for any slight fluctuation in circuit or tube parameters, the responses will move away from their sinusoidal steady-state solutions. We show in the following paragraph that when g_m decreases from the value of 6.425, the sinusoidal responses will decay in amplitude, whereas if the value of g_m exceeds 6.425, the value of $i_2(t)$ (as well as of i_1 and v_c) will increase without bound (if we disregard

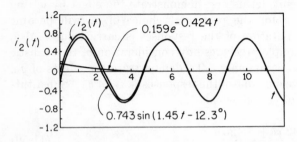

Fig. 11-15 *Waveform of the current $i_2(t)$ for $t \geq 0$ (switch is closed at $t = 0$) in the circuit of Fig. 11-12a, with $g_m = 6.425$ and the indicated initial conditions.*

the saturation limits of the tube and other circuit parameters), and the circuit is said to be unstable. In order to illustrate this unstable operation, let us assume that $g_m = 10$ (greater than 6.425). Substituting $g_m = 10$ in (11-58) yields

$$I_2(s) = \frac{13s + 11}{13s^3 + 4s^2 + 27s + 12} = \frac{s + 0.846}{(s + 0.433)(s^2 - 0.125s + 2.13)}$$

$$= \frac{0.174}{s + 0.433} + \frac{-0.174s + 1.098}{s^2 - 0.125s + 2.13} \tag{11-63}$$

Taking the inverse Laplace transform of (11-63), we obtain

$$i_2(t) = 0.174e^{-0.433t} + 0.762e^{0.0625t} \sin (1.46t - 13.1°) \tag{11-64}$$

We see that the first term on the right-hand side of $i_2(t)$ is an exponential decay whose steady-state value is zero. However, the $e^{0.0625t}$ factor in the second term causes the amplitude of $i_2(t)$ to increase as t increases. Assuming that the active circuit has no saturation or nonlinear limiting characteristics, the response of $i_2(t)$ will increase without bound as time progresses (Fig. 11-16).

We can now summarize our findings as follows:

In the circuit of Fig. 11-12, when $g_m = 0$, the circuit will exhibit responses whose amplitudes will decrease with time; when $g_m = 6.425$, the responses are in the form of constant-amplitude sinusoidal oscillations, and when g_m is greater than 6.425, the amplitudes of oscillations will increase with time.   The linear circuit is said to be unstable for g_m greater than 6.425.   We should also bear in mind that the only source of excitation assumed for this circuit is the initial voltage on the capacitor.

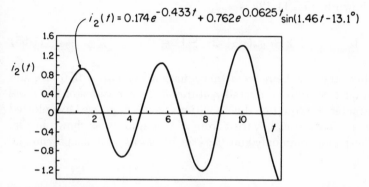

$$i_2(t) = 0.174e^{-0.433t} + 0.762e^{0.0625t}\sin(1.46t - 13.1°)$$

Fig. 11-16   Waveform of the current $i_2(t)$ for $t \geq 0$ (switch is closed at $t = 0$) in the circuit of Fig. 11-12a, with $g_m = 10$ and the indicated initial conditions.

If we desire to investigate the problem in a more quantitative manner, we inspect the expressions of $I_2(s)$ for $g_m = 0$, $g_m = 6.425$, and $g_m = 10$. We notice that the reason that the magnitude of $i_2(t)$ is convergent for $g_m = 0$ is that the roots of the denominator polynomial of $I_2(s)$ in (11-47) all lie in the left half of the s plane.   Therefore, when taking the inverse Laplace transform of this $I_2(s)$, the real parts of the roots, being negative, give rise to the $e^{-0.5t}$ term in (11-48).   Certainly, it is because of this damping term that the time response of $i_2(t)$ decreases with time.   For $g_m = 6.425$, two of the roots of the denominator polynomial of $I_2(s)$ lie on the $j\omega$ axis of the s plane; thus the response corresponds to an undamped sinusoid.   Finally, when $g_m = 10$, two of the roots of the denominator polynomial of (11-63) move into the right half of the s plane.   This accounts for the result that the term $e^{0.0625t}$ appearing in the expression for i_2 in (11-64), where 0.0625 is the real part of the complex roots of the denominator polynomial of $I_2(s)$.   From these observations we can conclude now that the dynamic behavior of the active network is completely controlled by the roots of the denominator polynomial of the transfer functions, or of the output response transforms. The numerator polynomial will only contribute to the magnitudes and phases of the output time responses, but will not affect the dynamic nature of the network, as observed from the results of the partial fraction expansions of $I_2(s)$. It is important to notice that the denominators of $I_1(s)$, $I_2(s)$, and $V_c(s)$ are all alike. These denominator polynomials, when set equal to zero, are called the *characteristic equation* of the network. The term characteristic equation originates from the characteristic equation of a linear differential equation. Therefore the characteristic equation of the active network shown in Fig. 11-12a is

$$3s^3 + 4s^2 + 7s + 2 + g_m(s^3 + 2s + 1) = 0 \qquad (11\text{-}65)$$

We have investigated the roots of this equation when $g_m = 0$, 6.425, and 10. In order to obtain an overall picture of the variations of the roots of this characteristic equation due to various values of g_m, we have plotted the loci of the roots as g_m is varied from zero to infinity as shown in Fig. 11-17. The plot is commonly known as the *root-locus*[1] plot of a polynomial

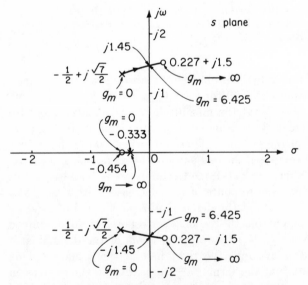

Fig. 11-17 Root-locus diagram of the polynomial
$3s^3 + 4s^2 + 7s + 2 + g_m(s^3 + 2s + 1) = 0$
when g_m is varied from zero to infinity.

when one of the parameters of the polynomial is varied from zero to infinity. The root-locus technique is used quite extensively in the analysis and design of feedback control systems.[2]

We have demonstrated by means of a numerical example the significance of the effect of the characteristic equation on the dynamic behavior of the system response. The characteristic equation was defined as the denominator of the transfer function equated to zero. Now we present a more general definition of the characteristic equation, using the state variables and the transfer functions.

Characteristic equation defined from the transfer function

The characteristic equation of a linear system can be defined as the equation obtained by equating the denominator of the transfer function to zero. The transfer function of a linear system is given by (11-18) as

$$\mathbf{G}(s) = \mathbf{C}(s\mathbf{I} - \mathbf{A})^{-1}\mathbf{B} + \mathbf{D} \tag{11-66}$$

$\mathbf{G}(s)$ can also be written

$$
\begin{aligned}
\mathbf{G}(s) &= \mathbf{C}\,\frac{[\Delta_{ij}]'}{|s\mathbf{I} - \mathbf{A}|}\,\mathbf{B} + \mathbf{D} \\
&= \frac{\mathbf{C}[\Delta_{ij}]'\mathbf{B} + |s\mathbf{I} - \mathbf{A}|\mathbf{D}}{|s\mathbf{I} - \mathbf{A}|}
\end{aligned} \tag{11-67}
$$

where Δ_{ij} represents the cofactor of the ijth element of the matrix $[s\mathbf{I} - \mathbf{A}]$, and $[\Delta_{ij}]'$ denotes the transpose of the matrix $[\Delta_{ij}]$.

Setting the denominator of $\mathbf{G}(s)$ equal to zero, we get

$$|s\mathbf{I} - \mathbf{A}| = 0 \tag{11-68}$$

which is defined as the characteristic equation of the system G.

The roots of the characteristic equation are often referred to as the *eigenvalues* of the coefficient matrix $\mathbf{A}$.

Let us use the state equations of (11-36) to (11-38) to illustrate the determination of the characteristic equation of a linear system. The coefficient matrix $\mathbf{A}$ of these state equations is

$$\mathbf{A} = \begin{bmatrix} 0 & 1 & -1 \\ -1 & -\tfrac{2}{3} & \tfrac{1}{3} \\ 1 & \tfrac{1}{3} & -\tfrac{2}{3} \end{bmatrix} \tag{11-69}$$

In determinant form the characteristic equation is obtained by substituting (11-69) in (11-68). We have

$$|s\mathbf{I} - \mathbf{A}| = \begin{vmatrix} s & -1 & 1 \\ 1 & s + \tfrac{2}{3} & -\tfrac{1}{3} \\ -1 & -\tfrac{1}{3} & s + \tfrac{2}{3} \end{vmatrix} = 0 \qquad (11\text{-}70)$$

Expanding the last determinant, we get, after simplification,

$$3s^3 + 4s^2 + 7s + 2 = 0 \qquad (11\text{-}71)$$

which is the characteristic equation of the network shown in Fig. 11-12. It is clear that (11-71) agrees with the denominator of (11-43), (11-44), or (11-45).

Characteristic equation defined from the signal flow graph

The characteristic equation of a linear system can be defined also from the signal flow graph and Mason's gain formula. The gain between a pair of input and output transform variables of a linear system is given by

$$G(s) = \frac{V_0(s)}{V_i(s)} = \frac{\displaystyle\sum_k G_k(s)\,\Delta_k(s)}{\Delta(s)} \qquad (11\text{-}72)$$

Since $G(s)$ is also a transfer function of the system, the characteristic equation is obtained by equating the denominator of $G(s)$ to zero. In general, however, it is improper to regard $\Delta(s) = 0$ as the characteristic equation, since $\Delta(s)$ is usually a quotient of two polynomials or functions. When the signal flow graph does not possess feedback loops, $\Delta(s) = 1$; then the characteristic equation must come from the denominator of $\sum_k G_k(s)\,\Delta_k(s)$. In general, if the transfer function is expressed as

$$G(s) = \frac{b_0 s^m + b_1 s^{m-1} + \cdots + b_{m-1} s + b_m}{a_0 s^n + a_1 s^{n-1} + \cdots + a_{n-1} s + a_n} \qquad (11\text{-}73)$$

the characteristic equation is given by

$$a_0 s^n + a_1 s^{n-1} + \cdots + a_{n-1} s + a_n = 0 \qquad (11\text{-}74)$$

11-6 TRANSFER FUNCTIONS AND IMPULSE SEQUENCES OF DISCRETE - DATA SYSTEMS

The transfer function of a linear discrete-data system is defined in the same way as that of a continuous-data system. We shall derive the transfer function from various possible viewpoints.

The state-equation approach

Consider that the output equation of a linear discrete-data system is given by

$$\mathbf{y}(kT) = \mathbf{Cx}(kT) + \mathbf{Dr}(kT) \tag{11-75}$$

Multiplying both sides of (11-75) by z^{-k} and taking the sum from $k = 0$ to $k = \infty$, we get

$$\sum_{k=0}^{\infty} \mathbf{y}(kT)z^{-k} = \sum_{k=0}^{\infty} \mathbf{Cx}(kT)z^{-k} + \sum_{k=0}^{\infty} \mathbf{Dr}(kT)z^{-k} \tag{11-76}$$

By definition of the z transform, (11-76) becomes

$$\mathbf{Y}(z) = \mathbf{CX}(z) + \mathbf{DR}(z) \tag{11-77}$$

Now, substituting the z-transformed state-transition equation (10-44) in (11-77), we have

$$\mathbf{Y}(z) = \mathbf{C}(z\mathbf{I} - \mathbf{A})^{-1}z\mathbf{x}(0+) + \mathbf{C}(z\mathbf{I} - \mathbf{A})^{-1}\mathbf{BR}(z) + \mathbf{DR}(z) \tag{11-78}$$

The transfer function is defined with the assumption of zero initial condition. Therefore, with $\mathbf{x}(0+) = \mathbf{0}$, (11-78) becomes

$$\mathbf{Y}(z) = [\mathbf{C}(z\mathbf{I} - \mathbf{A})^{-1}\mathbf{B} + \mathbf{D}]\mathbf{R}(z) \tag{11-79}$$

which represents the input-output transform relationship of a discrete-data system. The *transfer-function matrix*, or the *discrete transfer function*, is defined as

$$\mathbf{G}(z) = \mathbf{C}(z\mathbf{I} - \mathbf{A})^{-1}\mathbf{B} + \mathbf{D} \tag{11-80}$$

We must point out that the input-output relationship (11-79) and the transfer function (11-80) are derived for multiple inputs and outputs, with the single input-output as a special case.

The inverse z transform of $\mathbf{G}(z)$ is obtained from (11-80).

$$\mathcal{Z}^{-1}\mathbf{G}(z) = \mathcal{Z}^{-1}[\mathbf{C}(z\mathbf{I} - \mathbf{A})^{-1}\mathbf{B} + \mathbf{D}]$$
$$= \mathbf{g}(kT) = \mathbf{C}\boldsymbol{\Phi}(kT)\mathbf{B} + \mathbf{D}\delta(t) \qquad (11\text{-}81)$$

and $\mathbf{g}(kT)$ is regarded as the *impulse sequence*, or the *weighting sequence*, of the linear process.   In a strictly digital process, the impulse sequence $\mathbf{g}(kT)$ is interpreted as the sequence of output impulses (or numbers) of the system when a unit impulse is applied as inputs at $t = 0$ (Fig. 11-18).

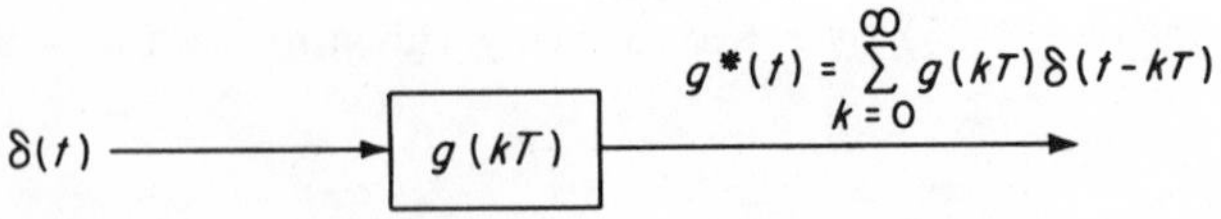

Fig. 11-18   *Impulse sequence of a digital process.*

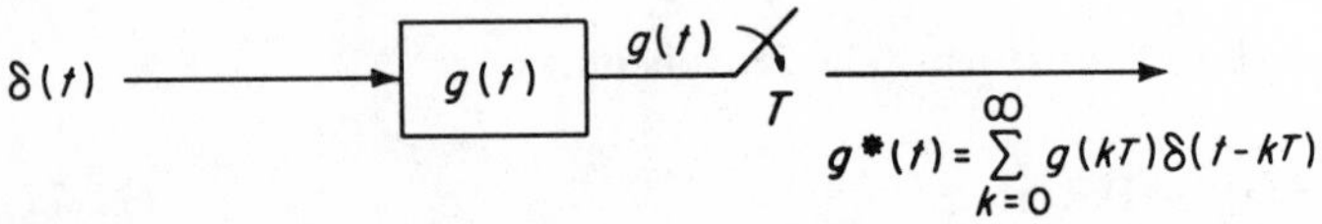

Fig. 11-19   *Impulse sequence of a continuous process.*

For a continuous-data system, $\mathbf{g}(kT)$ may have a physical significance as the sampled sequence of the impulse response of the system (Fig. 11-19).

The superposition approach

Let us refer to the block diagram shown in Fig. 11-20.   The inputs to the linear system whose impulse response is $\mathbf{g}(t)$ are described by the vector $\mathbf{r}^*(t)$, and the output vector $\mathbf{y}(t)$ is sampled to give $\mathbf{y}^*(t)$.   Invoking

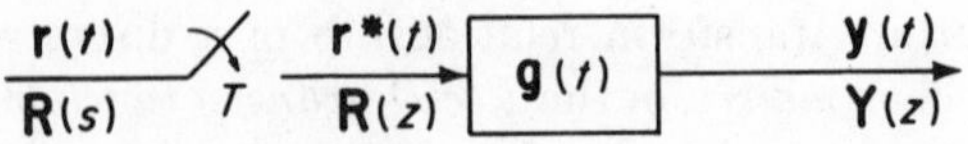

Fig. 11-20   *Block diagram of a linear discrete-data system with multi-inputs and multi-outputs.*

the principle of superposition, the continuous output vector $\mathbf{y}(t)$ is written

$$\mathbf{y}(t) = \sum_{k=0}^{\infty} \mathbf{g}(t - kT)\mathbf{r}(kT) \tag{11-82}$$

where, if there are j inputs and h outputs, $\mathbf{r}(kT)$ is a $j \times 1$ vector, $\mathbf{y}(kT)$ is an $h \times 1$ vector, and $\mathbf{g}(t)$ is an $h \times j$ matrix.   In (11-82), setting $t = nT$, multiplying both sides by z^{-n}, and summing from $n = 0$ to $n = \infty$, we get

$$\sum_{n=0}^{\infty} \mathbf{y}(nT)z^{-n} = \sum_{n=0}^{\infty} \sum_{k=0}^{\infty} \mathbf{g}(nT - kT)\mathbf{r}(kT)z^{-n} \tag{11-83}$$

Letting $p = n - k$, and when $n = 0$, $p = -k$, (11-83) becomes

$$\sum_{n=0}^{\infty} \mathbf{y}(nT)z^{-n} = \sum_{p=-k}^{\infty} \sum_{k=0}^{\infty} \mathbf{g}(pT)\mathbf{r}(kT)z^{-p}z^{-k} \tag{11-84}$$

For a physical system, the impulse response $g(t)$ is zero for $t < 0$; therefore the lower limit on the first summation sign in (11-84) can be changed from $p = -k$ to $p = 0$, and the expression becomes

$$\sum_{n=0}^{\infty} \mathbf{y}(nT)z^{-n} = \sum_{p=0}^{\infty} \sum_{k=0}^{\infty} \mathbf{g}(pT)\mathbf{r}(kT)z^{-p}z^{-k}$$

$$= \sum_{p=0}^{\infty} \mathbf{g}(pT)z^{-p} \sum_{k=0}^{\infty} \mathbf{r}(kT)z^{-k} \tag{11-85}$$

which is recognized to be

$$\mathbf{Y}(z) = \mathbf{G}(z)\mathbf{R}(z) \tag{11-86}$$

where

$$\mathbf{G}(z) = \sum_{p=0}^{\infty} \mathbf{g}(pT)z^{-p} \tag{11-87}$$

The difference-equation approach

The transfer function for a single input and single output system can be defined using the difference equation (5-111).   Taking the z transform on both sides of the difference equation and assuming zero initial condition, we get

$$(z^n + a_1 z^{n-1} + a_2 z^{n-2} + \cdots + a_{n-1} z + a_n) Y(z) = (b_0 z^n + b_1 z^{n-1}$$
$$+ \cdots + b_{n-1} + b_n) R(z) \quad (11\text{-}88)$$

The transfer function between $R(z)$ and $Y(z)$ may be defined as

$$G(z) = \frac{Y(z)}{R(z)} = \frac{b_0 z^n + b_1 z^{n-1} + \cdots + b_{n-1} z + b_n}{z^n + a_1 z^{n-1} + \cdots + a_{n-1} z + a_n} \quad (11\text{-}89)$$

The following example is used to illustrate the various advantages and applications of the three different forms of transfer functions defined above.

Example 11-4   Consider that a linear digital process is described by the difference equation

$$y(k + 2)T - 0.503 y(k + 1)T + 0.0497 y(kT) = r(kT) \quad (11\text{-}90)$$

It is apparent that the transfer function defined in (11-89) is more convenient for this case. Taking the z transform on both sides of the difference equation and assuming zero initial conditions, we have

$$z^2 Y(z) - 0.503 z Y(z) + 0.0497 Y(z) = R(z)$$

Therefore

$$G(z) = \frac{Y(z)}{R(z)} = \frac{1}{z^2 - 0.503 z + 0.0497} \quad (11\text{-}91)$$

However, if the difference equation (11-90) is originally given in state-equation form, i.e.,

$$\begin{bmatrix} x_1(k+1)T \\ x_2(k+1)T \end{bmatrix} = \begin{bmatrix} 0 & 1 \\ -0.0497 & 0.503 \end{bmatrix} \begin{bmatrix} x_1(kT) \\ x_2(kT) \end{bmatrix} + \begin{bmatrix} 0 \\ 1 \end{bmatrix} r(kT) \quad (11\text{-}92)$$

and

$$y(kT) = x_1(kT) \quad (11\text{-}93)$$

so that

$$A = \begin{bmatrix} 0 & 1 \\ -0.0497 & 0.503 \end{bmatrix} \quad B = \begin{bmatrix} 0 \\ 1 \end{bmatrix}$$

$$C = \begin{bmatrix} 1 & 0 \end{bmatrix} \quad D = \begin{bmatrix} 0 \end{bmatrix}$$

(11-94)

the transfer function is readily given by (11-80); i.e.,

$$G(z) = C(zI - A)^{-1}B + D$$

$$= \begin{bmatrix} 1 & 0 \end{bmatrix} \begin{bmatrix} \dfrac{z - 0.503}{z^2 - 0.503z + 0.0497} & \dfrac{1}{z^2 - 0.503z + 0.0497} \\ \dfrac{-0.497}{z^2 - 0.503z + 0.0497} & \dfrac{z}{z^2 - 0.503z + 0.0497} \end{bmatrix} \begin{bmatrix} 0 \\ 1 \end{bmatrix}$$

$$= \begin{bmatrix} \dfrac{1}{z^2 - 0.503z + 0.0497} \end{bmatrix}$$

(11-95)

It is apparent that (11-87) is applicable only when the system is described by its impulse sequence $g(kT)$.

11-7 APPLICATIONS OF z TRANSFORMS AND DISCRETE STATE EQUATIONS

The applications of the discrete state equations and the z transforms are numerous. They can be used not only to solve problems involving discrete-data networks and systems, but also continuous-data systems. Some examples of various types of applications of the topics discussed in the preceding sections of this chapter are presented below.

A ladder-network problem

The discrete state equations and z transformation can be used to solve ladder-network problems which would be difficult to solve by conventional means. The currents and voltages in the ladder network of Fig. 11-21

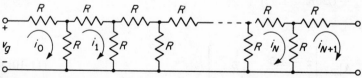

Fig. 11-21   A ladder network.

can be described by difference equations. In this case, instead of using time as the independent variable, it is advantageous to consider the transmission of current and voltage from one section of the network to the next as a process of state transition. The problem may involve (1) writing the equations for v and i at various points of the network, and (2) finding $i(k) = i_k$ as a function of V_g and N, where V_g is the input voltage, and N determines the number of sections of the network.

It is apparent that the ladder network can be divided into similar sections in a number of ways. Figure 11-22 shows that the network has been arbitrarily divided into identical T sections.

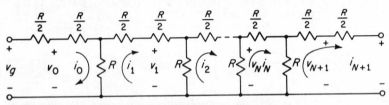

Fig. 11-22   *A ladder network divided into T sections.*

Let us designate i_k and v_k as state variables. Then, writing the voltage equations at both ends of the kth section, we get

$$v_k = 1.5Ri_k - Ri_{k+1} \tag{11-96}$$

$$v_{k+1} = -1.5Ri_{k+1} + Ri_k \tag{11-97}$$

Rearranging these two equations, we have the state equations

$$i_{k+1} = 1.5i_k - \frac{1}{R}v_k \tag{11-98}$$

$$v_{k+1} = -1.25Ri_k + 1.5v_k \tag{11-99}$$

from which

$$\mathbf{A} = \begin{bmatrix} 1.5 & -\dfrac{1}{R} \\ -1.25R & 1.5 \end{bmatrix} \tag{11-100}$$

Therefore

$$[z\mathbf{I} - \mathbf{A}] = \begin{bmatrix} z - 1.5 & \dfrac{1}{R} \\ 1.25R & z - 1.5 \end{bmatrix} \tag{11-101}$$

and

$$[z\mathbf{I} - \mathbf{A}]^{-1}z = \frac{z}{z^2 - 3z + 1} \begin{bmatrix} z - 1.5 & -\dfrac{1}{R} \\ -1.25R & z - 1.5 \end{bmatrix} \qquad (11\text{-}102)$$

The transition matrix $\mathbf{\Phi}(k)$ is obtained from the inverse z transform of (11-102), which is obtained using the inversion formula (10-26). Thus the state-transition equation of the network is

$$\begin{bmatrix} i_k \\ v_k \end{bmatrix} = \mathcal{L}^{-1} \left\{ \frac{z}{z^2 - 3z + 1} \begin{bmatrix} z - 1.5 & -\dfrac{1}{R} \\ -1.25R & z - 1.5 \end{bmatrix} \begin{bmatrix} i_0 \\ v_0 \end{bmatrix} \right\} \qquad (11\text{-}103)$$

From (10-26), we get

$$\mathcal{L}^{-1} \left[\frac{z(z - 1.5)}{(z^2 - 3z + 1)} \right] = \frac{1}{2\pi j} \oint \frac{z(z - 1.5)}{(z - 2.615)(z - 0.385)} z^{k-1} \, dz$$

$$= \sum \text{residues of } \frac{(z - 1.5)z^k}{(z - 2.615)(z - 0.385)} \quad \text{at } z = 2.615 \text{ and } z = 0.385$$

$$= 0.5[(2.615)^n + (0.385)^n] \qquad (11\text{-}104)$$

Similarly, the other elements of $\mathbf{\Phi}(k)$ are found, and (11-103) becomes

$$\begin{bmatrix} i_k \\ v_k \end{bmatrix}$$

$$= \begin{bmatrix} 0.5[(2.615)^k + (0.385)^k] & 0.448[-(2.615)^k + (0.385)^k]\dfrac{1}{R} \\ 0.56[-(2.615)^k + (0.385)^k]R & 0.5[(2.615)^k + (0.385)^k] \end{bmatrix}$$

$$\begin{bmatrix} i_0 \\ v_0 \end{bmatrix} \qquad (11\text{-}105)$$

From (11-105) we get

$$i_k = 0.5[(2.615)^k + (0.385)^k]i_0 + 0.448[-(2.615)^k + (0.385)^k]\frac{v_0}{R} \qquad (11\text{-}106)$$

Now we are ready to apply the initial conditions, or more appropriately for this problem, the boundary conditions, to (11-106). The boundary conditions, as observed from Fig. 11-22, are

$$v_0 = v_g - \frac{i_0}{2} R \qquad (11\text{-}107)$$

and

$$i_{N+1} = 0 \qquad (11\text{-}108)$$

Substituting (11-107) in (11-106) and letting $k = N + 1$, we get

$$i_{N+1} = 0 = 0.5[(2.615)^{N+1} + (0.385)^{N+1}]i_0 - 0.448[(2.615)^{N+1}$$
$$- (0.385)^{N+1}] \frac{1}{R} \left(v_g - \frac{i_0 R}{2} \right) \quad (11\text{-}109)$$

Solving for i_0 from (11-109), we have

$$i_0 = \frac{0.448[(2.615)^{N+1} - (0.385)^{N+1}]}{0.723(2.615)^{N+1} + 0.276(0.385)^{N+1}} \frac{v_g}{R} \qquad (11\text{-}110)$$

and from (11-107),

$$v_0 = \frac{(2.615)^{N+1} + (0.385)^{N+1}}{1.448(2.615)^{N+1} + 0.552(0.385)^{N+1}} v_g \qquad (11\text{-}111)$$

Once i_0 and v_0 are found in terms of v_g and N as in (11-110) and (11-111), respectively, the solutions of i_k and v_k for $k = 1, 2, \ldots, (N + 1)$ are given by (11-105).

The ladder network shown in Fig. 11-21 can also be analyzed with a different selection of state variables. Writing the loop equation of the loop with current i_{k+1}, $k = 0, 1, 2, \ldots, N + 1$, we get

$$i_{k+2} - 3i_{k+1} + i_k = 0 \qquad (11\text{-}112)$$

The state variables may be defined as

$$x_{1,k} = x_1(k) = i_k \qquad (11\text{-}113)$$
$$x_{2,k} = x_2(k) = i_{k+1} = x_{1,k+1} \qquad (11\text{-}114)$$

Notice that, in this case, the state variables $x_1(k)$ and $x_2(k)$ represent the currents i_k and i_{k+1}, respectively. Then (11-112) is written in state-equation form:

$$x_{1,k+1} = x_{2,k} \tag{11-115}$$

$$x_{2,k+1} = -x_{1,k} - 3x_{2,k} \tag{11-116}$$

and from these equations we get

$$\mathbf{A} = \begin{bmatrix} 0 & 1 \\ -1 & 3 \end{bmatrix} \tag{11-117}$$

$$[z\mathbf{I} - \mathbf{A}]^{-1}z = \frac{z}{z^2 - 3z + 1} \begin{bmatrix} z - 3 & 1 \\ -1 & z \end{bmatrix} \tag{11-118}$$

Notice that, although the matrix $\mathbf{A}$ in (11-117) is different from that of (11-100), because of the difference in the choice of state variables, the characteristic equation $z^2 - 3z + 1 = 0$ is the same by both methods.

The inverse z transform of $(z\mathbf{I} - \mathbf{A})^{-1}z$ brings

$\mathbf{\Phi}(k)$

$$= \begin{bmatrix} 1.1725(0.385)^k - 0.1725(2.615)^k & 0.448[(2.615)^k - (0.385)^k] \\ 0.448[(0.385)^k - (2.615)^k] & -0.1725(0.385)^k + 1.1725(2.615)^k \end{bmatrix} \tag{11-119}$$

The state-transition equations become

$$\begin{bmatrix} x_{1,k} \\ x_{2,k} \end{bmatrix}$$

$$= \begin{bmatrix} 1.1725(0.385)^k - 0.1725(2.615)^k & 0.488[(2.615)^k - (0.385)^k] \\ 0.448[(0.385)^k - (2.615)^k] & -0.1725(0.385)^k + 1.1725(2.615)^k \end{bmatrix}$$
$$\begin{bmatrix} x_{1,0} \\ x_{2,0} \end{bmatrix} \tag{11-120}$$

The boundary conditions, as observed from Fig. 11-21, are

$$x_{1,0} = i_0 = \frac{v_g}{2R} + \frac{i_1}{R} = \frac{v_g}{2R} + \frac{x_{2,0}}{2} \tag{11-121}$$

and

$$x_{1,N+1} = i_{N+1} = 0 \tag{11-122}$$

Letting $k = N + 1$ and substituting the two boundary conditions in (11-120), we have

$$x_{1,N+1} = 0 = [1.1725(0.385)^{N+1} - 1.1725(2.615)^{N+1}]x_{1,0}$$

$$+ 0.448[(2.615)^{N+1} - (0.385)^{N+1}]\left(2x_{1,0} - \frac{v_g}{R}\right) \quad (11\text{-}123)$$

Therefore

$$x_{1,0} = \frac{0.448[(2.615)^{N+1} - (0.385)^{N+1}]}{0.7235(2.615)^{N+1} + 0.2765(0.385)^{N+1}} \frac{v_g}{R} \quad (11\text{-}124)$$

which is identical with the result obtained earlier, in (11-110).

Although an all-resistor ladder network is used in this illustrative example, the method can also be applied to a ladder network with reactive elements.

A sampled-data control system

Perhaps the most extensive use of the z transformation is in the study of sampled-data control systems. Since the subject is well covered in the literature, we present just a simple illustration of the application here.

The block diagram of a feedback control system with a periodic sampling switch is shown in Fig. 11-23. The sampling switch samples

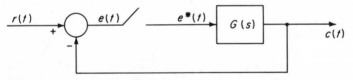

Fig. 11-23 *A sampled-data control system.*

the signal $e(t)$ once every T sec for an infinitesimally small duration. Therefore the output of the sampler can be denoted by

$$e^*(t) = \sum_{k=0}^{\infty} e(kT)\delta(t - kT) \quad (11\text{-}125)$$

The z transform of $e^*(t)$ is written

$$E(z) = \sum_{k=0}^{\infty} e(kT)z^{-k} \quad (11\text{-}126)$$

Using the transfer-function concept discussed in Sec. 11-6, the discrete transfer function of $G(s)$ is defined as

$$G(z) = \frac{C(z)}{E(z)} \tag{11-127}$$

The input-output transfer relations of the system is derived from the following algebraic relationships:

$$C(z) = G(z)E(z)$$
$$E(z) = R(z) - C(z)$$

Therefore

$$C(z) = \frac{G(z)}{1 + G(z)} R(z) \tag{11-128}$$

Given $r(t)$ and $G(s)$, the output signal $c(t)$ at the sampling instants of $t = 0, T, 2T, \ldots$ is completely defined by (11-128). However, it is necessary to point out that the z-transform solution specifies only $c(kT)$, and not $c(t)$. The true output of the system is $c(t)$, which is a function of t. Therefore, if the true output $c(t)$ is oscillatory, the sequence $c(kT)$ may not adequately describe the output between the sampling instants if T is relatively large. This difficulty may be regarded as one of the limitations of the z-transform method.

As an illustrative example, let us consider that, for the sampled-data system of Fig. 11-23, $T = 1$ sec, $r(t)$ is a unit-step-function input, and

$$G(s) = \frac{2}{s(s + 1)}$$

The z transform of $G(s)$ for $T = 1$ sec is

$$G(z) = \mathbb{Z}\left[\frac{2}{s(s + 1)}\right] = \frac{2(1 - e^{-T})z}{(z - 1)(z - e^{-T})}$$

$$= \frac{1.264z}{(z - 1)(z - 0.368)} \tag{11-129}$$

Substituting $G(z)$ from (11-129) in (11-128), we get

$$C(z) = \frac{1.264z}{(z - 1)(z - 0.368) + 1.264z} R(z) \tag{11-130}$$

For a unit step input,

$$R(z) = \frac{z}{z - 1} \tag{11-131}$$

Therefore (11-130) becomes

$$C(z) = \frac{1.264z^2}{(z - 1)(z^2 - 0.104z + 0.368)} \tag{11-132}$$

Expanding $C(z)$ into a power series in z^{-1} by long division, we have

$$C(z) = 1.264z^{-1} + 1.395z^{-2} + 0.943z^{-3} + 0.848z^{-4} + 1.004z^{-5}$$
$$+ 1.055z^{-6} + 1.002z^{-7} + \cdots \tag{11-133}$$

Since the coefficient of z^{-k} in the expanded $C(z)$ represents the value of $c(kT)$, the sampled output signal is written directly from (11-133).

$$c^*(t) = 1.264\delta(t - 1) + 1.395\delta(t - 2) + 0.943\delta(t - 3)$$
$$+ 0.848\delta(t - 4) + 1.004\delta(t - 5) + 1.055\delta(t - 6)$$
$$+ 1.002\delta(t - 7) + \cdots \tag{11-134}$$

It is apparent that, as time approaches infinity, the output approaches the input. This fact can also be verified by means of the final-value theorem stated in Sec. 10-2; i.e.,

$$\lim_{k \to \infty} c(kT) = \lim_{z \to 1} (1 - z^{-1})C(z)$$
$$= \lim_{z \to 1} \frac{1.264z}{z^2 - 0.104z + 0.368} = 1 \tag{11-135}$$

The output sequence $c(kT)$ is sketched as shown in Fig. 11-24. In this case, since the output signal $c(t)$ is well behaved between the sampling

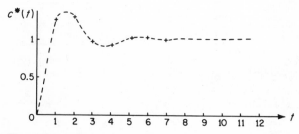

Fig. 11-24 Output response of the sampled-data system shown in Fig. 11-23.

instants, the true response may be approximated by drawing a smooth curve through the points of $c(kT)$.

11-8 STABILITY OF LINEAR SYSTEMS

From the illustrative example of Sec. 11-5, the relation between the transient response of a linear system with continuous data and its characteristic equation roots can be summarized as follows:

1   When all the roots of the characteristic equation are found in the left half of the s plane, the responses due to the initial conditions will decrease to zero as time approaches infinity.
2   If one or more pairs of simple roots are located on the imaginary axis, but with no roots in the right half of the s plane, the responses will be undamped sinusoidal oscillations.
3   If one or more roots are found in the right half of the s plane, the responses will increase in magnitude as time increases.

Usually, in linear-system theory, the last two categories are defined as *unstable* conditions.

The stability of a linear time-invariant system can be defined in a number of ways.   Strictly, in linear systems, stability is independent of the input excitations.   However, a well-known definition of stability is:

A system is said to be stable if its output is bounded for any bounded input.

In other words, let $c(t)$ be the output and $r(t)$ the input of a linear system.   Then

$$|r(t)| \leq N < \infty \qquad t \geq t_0 \tag{11-136}$$

$$|c(t)| \leq M < \infty \qquad t \geq t_0 \tag{11-137}$$

However, there are a few exceptions to the foregoing definition.   A differentiator gives rise to an impulse response at $t = t_0$ when it is subjected to a unit-step-function input $u(t - t_0)$.   In this case, the input is bounded but the output is not, since an impulse is known to have an infinite amplitude.   Also, when $u(t - t_0)$ is applied to an integrator, the output is a ramp function $(t - t_0)u(t - t_0)$ which is not bounded for $t > t_0$.   However, since a differentiator and an integrator are all useful systems, they are defined as stable systems.

The definition of stability given above may lead to several different ways of interpreting the stability criterion of linear time-invariant systems.   They are discussed below.

Stability defined according to impulse response

The definition of stability, given in the foregoing section, leads to an important requirement on the impulse response of a stable system.

Given a linear system with input $r(t)$, output $c(t)$, then

$$c(t) = \int_0^\infty r(t - \tau)g(\tau)\, d\tau \qquad (11\text{-}138)$$

where $g(\tau)$ is the impulse response of the system.

Taking the absolute value on both sides of (11-138) gives

$$|c(t)| = \left| \int_0^\infty r(t - \tau)g(\tau)\, d\tau \right| \qquad (11\text{-}139)$$

From the knowledge that the absolute value of an integral is no greater than the integral of the absolute value of the integrand, (11-139) is written

$$|c(t)| \leq \int_0^\infty |r(t - \tau)|\, |g(\tau)|\, d\tau \qquad (11\text{-}140)$$

Now, if $r(t)$ is a bounded signal, then, from (11-136),

$$|c(t)| \leq \int_0^\infty N|g(\tau)|\, d\tau = N \int_0^\infty |g(\tau)|\, d\tau \qquad (11\text{-}141)$$

Therefore, if $c(t)$ is to be a bounded output, the following condition must hold:

$$N \int_0^\infty |g(\tau)|\, d\tau \leq M < \infty \qquad (11\text{-}142)$$

or

$$\int_0^\infty |g(\tau)|\, d\tau \leq p < \infty \qquad (11\text{-}143)$$

A physical interpretation of (11-143) is that the area under the absolute-value curve of the impulse response $g(t)$, evaluated from $t = 0$ to $t = \infty$, must be finite.

Now we show that the requirement on the impulse response for stability can be linked to the restrictions on the characteristic-equation roots.

By definition, the transfer function $G(s)$ of the system and the impulse response $g(t)$ are related through the Laplace transform integral

$$G(s) = \int_0^\infty g(t)e^{-st}\,dt \tag{11-144}$$

Taking the absolute value on both sides of (11-144) gives

$$|G(s)| \leq \int_0^\infty |g(t)|\,|e^{-st}|\,dt \tag{11-145}$$

The roots of the characteristic equation are the poles of $G(s)$, and when s takes on these values, $|G(s)| = \infty$. Also, $s = \sigma + j\omega$; the absolute value of e^{-st} is $|e^{-\sigma t}|$. Equation (11-145) becomes

$$\infty \leq \int_0^\infty |g(t)|\,|e^{-\sigma t}|\,dt \tag{11-146}$$

If one or more roots of the characteristic equation are in the right half and on the imaginary axis of the s plane, $\sigma \geq 0$, and thus $|e^{-\sigma t}| \leq N = 1$. Equation (11-146) is written

$$\infty \leq \int_0^\infty N|g(t)|\,dt = \int_0^\infty |g(t)|\,dt \tag{11-147}$$

for Re $(s) = \sigma \geq 0$.

Since (11-147) contradicts the stability criterion given in (11-143), we conclude that, for the system to be stable, *the roots of the characteristic equation must all lie inside the left half of the s plane.* Another way of stating this stability criterion is that *the roots of the characteristic equation must all have negative real parts.*

Stability from the state-variable viewpoint

The stability condition of a linear time-invariant system can also be established from the state-variable approach. Since stability is independent of the input, the condition that $\mathbf{x}(t) = \mathbf{0}$, where $\mathbf{x}(t)$ is the state vector, can be regarded as the equilibrium state of the system. Now consider that the system is subjected to a disturbance of finite amplitude at $t = t_0$, so that the initial state is given by $\mathbf{x}(t_0) \neq \mathbf{0}$. If the system under zero input condition returns to its equilibrium state as t approaches infinity, it is said to be stable; otherwise, it is unstable. For linear systems the magnitude of the initial state is unimportant so long as it is finite. For nonlinear systems, however, different initial states may lead to entirely different stability conditions.

In view of the foregoing discussion, the stability condition from the state-variable viewpoint can be stated:

A system is said to be stable if, for any finite initial state $\mathbf{x}(t_0)$, *there is a positive number M [which depends on* $\mathbf{x}(t_0)$] *such that*

$$\|\mathbf{x}(t)\| < M \qquad all \; t \geq t_0 \tag{11-148}$$

and

$$\lim_{t \to \infty} \|\mathbf{x}(t)\| = 0 \tag{11-149}$$

where $\|\mathbf{x}(t)\|$ *represents the norm† of the state vector* $\mathbf{x}(t)$, *or*

$$\|\mathbf{x}(t)\| = \Big[\sum_{i=1}^{n} x_i(t)^2 \Big]^{\frac{1}{2}} \tag{11-150}$$

The condition stated in (11-148) implies that the transition of state for any $t > t_0$ as represented by the norm of the vector $\mathbf{x}(t)$ must be

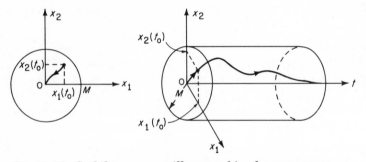

Fig. 11-25 *Stability concept illustrated in the state space.*

bounded. Equation (11-149) states that the system must reach its equilibrium point as t approaches infinity.

The stability criterion is illustrated by the second-order case shown in Fig. 11-25. The trajectory represents the transition of $\mathbf{x}(t)$ for $t \quad t_0$ from a finite initial state $\mathbf{x}(t_0)$. As shown on the figure, $\mathbf{x}(t_0)$ is represented by a point which is the tip of the vector obtained from the vector sum of $x_1(t_0)$ and $x_2(t_0)$. A cylinder with radius M forms the upper bound for the

† The norm of a vector is a generalization of the idea of length. $\|\mathbf{x}\|$ is always a real number.

trajectory points for all $t > t_0$, and as t approaches infinity, the system reaches its equilibrium point $\mathbf{x}(t) = \mathbf{0}$.

We now show that the definition of stability of linear systems given above leads to the same conclusion about the restrictions of the roots of the characteristic equation.

For zero-input conditions, the state-transition equation of the system is

$$\mathbf{x}(t) = \mathbf{\Phi}(t - t_0)\mathbf{x}(t_0) \tag{11-151}$$

where $\mathbf{\Phi}(t)$ is the state-transition matrix.

Taking the norm on both sides of (11-151) gives

$$\|\mathbf{x}(t)\| = \|\mathbf{\Phi}(t - t_0)\mathbf{x}(t_0)\| \tag{11-152}$$

An important property of the norm of a vector is

$$\|\mathbf{x}(t)\| \leq \|\mathbf{\Phi}(t - t_0)\| \, \|\mathbf{x}(t_0)\| \tag{11-153}†$$

Then the condition in (11-148) requires that $\|\mathbf{\Phi}(t - t_0)\| \, \|\mathbf{x}(t_0)\|$ be finite. Thus, if $\|\mathbf{x}(t_0)\|$ is finite as postulated, $\|\mathbf{\Phi}(t - t_0)\|$ must also be finite for $t > t_0$. Similarly, (11-149) leads to the condition that

$$\lim_{t \to \infty} \mathbf{\Phi}(t - t_0) = \mathbf{0} \tag{11-154}$$

In (9-27) the state-transition matrix is written

$$\mathbf{\Phi}(t) = \mathcal{L}^{-1}[(s\mathbf{I} - \mathbf{A})^{-1}] \qquad t \geq 0 \tag{11-155}$$

or

$$\mathbf{\Phi}(t) = \mathcal{L}^{-1} \frac{[\Delta_{ij}]'}{|s\mathbf{I} - \mathbf{A}|} \tag{11-156}$$

where $[\Delta_{ij}]'$ denotes the transpose of the matrix $[\Delta_{ij}]$, and Δ_{ij} is the cofactor of the ijth element of $[s\mathbf{I} - \mathbf{A}]$.

Since $|s\mathbf{I} - \mathbf{A}| = 0$ is the characteristic equation of the system, (11-156) implies that the time response of $\mathbf{\Phi}(t)$ is controlled by the roots of the characteristic equation. Thus condition (11-154) requires that the roots of the characteristic equation must all have negative real parts.

The discussions conducted in the preceding sections indicate that the

† This property is analogous to the relation between magnitudes of vectors: if $|\mathbf{A}| = |\mathbf{BC}|$, then $|\mathbf{A}| \leq |\mathbf{B}| \, |\mathbf{C}|$.

stability of linear systems can be tested by locating the roots of the characteristic equation in the s plane. The regions of stability and instability in the s plane are illustrated in Fig. 11-26. The imaginary axis, except the origin, is included in the unstable region.

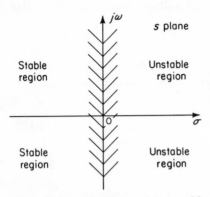

Fig. 11-26 Stable and unstable regions in the s plane.

As a concluding remark, it must be pointed out that the stability of nonlinear systems is a complex subject. Since the input condition and the initial state both affect the stability of a nonlinear system, it is necessary to define a variety of definitions of stability.

PROBLEMS

11-1   Find the voltage-ratio transfer function $V_2(s)/V_1(s)$ for each of the networks shown in Fig. P11-1.

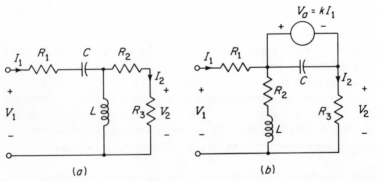

(a)   (b)

Fig. P11-1

11-2 Find the current-ratio transfer function $I_2(s)/I_1(s)$ for each of the networks shown in Fig. P11-1.

11-3 Find the output impedance (impedance seen across R_3) for each of the networks shown in Fig. P11-1.

11-4 Find the transfer impedance $z_{12}(j\omega)$ for each of the networks shown in Fig. P11-1.

11-5 Find the transfer admittance $y_{12}(j\omega)$ for each of the networks shown in Fig. P11-1.

11-6 The dynamic equations of a linear system is given by

$$\dot{x} = Ax + Br$$
$$\dot{y} = Cx + Dr$$

where

$$A = \begin{bmatrix} -5 & 2 \\ 0 & -1 \end{bmatrix} \qquad B = \begin{bmatrix} 0 \\ 2 \end{bmatrix} \qquad C = [0 \quad 1] \qquad D = 0$$

(a) Find the impulse-response matrix of the system.
(b) Find the transfer-function matrix of the system.

11-7 The output $c(t)$ of a linear time-invariant system when subjected to a step input of 0.1 unit is shown in Fig. P11-2.

(a) Sketch the impulse response of the system.
(b) Determine the transfer function of the system.

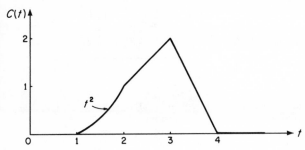

Fig. P11-2

11-8 Find the voltage $v_2(t)$ of the network shown in Fig. P11-3 for $t \geq 0$.

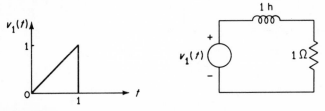

Fig. P11-3

368   Linear networks and systems

11-9 Find the impulse responses for $i_1(t)$, $i_2(t)$, and $v_c(t)$ of the network shown in Fig. P11-4.

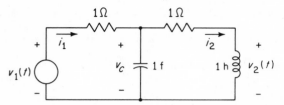

Fig. P11-4

11-10 Find the characteristic equation of the network shown in Fig. P11-4. Does the characteristic equation depend on which variable is considered the output?

11-11 An equivalent-circuit diagram of an N-stage amplifier is shown in Fig. P11-5. A sinusoidal voltage of amplitude V_g is applied to the input terminals from a generator of internal impedance Z_g. Find the voltage v_k and i_k, where $k = 0, 1, 2, \ldots, N$, in terms of the circuit parameters V_g and N.

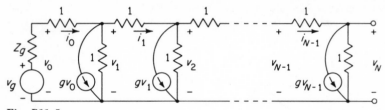

Fig. P11-5

11-12 The block diagram of a sampled-data control system is shown in Fig. P11-6.
(a) Write the dynamic equations of the system.
(b) Find the state-transition matrix $\Phi(kT)$ of the system.
(c) Find the impulse sequence of the system.

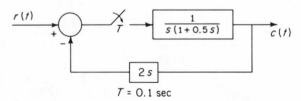

$T = 0.1$ sec

Fig. P11-6

TWELVE

STATE-TRANSITION SIGNAL FLOW GRAPHS

12-1 INTRODUCTION

The signal flow graph defined by Mason precludes consideration of initial conditions in the analysis of dynamic networks or systems. The conventional signal flow graphs and Coates' flow graphs are useful only for solving algebraic equations or transfer functions of systems for which the initial states are assumed to be zero. Also, we have demonstrated earlier that, at least from the standpoint of initial states, the state-variable analysis of dynamic networks is more convenient than the loop-and-node analysis. Now we introduce a consolidation between the state-variable and the signal-flow-graph concepts so that the advantages of both methods may be fully utilized.

The *state-transition signal flow graph*,[1] or the *state diagram*, for short, may be used to portray relationships between state variables of a system, including the initial states. The state diagram includes elements which

369

parallel analog-computer elements.   Therefore, once the state diagram of a system is drawn, if desired, the system may be programmed directly on a computer, following the relationships between the state variables exhibited on the state diagram.   In the Laplace domain the state diagram satisfies all the basic rules of Mason's signal flow graph.   Therefore Mason's gain formula can be applied to the state diagram to obtain the transfer functions of the system.   Furthermore, the state-transition equation of the system can also be easily written from the state diagram simply by use of Mason's gain formula.

12-2   ELEMENTS OF A STATE DIAGRAM

The state diagram is analogous to an analog-computer diagram, but we need not be concerned with the details and the mechanization of an analog computer in order to appreciate and understand the ideas of the state diagram.   We simply assume that an analog computer is a device which can compute by means of the following operations:

1   Multiplying a machine variable by a positive or a negative constant coefficient (usually done by an amplifier or a potentiometer)
2   Producing the sum of two or more machine variables (usually accomplished by summing amplifiers)
3   Producing the time integral of a machine variable, i.e., integration

These three computer operations are simply described hereafter as *multiplication by a constant, summing,* and *integration,* respectively.

The mathematical descriptions of these basic analog computations are as follows:

Multiplication by a constant

$$x_2(t) = ax_1(t) \qquad a = \text{const} \tag{12-1}$$

Integration

If the variables x_1 and x_2 are related by

$$\frac{dx_2(t)}{dt} = x_1(t) \tag{12-2}$$

then

$$x_2(t) = \int_{t_0}^{t} x_1(\tau) \, d\tau + x_2(t_0) \tag{12-3}$$

Summing

$$x_3(t) = x_0(t) + x_1(t) - x_2(t) \tag{12-4}$$

Because of the difficulties involved in realizing differentiation accurately, a conventional analog computer does not have a differentiator.

Taking the Laplace transform on both sides of these expressions, we have

$$X_2(s) = aX_1(s) \qquad \text{multiplication by} \qquad \text{a constant} \tag{12-5}$$

$$X_2(s) = \frac{X_1(s)}{s} + \frac{x_2(t_0)}{s} \qquad \text{integration} \tag{12-6}$$

$$X_3(s) = X_0(s) + X_1(s) - X_2(s) \qquad \text{summing} \tag{12-7}$$

Now since these are all algebraic equations, the signal-flow-graph representations (state diagrams) of the transform equations and the corresponding analog-computer diagrams are shown in Fig. 12-1.

The two integrator diagrams shown in Fig. 12-1b and c are mathematically identical, but the one in (b) accords with the true analog-computer diagram, whereas the one in (c) is simpler to draw.

12-3   STATE DIAGRAMS OF GENERAL HIGHER - ORDER SYSTEMS

Let us consider that a linear system is described by the following nth-order differential equation:

$$\frac{d^n y}{dt^n} + a_1 \frac{d^{n-1} y}{dt^{n-1}} + a_2 \frac{d^{n-2} y}{dt^{n-2}} + \cdots + a_{n-1} \frac{dy}{dt} + a_n y = r \tag{12-8}$$

where y is the output and r is the input.   It is of interest to show that the definition of the state variables, the state equations, the state-transition equation, and the transfer function of the system can all be obtained from the state diagram.

In general, the state diagram of a given system can be drawn in a number of ways and is not unique.   This also reflects the fact that the state variables of a given system are not uniquely defined.   The decision about the type of state diagram to be drawn depends upon how the system dynamics is initially described, that is, by differential equations or transfer functions, as well as the eventual objective of the state-diagram representation.   In the transfer-function case, the way the transfer function is given

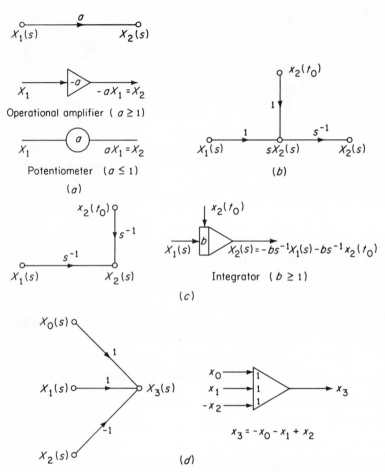

Fig. 12-1 *Basic elements of a state diagram and the corresponding analog-computer diagrams.* (a) *Multiplication by a constant.* (b) *Integration.* (c) *Integration.* (d) *Summing. The analog-computer elements are shown with phase shift between input and output of the amplifier and the integrator elements.*

also governs what type of state diagram is most easily obtained. A convenient way of drawing a state diagram for (12-8) is, first, to isolate the term with the highest derivative in the equation. The differential equation is written

$$\frac{d^n y}{dt^n} = -a_1 \frac{d^{n-1}y}{dt^{n-1}} - a_2 \frac{d^{n-2}y}{dt^{n-2}} - \cdots - a_{n-1} \frac{dy}{dt} - a_n y + r \qquad (12\text{-}9)$$

Now nodes representing the input r, $d^n y/dt^n$, $d^{n-1} y/dt^{n-1}$, . . . and output y are arranged in the order shown in Fig. 12-2a.   In terms of the Laplace-transform variable, $d^n y/dt^n$ is represented by $s^n Y(s)$, $d^{n-1} y/dt^{n-1}$ by $s^{n-1} Y(s)$, etc.   Since the signal at the node $s^n Y(s)$ is related to that at $s^{n-1} Y(s)$ by an integration with respect to t, the basic state-diagram configuration of Fig. 12-1b or c may be used.   When the nodes in Fig. 12-2a

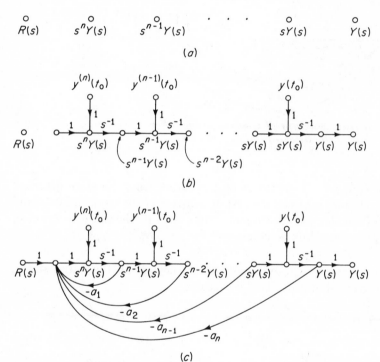

Fig. 12-2   State-diagram representation of the nth-order differential equation (12-8).

are properly connected by integrators and their associated initial conditions, the diagram in Fig. 12-2b results.   Completing the cause-and-effect relationship according to (12-9), the complete state diagram of the system is shown in Fig. 12-2c.   If we use the integrator diagram shown in Fig. 12-1c, a simpler state diagram for the same system is obtained as shown in Fig. 12-3.   The symbol $y^{(n)}(t_0)$ is used to indicate the nth-order derivative of $y(t)$ evaluated at $t = t_0$.

The state diagram provides information about the state equations of the system. In this case, it is convenient to designate the outputs of the integrators as the state variables. Therefore $Y(s) = X_1(s)$, $sY(s) = X_2(s)$, . . . , $s^{n-1}Y(s) = X_n(s)$, a total of n state variables.

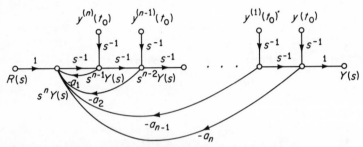

Fig. 12-3 *A state diagram of the nth-order differential equation (12-8), using the integrator diagram of Fig. 12-1c.*

The state equations are written by inspection from the state diagram, using the relations between the first derivatives of the state variables and the state variables and the input. Referring to the state diagram of Fig. 12-3, the procedure is as follows:

1   Delete all the integrator branches and neglect all the initial states; the diagram shown in Fig. 12-4 results.

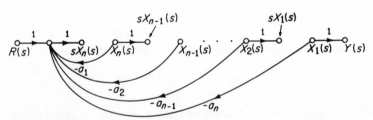

Fig. 12-4 *State diagram from which the state equations are written.*

2   From Fig. 12-4, write the variables at the input nodes of the integrators as functions of the state variables and the input.

The state equations are

$$\frac{dy}{dt} = \frac{dx_1}{dt} = x_2$$

$$\frac{dx_2}{dt} = x_3$$

$$\cdots \cdots \qquad\qquad\qquad (12\text{-}10)$$

$$\frac{dx_{n-1}}{dt^{n-1}} = x_n$$

$$\frac{dx_n}{dt^n} = -a_1 x_n - a_2 x_{n-1} - \cdots - a_{n-1} x_2 - a_n x_1 + r$$

which agree with the results obtained earlier, in Sec. 5-3.

The transfer function $Y(s)/R(s)$ of the system is obtained by applying Mason's gain formula to the state diagram while setting all initial states to zero.   From Fig. 12-2c or 12-3, we get

$$\frac{Y(s)}{R(s)} = \frac{s^{-n}}{\Delta(s)} \qquad\qquad\qquad (12\text{-}11)$$

where

$$\Delta(s) = 1 + a_1 s^{-1} + a_2 s^{-2} + \cdots + a_{n-1} s^{-n-1} + a_n s^{-n} \qquad (12\text{-}12)$$

When all the initial states are in force, the output variable $Y(s)$ can be written as a function of $R(s)$ and all the $x(t_0)$'s, using Mason's gain formula.   The inverse Laplace transform of $Y(s)$ is of the form of (5-97), which is the state-transition equation of the system.

As an illustrative example of the method of obtaining the state diagram, state equations, state-transition equation, and transfer function of a linear system, let us consider that a linear system is described by the differential equation

$$\frac{d^2 y(t)}{dt} + 3\frac{dy(t)}{dt} + 2y(t) = r(t) \qquad\qquad (12\text{-}13)$$

Following the procedure described above, the state diagram of the system is drawn as shown in Fig. 12-5.   In this case, the outputs of the integrators are conveniently defined as the state variables.   Therefore

$X_1(s) = Y(s)$ and $X_2(s) = sY(s)$.   The state equations of the system are

$$\frac{dx_1(t)}{dt} = x_2(t) \tag{12-14}$$

$$\frac{dx_2(t)}{dt} = -2x_1(t) - 3x_2(t) + r(t) \tag{12-15}$$

Notice that the first state equation is merely the definition of the state variables; the second equation is obtained by equating the variable dx_2/dt at the node $s^2Y(s)$ as a function of the state variables x_1 and x_2 and the input r, while neglecting the initial states and the integrators on the state diagram.

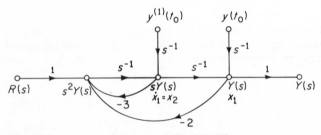

Fig. 12-5   *A state diagram of Eq. (12-13).*

The state-transition equation of the system is obtained by first writing the transformed state variables $X_1(s)$ and $X_2(s)$ in terms of $x_1(t_0)$, $x_2(t_0)$, and $R(s)$ from the state diagram in Fig. 12-5, using Mason's gain formula.   We have

$$X_1(s) = \frac{s^{-1}(1 + 3s^{-1})}{\Delta} x_1(t_0) + \frac{s^{-2}}{\Delta} x_2(t_0) + \frac{s^{-2}}{\Delta} R(s) \tag{12-16}$$

$$X_2(s) = \frac{-2s^{-2}}{\Delta} x_1(t_0) + \frac{s^{-1}}{\Delta} x_2(t_0) + \frac{s^{-1}}{\Delta} R(s) \tag{12-17}$$

where

$$\Delta(s) = 1 + 3s^{-1} + 2s^{-2} \tag{12-18}$$

After simplification, (12-16) and (12-17) are written

$$X_1(s) = \frac{1}{s^2 + 3s + 2} [(s + 3)x_1(t_0) + x_2(t_0) + R(s)] \tag{12-19}$$

$$X_2(s) = \frac{1}{s^2 + 3s + 2} [-2x_1(t_0) + sx_2(t_0) + sR(s)] \tag{12-20}$$

Now consider that the input is a unit step function applied at $t = t_0$; then $R(s) = 1/s$. Taking the inverse Laplace transform of (12-19) and (12-20) yields

$$x_1(t) = (2e^{-(t-t_0)} - e^{-2(t-t_0)})x_1(t_0) + (e^{-(t-t_0)} - e^{-2(t-t_0)})x_2(t_0)$$
$$+ (\tfrac{1}{2} - e^{-(t-t_0)} + e^{-2(t-t_0)}) \quad (12\text{-}21)$$

$$x_2(t) = -2(e^{-(t-t_0)} - e^{-2(t-t_0)})x_1(t_0) - (e^{-(t-t_0)} - e^{-2(t-t_0)})x_2(t_0)$$
$$+ (e^{-(t-t_0)} - e^{-2(t-t_0)}) \quad (12\text{-}22)$$

for $t - t_0$. Note that these state-transition equations are of the form

$$\mathbf{x}(t) = \mathbf{\Phi}(t - t_0)\mathbf{x}(t_0) + \int_{t_0}^{t} \mathbf{\Phi}(t - \tau)\mathbf{Br}(\tau)\,d\tau \quad (12\text{-}23)$$

Therefore we have demonstrated that the state diagram is very useful in determining the state-transition matrix $\mathbf{\Phi}(t)$, as well as the convolution integral on the right-hand side of (12-23).

The transfer function $Y(s)/R(s)$ of the system is determined from (12-19) by setting the initial states equal to zero. Thus

$$\frac{Y(s)}{R(s)} = \frac{X_1(s)}{R(s)} = \frac{1}{s^2 + 3s + 2} \quad (12\text{-}24)$$

When the right side of a differential equation also includes the derivatives of the input function, the state diagram cannot be drawn simply using the method just described. One difficulty is that the state diagram cannot include any differentiator, and therefore the derivatives of $r(t)$ must be achieved in some implicit way.

Consider the differential equation

$$\frac{d^n y}{dt^n} + a_1 \frac{d^{n-1} y}{dt^{n-1}} + a_2 \frac{d^{n-2} y}{dt^{n-2}} + \cdots + a_{n-1} \frac{dy}{dt}$$
$$+ a_n y = b_0 \frac{d^n r}{dt^n} + b_1 \frac{d^{n-1} r}{dt^{n-1}} + \cdots + b_{n-1} \frac{dr}{dt} + b_n r \quad (12\text{-}25)$$

One way of obtaining the state diagram for (12-25) is, first, to write the state equations of the system, and then the state diagram is drawn based on these equations. Another method is, first, to derive the transfer function $Y(s)/R(s)$ by taking the Laplace transform on both sides of (12-25) with zero initial conditions. The state diagram is then drawn from the transfer-function expression, using a method described in Sec. 12-4.

It is shown in Sec. 5.3 and Eqs. (5-51) and (5-52) that the nth-order differential equation (12-25) can be represented by the following matrix equations:

$$\frac{d\mathbf{x}}{dt} = \mathbf{A}\mathbf{x} + \mathbf{B}r \qquad (12\text{-}26)$$

and

$$y = \mathbf{C}\mathbf{x} + \mathbf{D}r \qquad (12\text{-}27)$$

where

$$\mathbf{A} = \begin{bmatrix} 0 & 1 & 0 & 0 & 0 & \cdots & 0 \\ 0 & 0 & 1 & 0 & 0 & \cdots & 0 \\ \cdot & \cdot & \cdot & \cdot & \cdot & \cdots & \cdot \\ 0 & 0 & 0 & 0 & 0 & \cdots & 1 \\ -a_n & -a_{n-1} & -a_{n-2} & -a_{n-3} & -a_{n-4} & \cdots & -a_1 \end{bmatrix}$$

$$(12\text{-}28)$$

$$\mathbf{B} = \begin{bmatrix} h_1 \\ h_2 \\ h_3 \\ \cdot \\ \cdot \\ \cdot \\ h_n \end{bmatrix} \qquad (12\text{-}29)$$

where the h's are functions of the differential equation coefficients, defined in (5-52). In (12-27),

$$\mathbf{C} = [1 \quad 0 \quad 0 \quad 0 \quad \cdots \quad 0] \qquad (12\text{-}30)$$

and

$$\mathbf{D} = b_0 \qquad (12\text{-}31)$$

Once the state equations and the output equation are written, the state diagram of the system is drawn as shown in Fig. 12-6.

12-4 DECOMPOSITION OF TRANSFER FUNCTIONS

One of the important advantages of working with the transfer functions of a linear system is that the input-output relationship can be represented

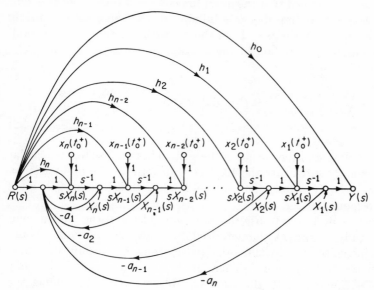

Fig. 12-6   State diagram portraying the differential equation (12-25).

by a function of s and the overall system can be described by a signal flow graph or a block diagram.   This is perhaps the most significant advantage of the transfer-function method over the ordinary differential-equation method.   Let us consider that three linear elements are connected in cascade as shown in Fig. 12-7.   The block G_1 may contain an electric

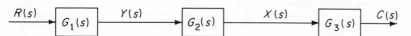

Fig. 12-7   A system containing three linear elements connected in cascade.

filter, G_2 may be an electronic amplifier, and G_3, say, a motor.   Without going into the details of the physical constructions of these elements, we may assume that the transfer functions of these elements are

$$G_1(s) = \frac{1 + 2s}{1 + 5s}$$
$$G_2(s) = 10$$
$$G_3(s) = \frac{1}{s(1 + 0.2s)}$$

It is also tacitly assumed that the input impedance of each element is zero and that the output impedance is infinite, so that there is no loading effect between the elements. Then the transfer function of the overall system is simply the product of the transfer functions of the three elements; i.e.,

$$\frac{C(s)}{R(s)} = \frac{C(s)}{X(s)} \frac{X(s)}{Y(s)} \frac{Y(s)}{R(s)} = G_1(s)G_2(s)G_3(s) = \frac{10(1 + 2s)}{s(1 + 5s)(1 + 0.2s)}$$
(12-32)

Now if we wish to find the output of the system in response to a particular input, we simply substitute the Laplace transform of the input $R(s)$ in (12-32) and solve for $C(s)$. The inverse Laplace transform of $C(s)$ gives the time response $c(t)$.

Often it is desirable to use the state variables and the analog computer to study a system characterized by transfer functions. Many linear components used in networks and systems are readily described by typical transfer functions. Therefore it is not at all unusual to mix the transfer function with the state-variable concept. In solving the problem, we first assign the state variables, then write the state equations, and finally draw the state-transition flow graph so that the solutions may be obtained either by means of a computer or by inspection of the flow graph. The procedure of expressing a transfer function by a state-transition flow graph or an analog-computer block diagram is termed the process of *decomposition*. In general, the process of decomposition can be classified under the following three categories.

Direct decomposition

The process of direct decomposition is best illustrated by an example. Consider that we wish to describe the transfer function in (12-32) by a state diagram. Equation (12-32) is written

$$\frac{C(s)}{R(s)} = \frac{10 + 20s}{s + 5.2s^2 + s^3}$$
(12-33)

Multiplying the numerator and the denominator of the right-hand side of (12-33) by $s^{-n}X(s)$, where n is the highest order of the numerator or the denominator in s (in this case, $n = 3$) and $X(s)$ is an auxiliary variable, we have

$$\frac{C(s)}{R(s)} = \frac{10s^{-3} + 20s^{-2}}{s^{-2} + 5.2s^{-1} + 1} \frac{X(s)}{X(s)}$$
(12-34)

In expression (12-34), since $X(s)$ is arbitrary, it can always be so chosen that the following relations are true:

$$C(s) = (10s^{-3} + 20s^{-2})X(s) \tag{12-35}$$

$$R(s) = (s^{-2} + 5.2s^{-1} + 1)X(s) \tag{12-36}$$

Now let us define the three state variables as x_1, x_2, and x_3. A quite arbitrary but convenient way of relating the state variable is defined as follows:

$$\frac{dx_3}{dt} = x \qquad X_3(s) = s^{-1}X(s)$$

$$\frac{dx_2}{dt} = x_3 \qquad X_2(s) = s^{-2}X(s)$$

$$\frac{dx_1}{dt} = x_2 \qquad X_1(s) = s^{-3}X(s)$$

In this way, the state variables will turn out to be the outputs of the integrators in the analog simulation. Writing (12-36) as

$$X(s) = R(s) - s^{-2}X(s) - 5.2s^{-1}X(s) \tag{12-37}$$

and substituting the relationships for the state variables, we have

$$X(s) = R(s) - X_2(s) - 5.2X_3(s) \tag{12-38}$$

From (12-35), the output $C(s)$ is also given by a linear combination of the state variables; hence

$$C(s) = 10X_1(s) + 20X_2(s) \tag{12-39}$$

The state diagram portraying the state equations in (12-38) and (12-39) is shown in Fig. 12-8.

In general, the state variables of the system need not be defined until the state diagram is constructed. In the case of the direct-decomposition scheme, it is customary to assign the outputs of the integrators as state variables. The state equations are then written from the state diagram by deleting the integrator branches and the initial states as shown in

Fig. 12-9.   Writing $\dot{\mathbf{x}}$ as functions of r and $\mathbf{x}$ yields (using Mason's gain formula)

$$\dot{x}_1 = x_2 \tag{12-40}$$

$$\dot{x}_2 = x_3 \tag{12-41}$$

$$\dot{x}_3 = -x_2 - 5.2x_3 + r \tag{12-42}$$

The method of direct decomposition can be used to define state variables and state equations of an nth-order linear system described by the differential equation (12-25).   In Sec. 12-3 the state diagram for

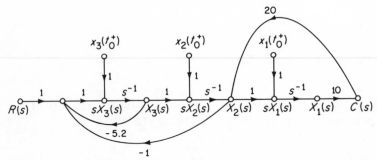

Fig. 12-8   State-diagram realization of the transfer function in Eq. (12-32) by direct decomposition.

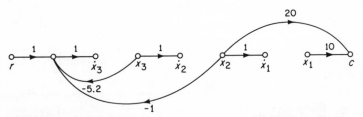

Fig. 12-9   Simplified state diagram of Fig. 12-8 for the purpose of writing state equations.

(12-25) is obtained by first writing the dynamic equations as described in (12-26) to (12-31).   However, with the decomposition method, the process is such that the state diagram is first drawn, and then the state variables and the state equations are written by inspection from the state diagram.   As a first step, we take the Laplace transform on both sides of (12-25), with all the initial conditions assumed to be zero. The transfer function is obtained as

$$\frac{Y(s)}{R(s)} = \frac{b_0 s^n + b_1 s^{n-1} + b_2 s^{n-2} + \cdots + b_{n-1}s + b_n}{s^n + a_1 s^{n-1} + a_2 s^{n-2} + \cdots + a_{n-1}s + a_n} \qquad (12\text{-}43)$$

Using the process of direct decomposition described above, the state diagram of the system is constructed as shown in Fig. 12-10. Defining

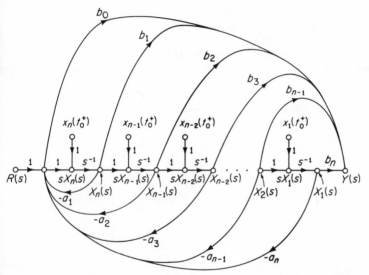

Fig. 12-10   State diagram of the system described by Eq. (12-25).

the state variables as the outputs of the integrators, the state equations are written directly from the state diagram shown in Fig. 12-11.

$$\begin{bmatrix} \dfrac{dx_1}{dt} \\ \dfrac{dx_2}{dt} \\ \cdot \\ \cdot \\ \cdot \\ \dfrac{dx_n}{dt} \end{bmatrix} = \begin{bmatrix} 0 & 1 & 0 & 0 & \cdots & 0 \\ 0 & 0 & 1 & 0 & \cdots & 0 \\ \cdot & \cdot & \cdot & \cdot & \cdots & \cdot \\ & & & & & \\ -a_n & -a_{n-1} & -a_{n-2} & -a_{n-3} & \cdots & -a_1 \end{bmatrix} \begin{bmatrix} x_1 \\ x_2 \\ \cdot \\ \cdot \\ \cdot \\ x_n \end{bmatrix} + \begin{bmatrix} 0 \\ 0 \\ \cdot \\ \cdot \\ \cdot \\ 1 \end{bmatrix} r$$

$$(12\text{-}44)$$

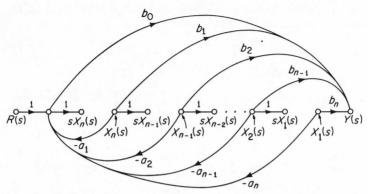

Fig. 12-11   State diagram of Fig. 12-10 with integrators and initial states deleted.

From the same diagram, the output equation is written

$$y = [(b_n - b_0 a_n)(b_{n-1} - b_0 a_{n-1})$$

$$\cdots \quad (b_2 - b_0 a_2)(b_1 - b_0 a_1)] \begin{bmatrix} x_1 \\ x_2 \\ \cdot \\ \cdot \\ \cdot \\ x_n \end{bmatrix} + b_0 r \qquad (12\text{-}45)$$

Parallel decomposition

Another method of decomposition relies on the partial fraction expansion of the transfer function into a sum of first-order terms, and then the direct decomposition is applied to each of the first-order terms. For instance, the transfer function of (12-32) is expanded by partial fraction expansion into

$$\frac{C(s)}{R(s)} = \frac{10}{s} - \frac{3.75}{s + 5} - \frac{6.25}{s + 0.2} \qquad (12\text{-}46)$$

Each of the terms on the right-hand side of (12-46) is of the form

$$\frac{Y_2(s)}{Y_1(s)} = \frac{A}{s + a} \qquad (12\text{-}47)$$

where A and a are constants.   Applying the direct-decomposition method outlined earlier, (12-47) becomes

$$\frac{Y_2(s)}{Y_1(s)} = \frac{As^{-1}}{1 + as^{-1}} \frac{X(s)}{X(s)} \tag{12-48}$$

The state-diagram representation of this first-order transfer function is shown in Fig. 12-12. The state diagram for the expression (12-46) is then realized by connecting the three simple first-order state models in

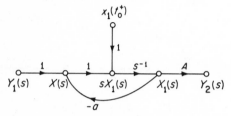

Fig. 12-12   State diagram of a first-order transfer function $A/(s + a)$.

parallel as shown in Fig. 12-13. Notice that, in this case, the outputs of the integrators are again designated as the state variables of the system.

The state equations are obtained again from the diagram by deleting the initial states and the integrators from Fig. 12-13.

$$\frac{dx_1(t)}{dt} = r(t) \tag{12-49}$$

$$\frac{dx_2(t)}{dt} = -5x_2(t) + r(t) \tag{12-50}$$

$$\frac{dx_3(t)}{dt} = -0.2x_3(t) + r(t) \tag{12-51}$$

Similarly, the output equation is written

$$c(t) = 10x_1(t) - 3.75x_2(t) - 6.25x_3(t) \tag{12-52}$$

One of the advantages of the parallel decomposition is that it gives a diagonal matrix for $\mathbf{A}$ if the transfer function has only simple poles. For example, from (12-49) to (12-51), we have

$$\mathbf{A} = \begin{bmatrix} 0 & 0 & 0 \\ 0 & -5 & 0 \\ 0 & 0 & -0.2 \end{bmatrix}$$

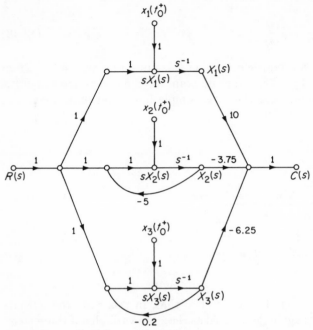

Fig. 12-13   State diagram of the transfer function in Eq. (12-32) by parallel decomposition.

which is a diagonal matrix.   A diagonal matrix for **A** not only simplifies the procedure of obtaining the state-transition matrix $\mathbf{\Phi}(t)$, but also can be used for the study of controllability and observability of the system.

Cascade decomposition

Still another decomposition is obtained by cascading first-order transfer functions to form higher-order ones.   For instance, the transfer function of (12-32) may be considered as the product of three parts.   Therefore the transfer function can be written

$$\frac{C(s)}{R(s)} = \frac{s + 0.5}{s + 0.2}\frac{1}{s + 5}\frac{20}{s} \tag{12-53}$$

or

$$\frac{C(s)}{R(s)} = \frac{1}{s + 0.2}\frac{s + 0.5}{s + 5}\frac{20}{s} \tag{12-54}$$

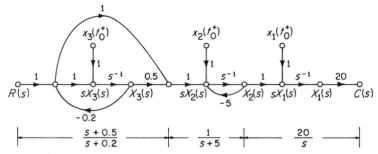

Fig. 12-14   State diagram of the transfer function in Eq. (12-32) by cascade decomposition.

or in other possible arrangements.   The cascade decomposition of (12-32), using the grouping of (12-53), is shown in Fig. 12-14.   In this case, the state variables are defined as the outputs of the integrators, and the state equations are

$$\frac{dx_1(t)}{dt} = x_2(t) \tag{12-55}$$

$$\frac{dx_2(t)}{dt} = -5x_2(t) + 0.5x_3(t) + r(t) \tag{12-56}$$

$$\frac{dx_3(t)}{dt} = -0.25x_3(t) + r(t) \tag{12-57}$$

There are other possible schemes of decomposition, but we can easily see why the above-mentioned methods are the most popular.   If a transfer function is of high order and is unfactored, the direct decomposition is preferred.   Referring to the state equations (12-49) to (12-51), we see that the differential equations for each state variable of the parallel decomposition is independent of the other state variables.   This simplifies the computational procedure considerably.   The cascade decomposition has a distinct advantage over the other methods from the standpoint of design and synthesis.   In the synthesis problem we often insert networks or devices in a system or network for the purpose of improving the system's performance.   Using the cascade decomposition, we only have to insert the state-transition flow graph of the compensating element into the original flow graph, without having to redraw the entire diagram.

Example 12-1   As an illustrative example of the various methods of decomposition, let us consider the transfer function

$$\frac{C(s)}{R(s)} = \frac{s+1}{s^2 + 2s + 2} \tag{12-58}$$

The decomposition of the transfer function by the three methods described above is carried out below.   The three state diagrams resulting from the various ways of decomposition are shown in Fig. 12-15.

Direct decomposition

$$\frac{C(s)}{R(s)} = \frac{s^{-1} + s^{-2}}{1 + 2s^{-1} + 2s^{-2}} \frac{X(s)}{X(s)} \tag{12-59}$$

$$C(s) = s^{-1}X(s) + s^{-2}X(s) \tag{12-60}$$

$$X(s) = R(s) - 2s^{-1}X(s) - 2s^{-2}X(s) \tag{12-61}$$

State equations:

$$\begin{bmatrix} \dfrac{dx_1(t)}{dt} \\ \dfrac{dx_2(t)}{dt} \end{bmatrix} = \begin{bmatrix} 0 & 1 \\ -2 & -2 \end{bmatrix} \begin{bmatrix} x_1(t) \\ x_2(t) \end{bmatrix} + \begin{bmatrix} 0 \\ 1 \end{bmatrix} r(t) \tag{12-62}$$

Output equation:

$$c(t) = x_1(t) + x_2(t) \tag{12-63}$$

Parallel decomposition

$$\frac{C(s)}{R(s)} = \frac{s + 1}{(s + 1 + j)(s + 1 - j)} = \frac{0.5}{s + 1 + j} + \frac{0.5}{s + 1 - j} \tag{12-64}$$

State equations:

$$\begin{bmatrix} \dfrac{dx_1(t)}{dt} \\ \dfrac{dx_2(t)}{dt} \end{bmatrix} = \begin{bmatrix} -(1 + j) & 0 \\ 0 & -(1 - j) \end{bmatrix} \begin{bmatrix} x_1(t) \\ x_2(t) \end{bmatrix} + \begin{bmatrix} 1 \\ 1 \end{bmatrix} r(t) \tag{12-65}$$

Output equation:

$$c(t) = 0.5x_1(t) + 0.5x_2(t) \tag{12-66}$$

Cascade decomposition

$$\frac{C(s)}{R(s)} = \frac{s + 1}{s + 1 + j} \frac{1}{s + 1 - j} \tag{12-67}$$

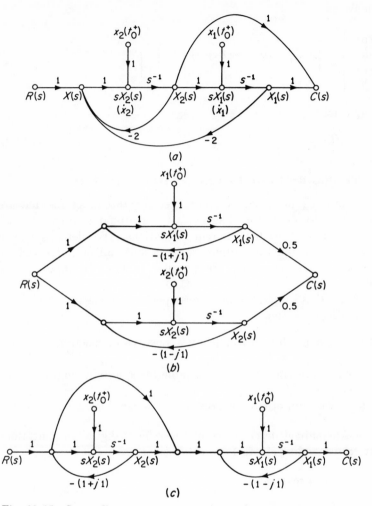

Fig. 12-15 State-diagram representations of

$$\frac{C(s)}{R(s)} = \frac{s+1}{s^2 + 2s + 2}$$

(a) *Direct decomposition.* (b) *Parallel decomposition.* (c) *Cascade decomposition.*

State equations:

$$
\begin{bmatrix} \dfrac{dx_1(t)}{dt} \\ \dfrac{dx_2(t)}{dt} \end{bmatrix} = \begin{bmatrix} -(1-j) & -(1+j) \\ 0 & -(1+j) \end{bmatrix} + \begin{bmatrix} 1 \\ 1 \end{bmatrix} r(t) \tag{12-68}
$$

Output equation:

$$
c(t) = x_1(t) \tag{12-69}
$$

12-5 STATE DIAGRAMS OF DISCRETE - DATA SYSTEMS

Since differential equations can be portrayed by state diagrams that are analogous to analog-computer diagrams, it is reasonable to expect that similar relationships exist for difference equations. We demonstrate in the following discussion that difference equations can be portrayed by discrete state diagrams which are parallel to digital-computer flow diagrams.

We assume that a digital computer can perform, at least, the following basic computing operations:

1   Multiplying a machine variable by a positive or negative constant coefficient
2   Time delay, involving storing a variable for a certain length of time before reusing it
3   Producing the sum of two or more machine variables

The mathematical descriptions of these basic digital computations and their corresponding z-transform expressions are given by:

Multiplication by a constant

$$
x_2(kT) = ax_1(kT) \tag{12-70}
$$
$$
X_2(z) = aX_1(z) \tag{12-71}
$$

Storing and time delay

$$
x_2(kT) = x_1(k+1)T \tag{12-72}
$$
$$
X_2(z) = zX_1(z) - zx_1(0^+) \tag{12-73}
$$

or

$$
X_1(z) = z^{-1}X_2(z) + x_1(0^+) \tag{12-74}
$$

Summing

$$x_3(kT) = x_0(kT) + x_1(kT) - x_2(kT) \qquad (12\text{-}75)$$

$$X_3(z) = X_0(z) + X_1(z) - X_2(z) \qquad (12\text{-}76)$$

The state-diagram representation of the three z-transform equations (12-71), (12-74), and (12-76) are obtained from the basic rules of the signal flow graphs and are shown in Fig. 12-16. Once the state diagrams

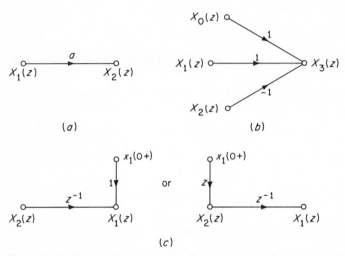

Fig. 12-16 Basic elements of a discrete state diagram. (a) Multiplication by a constant. (b) Summing. (c) Storing or time delay.

of the basic discrete operations are established, the state-diagram representation of a discrete-data system may be obtained using essentially the same rules as established for continuous-data systems.   If the transfer function of an nth-order linear process is given, the state diagram may be obtained by methods similar to the decomposition schemes discussed in Sec. 12-4.

Consider that the transfer function of a discrete-data system is given by

$$\frac{Y(z)}{R(z)} = \frac{b_0 z^n + b_1 z^{n-1} + \cdots + b_{n-1} z + b_n}{z^n + a_1 z^{n-1} + \cdots + a_{n-1} z + a_n} \qquad (12\text{-}77)$$

Since the denominator of (12-77) is not factored, the direct-decomposition method should be used here.   Multiplying the numerator and the denominator of (12-77) by $z^{-n}X(z)$, we have

$$\frac{Y(z)}{R(z)} = \frac{b_0 + b_1z^{-1} + \cdots + b_{n-1}z^{-n+1} + b_nz^{-n}}{1 + a_1z^{-1} + \cdots + a_{n-1}z^{-n+1} + a_nz^{-n}} \frac{X(z)}{X(z)} \tag{12-78}$$

from which

$$Y(z) = (b_0 + b_1z^{-1} + \cdots + b_{n-1}z^{-n+1} + b_nz^{-n})X(z) \tag{12-79}$$

and

$$X(z) = R(z) - (a_1z^{-1} + \cdots + a_{n-1}z^{-n+1} + a_nz^{-n})X(z) \tag{12-80}$$

Equations (12-79) and (12-80) are now represented by the state diagram shown in Fig. 12-17.

Important information which may be obtained from this state diagram, besides the state equations and the state-transition equations, is

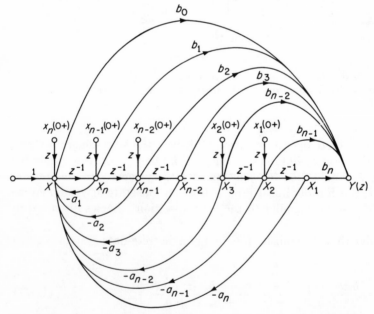

Fig. 12-17   State diagram of the discrete-data system described by Eq. (12-77).

the definition of the state variables.   For this, a convenient way of defining the state variables is to define them as the outputs of the delay units on the state diagram.   From Fig. 12-17, the state equations are written

$$x_1(k + 1)T = x_2(kT)$$
$$x_2(k + 1)T = x_3(kT)$$
$$\cdots \cdots \cdots \cdots \cdots \qquad (12\text{-}81)$$
$$x_{n-1}(k + 1)T = x_n(kT)$$
$$x_n(k + 1)T = -a_n x_1(kT) - a_{n-1} x_2(kT) - \cdots$$
$$- a_2 x_{n-1}(kT) - a_1 x_n(kT)$$

and the output equation is

$$y(kT) = b_n x_1(kT) + b_{n-1} x_2(kT) + \cdots + b_1 x_n(kT) + b_0 r(kT)$$
$$(12\text{-}82)$$

The following example illustrates the application of the various decomposition techniques to discrete-data systems.

Example 12-2   Consider that the transfer function of a discrete-data system is

$$\frac{C(z)}{R(z)} = \frac{K}{z^2 - 1.208z + 0.208} \qquad (12\text{-}83)$$

The three methods of decomposition of the transfer function are presented below.   The state diagrams resulting from the various ways of decomposition are shown in Fig. 12-18, and the diagrams from which the dynamic equations are written are shown in Fig. 12-19.   Notice that these diagrams are obtained by deleting the initial states and the delay units z^{-1} from the original state diagrams.

Direct decomposition

$$\frac{C(z)}{R(z)} = \frac{Kz^{-2}}{1 - 1.208z^{-1} + 0.208z^{-2}} \frac{X(z)}{X(z)} \qquad (12\text{-}84)$$
$$C(z) = Kz^{-2}X(z) \qquad (12\text{-}85)$$
$$X(z) = R(z) + 1.208z^{-1}X(z) - 0.208z^{-2}X(z) \qquad (12\text{-}86)$$

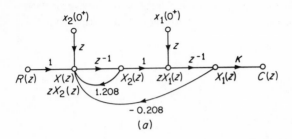

(a)

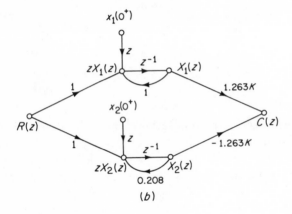

(b)

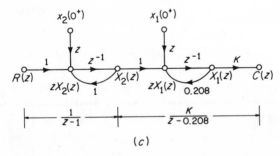

(c)

Fig. 12-18 *State-diagram representations of*

$$\frac{C(z)}{R(z)} = \frac{K}{(z-1)(z-0.208)}$$

(a) Direct decomposition. (b) Parallel decomposition. (c) Cascade decomposition.

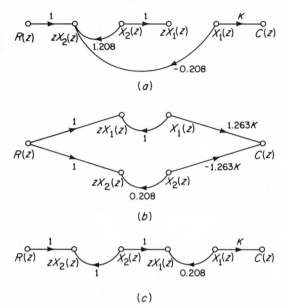

(a)

(b)

(c)

Fig. 12-19   State diagrams of Fig. 12-18 with all initial states and delay units deleted.

State equations:

$$\begin{bmatrix} x_1(k+1) \\ x_2(k+1) \end{bmatrix} = \begin{bmatrix} 0 & 1 \\ -0.208 & 1.208 \end{bmatrix} \begin{bmatrix} x_1(k) \\ x_2(k) \end{bmatrix} + \begin{bmatrix} 0 \\ 1 \end{bmatrix} r(k) \qquad (12\text{-}87)$$

Output equation:

$$c(k) = Kx_1(k) \qquad (12\text{-}88)$$

Parallel decomposition

$$\frac{C(z)}{R(z)} = \frac{K}{(z-1)(z-0.208)} = \frac{1.263K}{z-1} - \frac{1.263K}{z-0.208} \qquad (12\text{-}89)$$

State equations:

$$\begin{bmatrix} x_1(k+1) \\ x_2(k+1) \end{bmatrix} = \begin{bmatrix} 1 & 0 \\ 0 & 0.208 \end{bmatrix} \begin{bmatrix} x_1(k) \\ x_2(k) \end{bmatrix} + \begin{bmatrix} 1 \\ 1 \end{bmatrix} r(k) \qquad (12\text{-}90)$$

Output equation:

$$c(k) = 1.263Kx_1(k) - 1.263x_2(k) \tag{12-91}$$

Cascade decomposition

$$\frac{C(z)}{R(z)} = \frac{K}{(z-1)(z-0.208)} = \frac{1}{z-1}\frac{K}{z-0.208} \tag{12-92}$$

State equations:

$$\begin{bmatrix} x_1(k+1) \\ x_2(k+1) \end{bmatrix} = \begin{bmatrix} 0.208 & 1 \\ 0 & 1 \end{bmatrix} \begin{bmatrix} x_1(k) \\ x_2(k) \end{bmatrix} + \begin{bmatrix} 0 \\ 1 \end{bmatrix} r(k) \tag{12-93}$$

Output equation:

$$c(k) = Kx_1(k) \tag{12-94}$$

12-6 STATE DIAGRAMS OF MULTIVARIABLE SYSTEMS

The discussions of state diagrams in the preceding sections are restricted to systems with one input and one output, i.e., single-variable systems. We noticed that, if the input-output relationship of the system is given in terms of a transfer function which has no cancellation of poles and zeros, the number of integrators (or delays in the discrete-data case) is equal to the order of the transfer function.   Therefore the minimum number of state variables required to describe the system is determined once the transfer function is given.

If a system has more than one input and output, the problem of constructing the state diagram is more involved, especially when the condition of minimum number of integrators (delays) and state variables must be achieved.

Figure 12-20 gives the block-diagram representation of a linear system with two inputs and two outputs.   The transfer-function relationships between the inputs and outputs can be represented by the following transfer-matrix relationship:

$$\begin{bmatrix} C_1(s) \\ C_2(s) \end{bmatrix} = \begin{bmatrix} G_{11}(s) & G_{12}(s) \\ G_{21}(s) & G_{22}(s) \end{bmatrix} \begin{bmatrix} R_1(s) \\ R_2(s) \end{bmatrix} \tag{12-95}$$

or

$$\mathbf{C}(s) = \mathbf{G}(s)\mathbf{R}(s) \tag{12-96}$$

The problem with which we are concerned in the multivariable system is: Given the transfer-function matrix $\mathbf{G}(s)$, how can a state diagram utilizing a minimum number of integrators be realized? The condition of a minimum number of integrators is not merely important from the point of view of achieving minimum complexity in the physical simulation of the system, but it is also essential for the design of optimal-control systems.

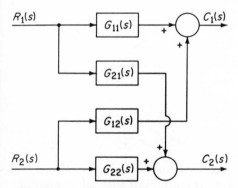

Fig. 12-20 Block-diagram representations of a system with two inputs and two outputs.

Let us consider that the transfer-function matrix for the multivariable system of Fig. 12-20 is given by

$$\mathbf{G}(s) = \begin{bmatrix} \dfrac{1}{s(s+1)} & \dfrac{1}{s} \\ \dfrac{1}{s} & \dfrac{2}{s(s+1)} \end{bmatrix} \tag{12-97}$$

One might jump to a conclusion and represent the system by the state diagram shown in Fig. 12-21, which has six integrators. It is natural to ask if the number of integrators can be reduced. A close inspection of

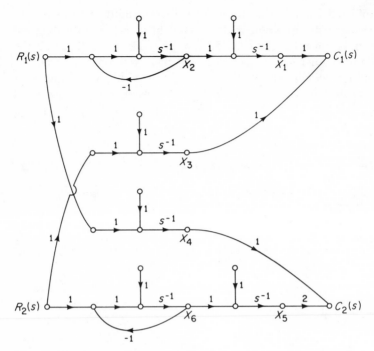

Fig. 12-21   A state-diagram realization of Eq. (12-97) using six integrators.

the state diagram of Fig. 12-21 reveals that a number of these six integrators can indeed be shared by the various input-output channels if a parallel decomposition is applied to each of the transfer functions of $\mathbf{G}(s)$.   Therefore the final state diagram with minimum complexity contains only four integrators, as shown in Fig. 12-22.

In general, a more reliable method of determining the minimum number of integrators in the state-diagram realization of $\mathbf{G}(s)$ exists.   The method relies on the partial fraction expansion of $\mathbf{G}(s)$.   The partial fraction of a transfer matrix $\mathbf{G}(s)$ is carried out in a manner similar to that of a scalar transfer function $G(s)$.   If $\mathbf{G}(s)$ contains transfer functions which have poles at $s = s_1$, s_2, and s_3, it can be expanded into

$$\mathbf{G}(s) = \frac{\mathbf{K}_1}{s + s_1} + \frac{\mathbf{K}_2}{s + s_2} + \frac{\mathbf{K}_3}{s + s_3} \qquad (12\text{-}98)$$

where $\mathbf{K}_1$, $\mathbf{K}_2$, and $\mathbf{K}_3$ are matrices containing constant coefficients.   For instance, the $\mathbf{G}(s)$ in (12-97) has poles at $s = 0$ and $s = -1$; it is expanded into

$$\mathbf{G}(s) = \begin{bmatrix} \dfrac{1}{s} - \dfrac{1}{s+1} & \dfrac{1}{s} \\ \dfrac{1}{s} & \dfrac{2}{s} - \dfrac{2}{s+1} \end{bmatrix} = \frac{1}{s}\begin{bmatrix} 1 & 1 \\ 1 & 2 \end{bmatrix} + \frac{1}{s+1}\begin{bmatrix} -1 & 0 \\ 0 & -2 \end{bmatrix}$$

(12-99)

Once $\mathbf{G}(s)$ is expanded by partial fraction expansion, the minimum number of integrators in the state diagram is equal to the sum of the ranks of the coefficient matrices $\mathbf{K}_1, \mathbf{K}_2, \ldots$. Furthermore, the number of times that a pole is used in the state-diagram realization is equal to the rank of its corresponding coefficient matrix. Therefore, from (12-99), the ranks of the two coefficient matrices are all equal to *two*, meaning that the state-diagram descriptions of $1/s$ and $1/(s+1)$ are each used twice in the complete state diagram. This fact is verified by the state diagram of Fig. 12-22.

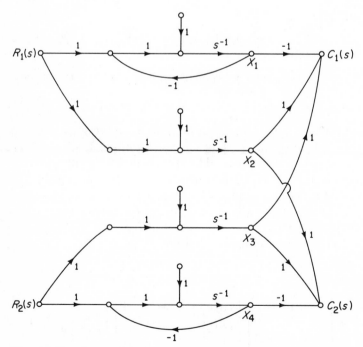

Fig. 12-22   A state-diagram realization of Eq. (12-97) using only four integrators.

Example 12-3 Consider that a multivariable system has the transfer matrix

$$\mathbf{G}(s) = \begin{bmatrix} \dfrac{1}{s(s+1)(s+2)} & \dfrac{2}{s(s+1)(s+2)} \\ \dfrac{1}{(s+1)(s+2)} & \dfrac{2}{(s+1)(s+2)} \end{bmatrix} \qquad (12\text{-}100)$$

Performing the partial fraction expansion on each of the transfer functions and collecting the terms with identical poles yields

$$\mathbf{G}(s) = \frac{1}{s}\begin{bmatrix} \tfrac{1}{2} & 1 \\ 0 & 0 \end{bmatrix} + \frac{1}{s+1}\begin{bmatrix} -1 & -2 \\ 1 & 2 \end{bmatrix} + \frac{1}{s+2}\begin{bmatrix} \tfrac{1}{2} & 1 \\ -1 & -2 \end{bmatrix} \qquad (12\text{-}101)$$

The ranks of the coefficient matrices are determined as follows:

$$\mathbf{K}_1 = \begin{bmatrix} \tfrac{1}{2} & 1 \\ 0 & 0 \end{bmatrix} \qquad \text{rank 1}$$

$$\mathbf{K}_2 = \begin{bmatrix} -1 & -2 \\ 1 & 2 \end{bmatrix} \qquad \text{rank 1 (elements in row 2 are } -1 \text{ times those of row 1)}$$

$$\mathbf{K}_3 = \begin{bmatrix} \tfrac{1}{2} & 1 \\ -1 & -2 \end{bmatrix} \qquad \text{rank 1 (elements in row 2 are } -2\text{-times those of row 1)}$$

Therefore the minimum number of integrators in the state-diagram realization of $\mathbf{G}(s)$ is *three*, and each of the realizations of $1/s$, $1/(s+1)$, and $1/(s+2)$ is used exactly once. The state diagram for the system is drawn as shown in Fig. 12-23, by first constructing the diagrams for the first-order poles at $s = 0$, -1, and -2 and then connecting the input and output branches according to the coefficient matrices in (12-101). The state equations of the system may be written from the state diagram in the usual manner. Therefore, from Fig. 12-23,

$$\begin{bmatrix} \dfrac{dx_1(t)}{dt} \\ \dfrac{dx_2(t)}{dt} \\ \dfrac{dx_3(t)}{dt} \end{bmatrix} = \begin{bmatrix} 0 & 0 & 0 \\ 0 & -1 & 0 \\ 0 & 0 & -2 \end{bmatrix} \begin{bmatrix} x_1(t) \\ x_2(t) \\ x_3(t) \end{bmatrix} + \begin{bmatrix} \tfrac{1}{2} & 1 \\ -1 & -2 \\ \tfrac{1}{2} & 1 \end{bmatrix} \begin{bmatrix} r_1(t) \\ r_2(t) \end{bmatrix} \qquad (12\text{-}102)$$

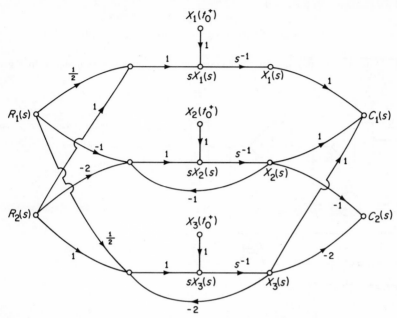

Fig. 12-23   *A state-diagram realization of Eq. (12-100) with a minimum number of integrators.*

and the output equation is

$$\begin{bmatrix} c_1(t) \\ c_2(t) \end{bmatrix} = \begin{bmatrix} 1 & 1 & 1 \\ 0 & -1 & -2 \end{bmatrix} \begin{bmatrix} x_1(t) \\ x_2(t) \\ x_3(t) \end{bmatrix} \qquad (12\text{-}103)$$

PROBLEMS

12-1   (a)   Draw a state diagram for the network shown in Fig. P12-1.   The flow graph should not have any differentiators.

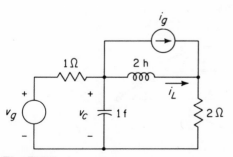

Fig. P12-1

(b)   Find $v_c(t)$ for $t > 0$.

$$v_g(t) = u(t) \qquad i_g(t) = u(t) \qquad i_L(0+) = 0 \qquad v_c(0+) = 0$$

12-2   Draw a state diagram for the analog-computer block diagram shown in Fig. P12-2.

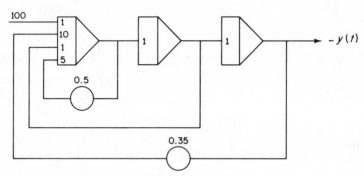

Fig. P12-2

12-3   Draw state diagrams for the systems described by the following differential equations:

(a) $\dfrac{d^3y}{dt^3} + 3\dfrac{d^2y}{dt^2} + 2\dfrac{dy}{dt} + y = 2r$

(b) $2\dfrac{d^2y}{dt^2} + 5\dfrac{dy}{dt} + y = \dfrac{dr}{dt} + 0.5r$

(c) $\dfrac{d^2y}{dt^2} + 1.5\dfrac{dy}{dt} + 2y + \displaystyle\int_0^t y\,dt = r$

12-4   A state diagram of a physical system is shown in Fig. P12-3.
(a)   Write the dynamic equations of the system.
(b)   Write the transfer function of the system.

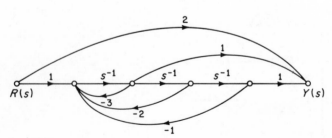

Fig. P12-3

12-5 Draw state diagrams for the following transfer functions by means of direct decomposition:

(a) $G(s) = \dfrac{1}{s(s + 1)(s + 2)}$

(b) $G(s) = \dfrac{2}{s^2(s + 1)}$

(c) $G(s) = \dfrac{5(s + 4)}{s + 1}$

(d) $G(s) = \dfrac{s + 1}{s^2 + 4s + 4}$

12-6 Draw state diagrams for the transfer functions in Prob. 12-5 using the method of cascade decomposition.

12-7 Draw state diagrams for the transfer functions in Prob. 12-5 using the method of parallel decomposition.

12-8 Draw state diagrams for the following transfer function by means of the three methods of decomposition.   Compare the results and make comments.

$$G(s) = \frac{s + 2}{s(s^2 + 5s + 6)}$$

12-9 Show that, for transfer functions with simple poles, parallel decomposition will always lead to state equations whose **A** matrix is a diagonal matrix.

12-10 Draw a state diagram for the control system shown in Fig. P12-4.

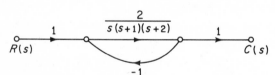

Fig. P12-4

12-11 The signal flow graph of a feedback control system is shown in Fig. P12-5.

(a) Define the state variables of the system and write the dynamic equations in vector-matrix form.

(b) Find the state-transition matrix $\mathbf{\Phi}(t)$.

(c) Solve the state equations and express the state variables in terms of the initial state $\mathbf{x}(t_0)$ with zero input, $r(t) = 0$.

(d) What are the solutions of the state equations if the input is a unit step function and $\mathbf{x}(0) = \mathbf{0}$?

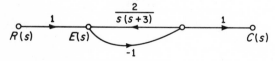

Fig. P12-5

12-12   The transfer function of a discrete-data system is given by

$$\frac{C(z)}{R(z)} = \frac{z + 1}{4z(z - 0.5)}$$

Write a set of state equations for the system in which the matrix **A** is a diagonal matrix.

12-13   The transfer matrix of a linear system with two inputs and two outputs is given by

$$\mathbf{G}(s) = \begin{bmatrix} \dfrac{1}{s} & \dfrac{1}{s(s + 1)} \\ \dfrac{1}{s(s + 1)} & \dfrac{1}{s} \end{bmatrix}$$

Draw a state diagram for the system with a minimum number of integrators.

BIBLIOGRAPHY

1   Kuo, B. C.: State Transition Flow Graphs of Continuous and Sampled Dynamic Systems, *WESCON Conv. Records*, 18.1, August, 1962.
2   Korn, G. A., and T. M. Korn: "Electronic Analog Computers," 2d ed., McGraw-Hill Book Company, New York, 1956.
3   Johnson, C. L.: "Analog Computer Techniques," 2d ed., McGraw-Hill Book Company, New York, 1963.

INDEX